INDUSTRIAL HEAT TRANSFER

INDUSTRIAL HEAT TRANSFER

By

F. W. HUTCHINSON

Professor of Mechanical Engineering
University of California

THE INDUSTRIAL PRESS 93 Worth St., New York 13, N. Y.

Publishers of AIR CONDITIONING, HEATING AND VENTILATING

SECOND PRINTING
PRINTED IN THE UNITED STATES OF AMERICA

For

KATHLEEN

PREFACE

The intent of this book is to provide a selective, rather than a comprehensive, coverage of the field of heat transmission. Emphasis throughout has been placed on those equations which find widest industrial application and which are of the greatest practical importance. The text section has been kept as brief as possible and, with few exceptions, graphical solutions have been provided at the end of each chapter for all of the major equations which are presented in that chapter.

The primary objective in the arrangement of material has been to select equations of maximum usefulness and to provide, through graphical solutions, means of applying these equations with a minimum of calculation and cross reference. The graphs equal in accuracy the equations from which they are constructed and permit direct visual solution without need of computation. Since many of the heat transfer equations involve exponential relationships among dimensionless groups, it is frequently helpful and timesaving to use a direct-reading graph rather than resort to other methods of mathematical solution.

Of particular interest to the industrial engineer will be the section covering forced convection of gases or liquids, whether heating or cooling, while flowing within or outside of pipes. Analytical solutions for these cases would require the determination of viscosity, specific heat, thermal conductivity, and density all as functions of temperature. The graphs simplify these cases by permitting direct evaluation, without requiring determination of any physical properties, of the heat transfer characteristics of each particular fluid. The graphical solutions obviously cannot give information which is not inherent in the equations, but they do permit the user to take from the graphs, in a matter of minutes, the information that was built into them over a period of hours.

The scales used in constructing the graphs have been so selected that the accuracy to which each graph can be read will equal or exceed the limits of accuracy of the equation from which it is constructed. In some cases scale restrictions may cause problems to fall outside the range of the graph; when this occurs the solution will have to be obtained by calculation from the equation.

As an aid to the user, the page opposite each graph gives the equation, its limitations, its extension, and a reference to the discussion of that equation in the text. A numerical example line is presented in each case and its solution shown by a dashed example line on the graph. Numerical examples have been selected not only to show the use of the particular graphs, but to illustrate typical applications of heat transfer problems.

The selection of material for inclusion in this book is in large measure from such standard references* as those of Jakob[2], McAdams[1], and Stoever[3]; the author gladly acknowledges indebtedness to these authors and recommends their books for a more comprehensive treatment of this subject.

The author wishes to express his thanks to Clifford Strock for encouragement in the preparation of this material and to D. Doble, S. Lift, B. Pater, and M. Orange for their help in preparation of the graphs.

F. W. Hutchinson

Berkeley, California
November, 1951

*All references throughout the text are to items listed in the bibliography.

CONTENTS

NOMENCLATURE

The following list includes the most commonly used terms. Special terms are sometimes used in the text, but in all such cases the symbols are defined.

A Area normal to flow of heat, sq ft

c_p Specific heat at constant pressure, Btu/(lb)(°F)

C Conductance for a thermal system in which A is constant, Btu/(hr)(sq ft)(°F)

C' Conductance for any thermal system, Btu/(hr)(°F)

D Diameter, ft

F Shape factor or emissivity factor for radiant exchange, dimensionless

g Acceleration due to gravity, ft/(sec)(sec) or ft/(hr)(hr)

Gr Grashof's number, dimensionless

h Film coefficient of heat transfer, Btu/(hr)(sq ft)(°F)

k Thermal conductivity, Btu/(hr)(sq ft)(°F/ft)

L Distance along the path of heat flow, ft

Nu Nusselt's number, dimensionless

Pr Prandtl's number, dimensionless

q Rate of heat transmission, Btu/hr

R Thermal resistance for a system in which A is constant, (hr)(sq ft)(°F)/Btu

R' Thermal resistance for any system, (hr)(°F)/Btu

Re Reynolds' number, dimensionless

t Temperature, °F (also used for transmissivity, dimensionless)

T Absolute temperature, °F + 460

U Overall coefficient for a system in which A is constant, Btu/(hr)(sq ft)(°F)

U' Overall coefficient of heat transfer for any system, Btu/(hr)(°F)

V Fluid velocity, ft/sec or ft/hr (also used as wind velocity, mph)

w Flow rate, lb/hr or lb/(hr)(sq ft), w' being used for lb/(hr)(tube)

W Weight, lbs

x Distance or thickness, ft

α (alpha) Thermal diffusivity, ft^2/hr

β (beta) Coefficient of volumetric expansion 1/°F

θ (theta) Time, hr

π (pi) Constant, equal to 3.1416, dimensionless

ρ (rho) Density, lbs/(cu ft)

ϕ (phi) Angle, degrees (also used to indicate "is a function of"

ω (omega) Solid angle

Δ (delta) Indicates (when used as a prefix) a difference or change of some quantity as temperature, time, or distance

μ (mu) viscosity, lb/(hr)(ft), or lb/(sec)(ft), or centipoises.

CHAPTER I

Introduction

This book is so arranged that the text and the graphical solutions are independent of one another. For purposes of study or for review of theory, some readers may wish to start at the beginning and go through the text section of each chapter before going on to the graphical solutions. For the practicing engineer, however, the text section will be of lesser interest as he will find that the graphical solutions are complete in themselves and, in general, permit the direct solution of many practical problems without other reference. On the page facing each graphical solution is an explanatory title, a statement of the equation for which the graph has been constructed, a summary of the limitations and extensions, and a numerical example showing the method of applying the graphical solution. Each graph is an entirely self-contained unit and such cross-references as do occur are intended primarily for the convenience of students.

Once the reader has become familiar with the contents and arrangement of the book, he will normally refer directly to the list of graphical solutions to find the one, or ones, directly applicable to the particular problem for which he is seeking a solution. The graphs do not provide information that could not be obtained by other means, but the user will find that they make that information available with an economy of both time and effort.

1.1. Energy in Transition as Heat. Since energy in the form of heat is transferred in three basically different ways, conduction, convection, and radiation, it is inconvenient to define heat in terms of the form adopted while in transition. A more satisfactory procedure is to identify heat as any transfer of energy which occurs whenever certain conditions are established. Thus, irrespective of which of the three forms of transfer is occurring, a necessary and sufficient condition for heat flow is the maintenance, or the transient existence, of a difference in temperature between the two thermally connected materials between which the energy transfer is taking place.

Common experience tells us that whenever a hot object is placed in a cool room the object undergoes a loss of temperature with respect to time and, since temperature is an indication of the quantity of kinetic internal energy in storage, it appears that stored energy must be flowing from the hot object to the cooler room; this energy transfer is defined as heat. When the situation is reversed and a cold object is introduced into a warm room the temperature of the object is observed to rise, hence internal kinetic energy is going into storage in the object; the flow of this energy from the room or surroundings to the object is likewise defined as heat. Thus, energy transfer as heat occurs because of a temperature difference within the thermal system.

1.2. The Three Mechanisms of Heat Transmission. Since any energy transfer which occurs because of a temperature difference is, by definition, heat, we must expect the term to include widely divergent methods of energy flow. Three such methods can be readily classified in terms of the different relationship, existing in each case, between the energy and the working substance:

(1) RADIATION. When energy transfer takes place between two objects at different temperatures by means of a flow of massless particles, photons, which are not part of nor associated with the working substance, the transfer is said to be by radiation. Radiant heat transmission is characterized by the complete independence of the energy quanta of any intermediate substance. Radiation, therefore, would readily occur through a perfect vacuum. In common experience the most vivid evidence of radiant transfer is that represented by the solar energy which passes through interstellar space (where conditions are infinitesimally close to those existing in a perfect vacuum) on its way to the earth's surface. Thus, radiation can occur without the presence of any "bridge" of working substance. As a corollary, radiation usually does not occur when a working substance is present, that is, radiation, in the wavelengths associated with ordinary thermal systems, does not take place through either a liquid or a solid. Through most gases radiation occurs as though the gas were not present, carbon dioxide being a marked exception and water vapor another exception.

(2) CONDUCTION. Whenever the molecules of a working substance, whether liquid, solid, or vapor, are restrained so that no appreciable relative translatory motion occurs among them, the kinetic energies of the various molecules will be largely due to vibration. If a temperature difference exists in the working substance, some adjacent molecules will necessarily be at different temperatures hence will possess different degrees of vibratory motion. In this case the molecule which is vibrating most rapidly will transfer some of its motion to the slower-moving molecule next to

it, the one then undergoing a decrease in temperature and the other an increase. In this way, thermal energy will be transferred by the mechanism of conduction from the region of higher to the region of lower temperature. The process will continue spontaneously until the entire system has reached a uniform equilibrium temperature. If external conditions prevent attainment of a uniform temperature, as, for example, when one end of a copper rod is placed in a fire and the other end in an icebox, heat will continue to flow by conduction from the region of higher to the region of lower temperature.

In contrast to radiation, conduction only occurs when a working substance is present and when the molecules of that working substance retain practically fixed positions with respect to one another. Thus, conductive heat flow would always occur through solids, but would take place in liquids and vapors only if special conditions prevented or greatly reduced the normal translatory motion of the molecules within these materials.

(3) CONVECTION. All materials undergo some change in specific volume (hence in density) as a function of temperature. In solids, the restraining forces between molecules are sufficient to hold them in relatively fixed positions with respect to one another. This prevents any tendency of the molecules to move so as to equalize the density throughout the solid. Thus, for example, a vertical copper rod may be cold at the top and warm near the bottom, but the heavier, colder, material will not be able to "sink" through the rod and displace the lighter, hotter, material.

With liquids, vapors, and gases the situation is markedly different and any difference in density immediately leads to downward flow of the heavier material and upward flow of the lighter. But since differences in density, at constant pressure, are always due to differences in temperature, it follows that for liquids, gases, and vapors there will always be mass flow associated with temperature gradient and a net transfer of internal kinetic energy from the region of higher to the region of lower temperature. Admittedly the "flow" in this case is of fluid and not of energy, the energy merely being carried by the fluid in stored form; however, since the net effect is a transfer of energy, and since it occurs because of and in the direction of a temperature gradient, this mechanism of transfer is grouped under the classification "heat" and referred to as convective heat transmission.

Convection is fundamentally a mixing process and any method of increasing the rate of mixing will correspondingly increase the rate of convective transfer. When mixing takes place solely through the effect of gravity on macroscopic fluid volumes of different density, the process is said to be one of *free convection*. If the mixing process is initiated or accelerated by mechanical means (as a pump, fan, or any type of stirring device) the process is defined as *forced convection*. Effectiveness of convection as a mechanism of heat transmission obviously depends on the difference of energy intensity as determined by temperature gradient and on the rate of mass transfer as influenced by pressure gradient throughout the fluid.

SUMMARY. The three different mechanisms of heat transmission are characterized by three fundamentally different relationships between energy and mass. In radiant transfer the energy is transferred without any connection between the masses involved and the effect of any material present between the masses is to reduce or to eliminate entirely the radiant transmission. In conductive transfer the energy flows because of inter-molecular relationships in the working substance. The presence of mass is necessary for conductive transfer and the molecular arrangement must be such that there is no appreciable relative translatory motion, except that of vibration, among the molecules of the working substance. In convective transfer, the presence of mass is not only a requirement, but in addition there must be macroscopic transfer of the mass from the warmer to the cooler region and vice versa.

1.3. Steady, Periodic, and Transient Heat Transmission. In heat transfer analyses, interest centers not only on the quantity of energy which flows but on the rate of transfer; rate is here represented by the symbol q and is expressed in Btu per hour. Since the Btu is a unit of work, it follows that heat transfer rate evaluates work rate or power. For heat loss through the wall of a heated room at a rate of 2545 Btu per hour one might with equal correctness refer to it as a heat loss of 1 horsepower, or, for a rate of loss of 3413 Btu per hour, one could say with accuracy that the "leakage" amounted to 1 kilowatt.

Since the rate of heat transfer involves time, it is evident that a classification of heat transfer processes can be set up in terms of the way in which energy flow varies as a function of time. When the rate of energy flow with respect to time is not a variable, that is, when it is constant, conditions at any point in the system do not change and the system is then said to be in steady state. A steady-state condition from the thermodynamic point of view is therefore one in which at any point in the system the rate of efflux of energy is equal to the rate of influx of energy.

Steady-state systems are by far the most common and the most important in general engineering applications. Typical examples are the flow of heat from products of combustion to the tubes of a steam boiler, the flow from a refrigerated space to the cooling surfaces of the evaporator, and the flow out through the walls of a gas turbine or of a thermo-jet. In all such cases, the state of the working substance at a given point in the thermodynamic cycle (hence at a given position in the particular equipment) does not change with time and the rate of heat loss and gain is therefore fixed and constant at each point in the cycle.

A second classification, periodic heat transfer, includes systems in which the state at a given point varies through some known cycle and thus returns periodically to a particular value. In any type of reciprocating engine, for example, the gases within the cylinder go through a periodic change of temperature. Similarly, the heat losses and heat gains related to air conditioning vary as a function of diurnal (as well as longer period) temperature changes. Periodic systems are much more complex than those of steady state; however, when the temperature-time curve can be plotted, all other conditions throughout the system will necessarily have definite values at a given time and the system will be defined. The problem then becomes one of investigating temperature conditions throughout the path of heat flow in terms of the way in which boundary temperatures, for that particular path, are known to vary with time.

The third classification is that of transient heat flow. For systems of this type, temperatures, at particular points, vary with time along a non-recurring temperature-time curve. A typical example is the warm-up period when an engine, turbine, boiler, or other thermal unit is first started and the similar heating or cooling period which occurs whenever the load on the system is increased or decreased. Fortunately, however, the transient operation of thermodynamic equipment is usually limited to brief intervals and represents a departure from the intended cycle hence it is rarely necessary to make a detailed or exact analysis of such a system during the transient period. One important exception to this statement is in reverse-cycle thermodynamics, refrigeration, where the transient interval during cooling of the refrigerated space is a major factor in determining the size of equipment needed to bring down the temperature within a specified time. Another refrigeration application is the analysis of the capacity requirements of a "stand-by" or emergency unit that would adequately delay the warming of the refrigerated space following failure of the regular refrigerating equipment. In power and process applications, however, transient effects can usually be disregarded.

1.4. Combined Heat Transfer. By far the greater number of systems of interest to the engineer involve heat transfer through a number of different series-connected sections, the transfer not infrequently occurring by two or more mechanisms in parallel for a given step of the series. Consider, as an example, the flow of heat from the incandescent products of combustion in the firebox of a boiler through the boiler wall and to the outside air. In this system, energy is liberated from chemical storage in the fuel as a result of combination of the carbon and the hydrogen with oxygen. The liberated energy first evidences itself as internal energy, kinetically stored by virtue of high temperature, in the products of combustion. These products consist in part of gases at high temperature and in part of incandescent carbon particles. Since the firebox walls bound the space in which incandescent and high temperature materials are formed, they are necessarily at the lowest temperatures which exist interior to the system and heat will flow to them by the parallel processes of convection from the hot gases and vapors and radiation from the incandescent solid surfaces and from such nonluminous products of combustion as carbon dioxide and water vapor. Once this energy has been received at the inner surface of the walls, it must be transferred by the mechanism of conduction to the embedded tubes (for water cooled walls) or through the walls to the outer surface. From the outer surface transmission again occurs, this time by the combined mechanisms of convection to the surrounding air and radiation to such surfaces as are able to "see" the exterior surface of the firebox wall. Thus, for this system, the processes whereby the thermal energy released in the products of combustion escapes from the combustion chamber are convection plus radiation to the interior surface followed by conduction through the solid wall followed by convection and radiation from the exterior surface to the surroundings; a total of five separate heat transfer processes are involved in transferring that portion of the thermal energy which escapes from the interior of the combustion space to the surroundings.

There are many other examples of the series flow of heat, by more than one mechanism, through the various thermal resistances of any system. Examination of but a few such cases will suffice to show that it would be most convenient to express all heat transfer relationships, regardless of the mechanism by which transfer occurs, in terms of the same general equation. From the considerations of section 1.2, it is evident that the three mechanisms of heat transmission differ widely, but, to permit the development of a general equation for combined transmission, methods have been developed for expressing heat transfer by all mechanisms in terms of one irrational but empirically acceptable equation,

$$dq = C'dt \tag{1.1}$$

which states that the differential heat transfer rate, dq, in Btu per unit time, is equal to the product of some coefficient C' and the differential temperature difference dt.

Recognition of the desirability of establishing a general equation in the form of 1.1 will justify some of the seemingly irrational steps taken in subsequent analyses of the three mechanisms of heat transmission. Assuming that all three mechanisms can be expressed in the form of equation 1.1, it is then evident that whenever two or more mechanisms are found to act in parallel the total heat transfer across that part of the path would be given by an equation of the form,

$$dq = (C'_{\text{conduction}} + C'_{\text{convection}} + C'_{\text{radiation}})\,dt$$
$$= (C_c' + C_v' + C_r')\,dt \tag{1.2}$$

whereas for series heat transfer the general equation would take the form,*

$$q = \frac{1}{\dfrac{1}{C_c'} + \dfrac{1}{C_v'} + \dfrac{1}{C_r'}}(t_2 - t_1) \tag{1.3}$$

The C' terms in equation 1.3 are called conductances and have units of Btu per hour per degree Fahrenheit temperature difference.

* This equation can be written by direct analogy with an electrical circuit or can be derived as follows:

Consider heat transfer along three paths in series: by conduction across the path for which the temperature difference is $t_2 - t$; by convection across the path for which the temperature difference is $t - t'$; by radiation across the path for which the temperature difference is $t' - t_1$. The standard equations expressing heat transmission along each of these paths are then,

$$q_{\text{conduction}} = q_c = C_c'\,(t_2 - t)$$
$$q_{\text{convection}} = q_v = C_v'\,(t - t')$$
$$q_{\text{radiation}} = q_r = C_r'\,(t' - t_1)$$

Now solving each of the above equations for its temperature difference,

$$(t_2 - t) = q_c/C_c'$$
$$(t - t') = q_v/C_v'$$
$$(t' - t_1) = q_r/C_r'$$

Adding these three equations and noting that for series heat transfer in steady state a necessary condition is that the rate of heat transfer through each section of the series path be the same and equal to the overall rate, q,

$$(t_2 - t) + (t - t') + (t' - t_1) = (t_2 - t_1) = q/(1/C_c' + 1/C_v' + 1/C_r')$$

or,

$$q = \frac{(t_2 - t_1)}{\dfrac{1}{C_c'} + \dfrac{1}{C_v'} + \dfrac{1}{C_r'}}$$

Analogous to equation 1.3, a general equation can be written for any series path consisting of n parts,

$$q = \left[\frac{1}{\frac{1}{C_1'} + \frac{1}{C_2'} + \frac{1}{C_3'} + \frac{1}{C_4'} + \cdots + \frac{1}{C_n'}}\right](t_2 - t_1) = U'(t_2 - t_1) \tag{1.4}$$

where U' is defined by the bracketed coefficient and is evaluable in terms of the conductances of the system; the units of U', like C', are Btu per hour per degree Fahrenheit and this term is called the overall coefficient of heat transfer. It will be noted that no area is explicitly included in equation 1.4, but the various areas of the elements of path will be shown to appear as part of the conductances, hence, to be implicit in U'.

By analogy with electrical systems, it is often desirable to rewrite equation 1.4 in terms of the reciprocals of the conductances, or thermal resistances, R'. The equation then becomes,

$$q = (t_2 - t_1)/(R_1' + R_2' + R_3' + R_4' + \cdots + R_n') = (t_2 - t_1)/R' \tag{1.5}$$

where R' is the total resistance of the series system and is equal to the reciprocal of the overall coefficient of heat transfer.

Evaluation of the various conductances or resistances of any system requires analysis of many factors. The geometry of each path in the system, the characteristics of radiating surfaces, and the physical properties of the materials through which conductive or convective transfer occur are all items which must be fully investigated before each separate conductance or resistance can be evaluated. In large measure the considerations taken up in the following chapters have to do with explicit evaluation of individual conductances and resistances of heat transfer systems. Once the individual values are evaluated the overall coefficient for any system can be readily obtained by considering the total path as a combination of series paths, any one of which may have parallel heat flow by two or more mechanisms, and making use of the two basic relationships:

(1) For parallel heat flow along any thermal path, the combined conductance of the path is equal to the sum of the individual conductances;

$$C' = C_1' + C_2' + C_3' + \cdots + C_n' \tag{1.6}$$

(2) For series heat flow the combined conductance, now called the overall coefficient, is equal to the reciprocal of the sum of the individual resistances;

$$U' = 1/(R_1' + R_2' + R_3' + R_4' + \cdots + R_n') = 1/R' \tag{1.7}$$

noting that the resistance for any section of a series path is the reciprocal of the combined conductance for that section of the path as given by equation 1.6. With known overall coefficient the rate of heat transfer for any steady-state system is then given by equation 1.4.

1.5. Evaporative Cooling. In many cases in practice where rapid removal of energy is essential the three mechanisms of normal heat transmission are unsatisfactory because of time delay due to irreducible thermal resistances. When this situation exists it is sometimes possible to localize the process of actual heat transmission, thereby reducing the resistance by reducing the length of path, and then carrying the energy away in stored form in a working substance. One of the most common examples of a combined process of this kind is that of putting a fire out by wetting it. To stop the fire it is necessary to transfer heat out of the combustible material so rapidly that its temperature will drop below the ignition point. No satisfactory means exists for connecting the flaming material with a thermal path along which sufficiently rapid loss of energy by conduction, convection, or radiation could occur; the alternative procedure is to bring into contact with the fire some fluid which on receiving heat will undergo phase change, leaving the region of the fire as a vapor and carrying with it the large quantity of energy that is added during vaporization. In this case the actual process of heat transfer from fire to water occurs with great rapidity in a very localized area; the energy is then carried away by mass transfer.

Another common example of a mass-transfer evaporative-cooling process is that represented by the action of the human sweat glands. For an occupant resting or doing light work in an average comfortable atmosphere the necessary loss of body heat occurs by the mechanisms of convection to the surrounding air and radiation to the surrounding surfaces. For a man doing heavy work, however, or for an occupant of a hot space, the resistance to convective and radiant loss is such that these two mechanisms become incapable of removing body heat at the rate at which it is produced. Under this circumstance the human body utilizes the emergency device of discharging moisture from the sweat glands to wet the body surface and thus provides the necessary increase in heat loss through the agency of evaporative cooling. Curiously, therefore, the thermal value of body moisture is realized *only* if the moisture is allowed to evaporate from the body surface; "mopping one's brow" is a thermally undesirable action since it removes moisture in liquid form which, if allowed to evaporate, would carry away a large part of the latent heat of vaporization.

In the human thermal system evaporative loss occurs, normally, due to the operation of the insensible perspiration glands at a rate which remains fixed at approximately 100 Btu per hour. The sweat glands, which secrete a chemically different fluid from normal perspiration, permit evaporative losses of the order of 1000 Btu per hour, but they are only intended for emergency service and are incapable of secreting moisture in amounts which would permit maintenance of this rate of evaporative cooling for any extended length of time.

In the field of industrial engineering evaporative coolers and condensers find extensive application. They are used in steam power plants, in refrigeration and air conditioning systems, and for many purposes in the process industries.

CHAPTER II

Conduction

2.1. Heat Transfer by Conduction. The basic equation for steady state conductive heat transfer is that of Fourier,

$$q = -\int (kA)\,(dt/dL) \tag{2.1}$$

where,

q = rate of heat transfer by conduction, Btu/hr

k = thermal conductivity of the material through which transfer is occurring, Btu/(hr) (sq ft) (°F/ft)

A = area normal to the path of heat flow, sq ft

dt/dL = temperature gradient, °F/ft

In the general case both k and A must remain under the integral sign as either or both of them may vary with position along the path. The negative sign on the right hand side of equation 2.1 indicates that the temperature decreases as the length of path, L, increases.

For a homogeneous material the value of the thermal conductivity will vary only with temperature, and, in many practical cases, the variation will be found so slight as to be negligible for purposes of engineering calculations. For most metals k decreases with temperature increase whereas for most nonmetals it undergoes a slight increase with increasing temperature; in neither case is the change, for solids, of appreciable engineering importance. With liquids and gases the variation is much more pronounced, but the simple conduction equation is rarely applicable to fluids because of convection effects. For engineering application, therefore, the conduction equation can usually be written,

$$q = -k \int (A/dL)\,dt \tag{2.2}$$

2.2. Conduction Through a Plane Surface. When conduction occurs through a plane surface, such as a wall, the area does not vary with length hence can be taken outside the integral sign; at the same time the variation of t with L will be linear, for constant k, so the conduction equation will integrate to the form,

$$q = -kA(t_1 - t_2)/(L_1 - L_2) = \frac{kA}{(L_2 - L_1)}(t_1 - t_2) \quad (2.3)$$

where subscripts *1* and *2* represent initial and final values along the path. The equation can more conveniently be written,

$$q = (kA/L)(t_h - t_c) = C_c'(t_h - t_c) \quad (2.4)$$

(For graphical solution refer to Fig. 2.1, p. 23)

where the subscripts h and c designate hot and cold, L is the length of path along which heat is flowing, and the conductance C_c' is defined by,

$$C_c' = kA/L \quad (2.5)$$

The thermal resistance for this system is then $R_c' = 1/C_c' = L/kA$.

From equation 2.5 it is evident that the conductance of a plane path varies directly with the cross-section area and the thermal conductivity and inversely with the length. The resistance to thermal flow can be visualized as being similar to the resistance offered to fluid flow except that for conduction there is a property of the path (thermal conductivity) which is of controlling importance whereas for fluid flow the corresponding property (viscosity) is associated with the flowing material rather than with the conduit through which flow occurs.

2.3. Thermal Conductivity. Solving equation 2.4 for the thermal conductivity we obtain,

$$k = (L)(q)/(A)(\Delta t) \quad (2.6)$$

which shows that the conductivity has physical meaning as it is numerically equal to the quantity of heat that would flow in unit time through a path of unit area, unit length, and with unit temperature difference. Thus if a 1°F temperature difference were maintained between two opposite faces of a 1 foot copper cube (the four other sides being perfectly insulated) the experimentally determined heat flow through the block in one hour, 240 Btu, would be numerically equal to the thermal conductivity of copper.

The variation in the thermal conductivities of different materials is so great, the extreme ratios being of the order of 10,000 to 1, that care must be exercised in selecting an accurate value for the material through which conductive heat transfer is to be evaluated. Most metals have high thermal conductivities of the order of 30 Btu/(hr) (sq ft) (°F/ft) or more whereas most materials used for purposes of insulation have conductivities less than 1/1000 of this value. The low thermal conductivity of most insulants, however, is not due to the material itself, but rather to the small pockets of "dead" air which are trapped in the interstices of porous insulating materials. Still air has a conductivity of the order of 0.01 Btu/(hr) (sq ft) (°F/ft) hence a material which traps large numbers of small air pockets will be highly resistant to heat flow. The effectiveness of such insulants as fibre board, cork, and mineral wool is derived largely from the entrapped air rather than from the solid matter.

The thickness of solids through which conductive heat transfer takes place is usually an inch or less rather than being measurable in feet. For this reason it is frequently convenient to define the thermal conductivity in Btu/(hr) (sq ft) (°F/inch) and thus permit the use of L'', measured in inches, in equation 2.4. Such units are frequently employed in practice, hence, in looking up values of k it is essential to check the units in which it is given in order to assure correct use. The value of k when expressed in inches is 12 times greater than when the units are in feet; throughout this text both k and L will always be expressed in the consistent and basic units of feet. (For typical values of k see Table I in the Appendix).

Although it is common practice to classify materials as either conductors or insulants, the engineer should remain aware of the fact that *any* material will act as an insulant if it is present in sufficient quantity. Certainly it is far more economical to insulate a house with a few inches of mineral wool rather than with many feet of copper, but since all materials afford resistance to thermal transfer they all serve in some measure as insulants. The primary distinction between a thermal conductor and a thermal insulator is not so much with respect to what the material does but rather what it is intended to do. Both insulators and conductors provide thermal resistance, however, the intent of the conductor is to facilitate the transfer of heat whereas the intent of the insulator is to minimize heat transfer.

2.4. Conduction through a Homogeneous Non-Plane Surface. In many cases the flow of heat occurs through solids in which the area normal to the path of heat flow varies as a function of the distance along the path. In such cases the area for use in equation 2.4 must be a mean value determinable from the particular path. With complete generality, the conductance for transfer by conduction along any homogeneous path can be defined by the equation,

$$C_c' = (kA_m)/L = 1/R' \tag{2.7}$$

where:

(1) For uni-directional heat flow A_m is equal to the fixed cross-section area of the path.

(2) For two-directional heat transfer A_m is the mean area and can, in general, be evaluated by noting that:

(a) When the area increases or decreases continuously in the direction of heat flow, the mean area can be taken as equal to the arithmetical average of the maximum and minimum areas (with maximum error of 4%) provided the maximum area is not more than twice as great as the minimum; thus,

$$A_m = (A_{max} + A_{min})/2 \text{ when } A_{max}/A_{min} < 2 \quad (2.8)$$

(b) When the area increases or decreases continuously in the direction of heat flow and the ratio of maximum to minimum area exceeds 2, the logarithmic mean area should be used,

$$A_m = (A_{max} - A_{min})/[\log_e (A_{max}/A_{min})] \quad (2.9)$$

(For graphical solution refer to Fig. 2.2, p. 25)

(3) For heat flow in three directions such as out through a sphere, the geometric mean area should be used,

$$A_m = [(A_{max})(A_{min})]^{1/2} \quad (2.10)$$

(For graphical solution refer to Fig. 2.3, p. 27)

In problems involving heat transfer through the walls of a pipe or tube, equation 2.7 can be re-written in the somewhat more convenient form,

$$C_o' = (k/L)(A_m/A_o)(A_o) = A_o/R_{co} \quad (2.11)$$

(For graphical solution refer to Figs. 2.4 & 2.5, pp. 29 & 31)

where R_{co} is the thermal resistance of the tube wall per square foot of outside surface area and A_o is the outside surface area in square feet.

2.5. Conduction through Composite Solids. In many cases heat flows by conduction through a series of solids. For an insulated pipe, for example, conduction occurs through the pipe wall and then through the insulating material. The composite wall of an insulated house or a cold storage warehouse may have many thermally different wall sections in series. In all such cases, for heat flow in one, two, or all three directions, the general conduction equation takes the form,

$$q = U'(t_h - t_c) \quad (2.12)$$

where t_h and t_c are temperatures of the hot and cold *surfaces*, respectively, and the value of the coefficient U' may be found from the equation,

$$U' = \frac{1}{(L_1/k_1A_1) + (L_2/k_2A_2) + \cdots + (L_n/k_nA_n)}$$

$$= \frac{1}{\frac{1}{C_1'} + \frac{1}{C_2'} + \cdots + \frac{1}{C_n'}} \qquad (2.13)$$

in which the area in each conductance term is the mean area for that particular length of path.

2.6. Conduction in the Unsteady State. With steady-state heat transfer the temperature at any fixed point along the path does not change with time, hence the medium, such as a copper rod or a pipe wall, merely provides a thermal "conduit" through which the energy flows, but does not provide either a source or a sink for energy; in short, the energy content of the medium does not change during, or as a result of, the flow of heat through it. With unsteady-state heat transfer the situation is markedly different; the temperature along the path changes with time hence energy flows into or from storage in the medium as well as flowing through it. Thus for unsteady-state analyses, the thermal capacity of the medium, the product of specific heat and weight density, must be considered as well as the thermal conductivity.

Consider a copper rod of fixed cross-section which is in equilibrium at a uniform temperature t_1; since the rod is homogeneous its internal energy has a fixed value at all points and is equal to the specific heat of the rod multiplied by its weight density and its temperature. If, now, the left end of this rod is heated to fixed temperature t_2 and if the sides are perfectly insulated, the temperature at every point of the rod to the right of its left end will come to some equilibrium value greater than t_1 and less than t_2. Taking the thermal conductivity of copper as constant with respect to temperature, the equilibrium temperature gradient through the rod will be a straight line and the equilibrium distribution of internal energy will likewise vary linearly. If the rod were made of some material for which the thermal capacity was only one-half as great as that of copper but for which the conductivity was the same, it is evident that the quantity of internal energy going into storage during the transient heat-up period would be only one-half as much as for the copper rod, but that once steady state was reached, the rate of heat flow through both rods would be equal and the temperature gradients would be identical.

The above example shows that the influence of thermal capacity on rate of heat transfer is present only during the period of transience; the greater the thermal capacity the longer will be the transient interval. By a crude analogy one can compare the initial flow of heat into a rod at uniform temperature with the initial flow of water out over dry earth; the rate at which the water moves out from the point of initial flow will depend on how rapidly it is absorbed; thus, over clay or other relatively non-porous material, the water would rapidly flow across the surface whereas with sand or equivalent porous material, the initial absorption would be so great that there would be little tendency for the process of wetting to extend very far beyond the point at which the water was released. Similarly, with heat flow into the cold rod, all of the heat which enters at the warm end will flow through the rod only if the temperature gradient corresponds to that for steady-state conditions. Initially the temperature at all points throughout the rod will be lower than the steady-state value, hence the energy which enters as heat will be rapidly absorbed into the rod and will go into storage as kinetic internal energy with a consequent temperature rise in the section of rod which absorbs heat. For a medium of low thermal capacity, the amount of energy absorbed in reaching steady state is less for a given value of thermal conductivity, hence the rate at which the energy flow moves out from the source is greater and the time interval for reaching steady state is considerably decreased.

From the above discussion it appears that two factors, thermal conductivity and thermal capacity, have opposite effects during the period of transience; a high value of conductivity decreases the time required for achieving a steady-state whereas a high value of thermal capacity increases the quantity of energy absorbed by the medium thereby increasing the interval of time before steady-state is reached. These two factors are accordingly grouped in a term which is also a fluid property, thermal diffusivity, α. It is defined as the ratio of thermal conductivity to thermal capacity, $k/\rho c_p$. Thermal diffusivity is indicative of the rate at which a change of temperature is experienced through the working substance. In effect, the numerator of the thermal diffusivity, thermal conductivity, shows the tendency toward rapid travel of temperature change through the working substance whereas the denominator, thermal capacity, varies directly as the resistance to temperature diffusion (represented by the ability of the material to absorb thermal energy during the process of a temperature change).

The general equation for conduction through a homogeneous solid, when k is taken as constant, is given by the equation,

$$dt/d\theta = \alpha \left(\frac{\partial^2 t}{\partial x^2} + \frac{\partial^2 t}{\partial y^2} + \frac{\partial^2 t}{\partial z^2} \right) \qquad (2.14)$$

For uni-directional heat transfer equation 2.14 simplifies to,

$$dt/d\theta = \alpha(\partial^2 t/\partial x^2) \qquad (2.15)$$

which can be solved analytically for many of the cases which occur in practical problems. When mathematical solution is difficult or seemingly impossible, equation 2.15 can often be solved by the approximate methods discussed in the two sections which follow.

2.7. Approximate Methods of Unsteady-State Analysis: Holme Method. Because of the mathematical complexity of analytical procedures for analysis of transient and periodic heat flow, a number of approximate methods have been developed. Of these the method attributed to Holme[6] is particularly suitable for problems involving unsteady-state heat conduction through relatively thin walls or for heat flow to-or-from objects having a large surface-volume ratio. In essence the Holme method establishes an idealized system thermally equivalent to the actual one. The material through which heat is flowing under unsteady conditions is then visualized as passing through a succession of states (as a function of time) each of which is characterized by a temperature gradient identical with that which would exist if the conditions, at that particular time, were representative of steady-state.

Referring to Fig. A, the gradient *ab* represents steady-state conditions for heat transfer from surface-to-surface through a solid when the hot and cold surface temperatures are t_h and t_c. If the temperature of the warm surface is suddenly raised to a new value t_h' and held constant, the gradients through the solid at various times during the transient interval (until steady-state is again realized) would depart from linearity and would have shapes as indicated in a qualitative way by the dashed lines. After steady-state was regained the final gradient would be as shown by the line *a'b* and the quantity of energy which would have entered storage in the solid during the transient interval would be proportional to the average temperature change hence would be indicated by the distance *ys* on the figure.

In approximating the above situation the Holme method assumes that during a brief interval immediately following the rise in surface temperature the rate of heat flow to the solid remains constant at its initially impressed instantaneous value, q_i, which is determinable, for practical problems, from conditions external to the hot surface. This impressed instantaneous rate of heat flow is assumed to go in part to maintain the original (as fixed by gradient *ab*) rate of heat flow through the solid and in part to enter storage; the initial rate at which energy goes to storage is then

$$q_s = q_i - (kA/L)(t_h - t_c) \qquad (2.16)$$

If the time interval is taken as $\Delta\theta$, the quantity of heat assumed to enter storage is $\Delta\theta q_s$ and the resultant average temperature rise of the solid during the $\Delta\theta$ period is $\Delta\theta q_s/Wc_p$ where W is the weight of

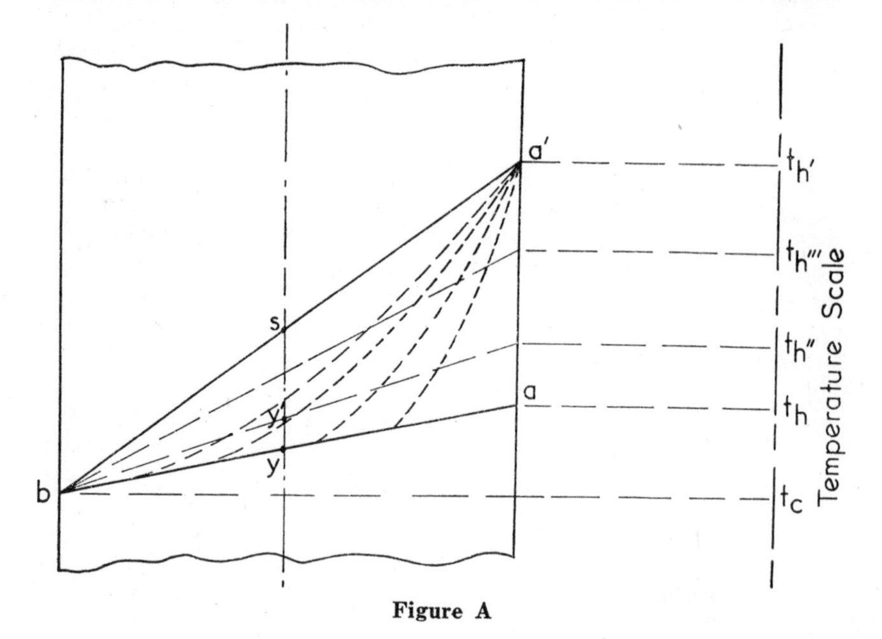

Figure A

the solid and c_p is its specific heat. Now refer to Fig. A and lay off the distance yy' corresponding to the calculated temperature change of the solid. Through point y' draw the steady-state gradient, thereby determining an "equivalent" temperature, t_h'', of the heated surface after time interval $\Delta\theta$. As a next step evaluate the rate of heat flow to storage during a second time interval $\Delta\theta_2$

$$q_{s_2} = q_{i_2} - (kA/L)(t_h'' - t_c) \tag{2.17}$$

where q_{i_2} is less than the original value, q_i, and must be determined from a knowledge of external conditions. The quantity of heat going to storage during this second interval is less than during the first and is equal to $\Delta\theta_2 q_{s_2}$ and the corresponding temperature rise of the solid during the second time interval is then $\Delta\theta_2 q_{s_2}/Wc_p$; the new temperature gradient, $t_h''' - t_c$, is constructed in the same manner as before and the analysis continued until steady state is realized.

Since the Holme method assumes instant distribution of the heat-up effect through the entire solid it is evident that the time indicated as necessary for realizing steady state after the sudden change of surface temperature will be less than that actually required; the Holme method is useful, however, as a means of determining the minimum time for return of steady state. The accuracy of the method as applied to a particular problem will depend on the conductivity and diffusivity of the solid and on its mass; for heavy solids the influence of a sudden change at one side will not be experienced at the other side for an extended time interval (some European cathedrals have walls so heavy that the effect of summer outside-air temperatures is not experienced at the inside surface of the walls until winter; a six months lag of this kind permits the summer sun to provide winter heat and winter cold to provide summer cooling effect).

In general the Holme method is suitable for problems involving heat flow to-or-from a large source or receiver through a transfer surface of only moderate resistance or for thermally "heavy" systems in which the transient boundary condition is impressed very slowly.

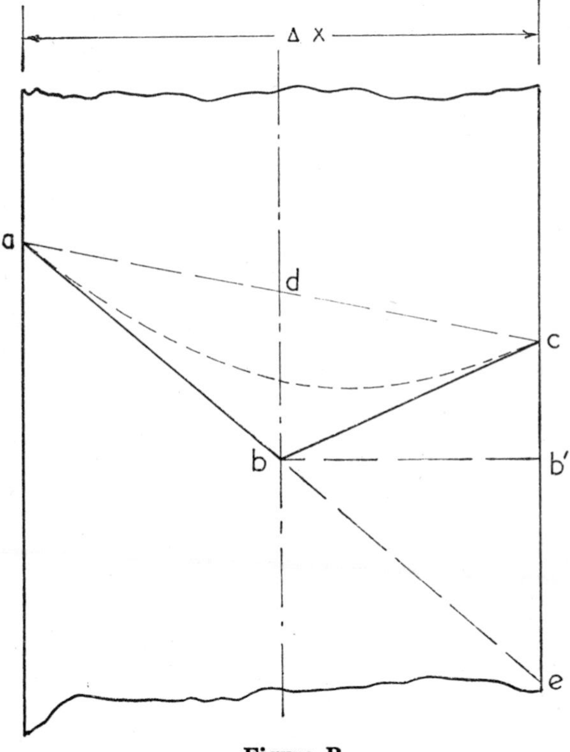

Figure B

2.8. Approximate Methods of Unsteady-State Analysis: Schmidt Method. In contrast with the Holme method, E. Schmidt[7] has developed a graphical procedure applicable to either transient or periodic problems and providing an accuracy as great as the requirements of the problem may indicate. The Schmidt method makes use of the principle of finite differences and is adaptable to graphical methods of solution which greatly simplify the problem though at the expense of considerable routine drafting. To develop the basic equation of the Schmidt procedure consider (Fig. B) a small width, Δx, of a homogeneous wall. The actual unsteady state temperature gradient through this section is shown by the dashed line whereas the tangents, ab and bc, to this gradient at the left and right sides of the small width are, respectively, the instantaneous gradients at these edges. Now extend the line ab to intersect the right side of Δx at point e and connect points a and c with a straight line which intersects the center line of the Δx section at d. The instantaneous rate of heat flow into the elementary wall section through the left side is then, from Fig. B,

$$q_l = -kA(dt/dL)_l = +kA(b'e/0.5\Delta x) = 2kA(b'e/\Delta x) \qquad (2.18)$$

and the instantaneous rate of heat flow into the same wall section from the right side is,

$$q_r = -kA(dt/dL)_r = +kA(b'c/0.5\Delta x) = 2kA(b'c/\Delta x) \qquad (2.19)$$

The instantaneous rate at which heat is going into storage in the wall element is the sum of the rates at which heat is crossing the left and right boundaries hence the quantity of energy that goes to storage in a small time interval $\Delta\theta$ is,

$$Q_{to\ storage} = 2kA\Delta\theta[(b'e + b'c)/\Delta x] = 2kA\Delta\theta(ce/\Delta x) \qquad (2.20)$$

But during the time interval $\Delta\theta$ the internal energy of the wall element will have to increase by an amount equal to the energy which flows in through the sides; the mean temperature of the element will therefore increase by an increment of Δt and we can write,

$$Q_{to\ storage} = \rho c_p(\Delta x)A(\Delta t) = 2kA\Delta\theta(ce/\Delta x) \qquad (2.21)$$

where ρ is the weight density of the wall and c_p is its specific heat. But from Fig. B the distance ce, by similar triangles, is seen to be equal to $2(bd)$ so substituting for ce and solving for bd,

$$bd = \rho c_p A(\Delta x)(\Delta t)(\Delta x)/(4kA\Delta\theta) = \rho c_p(\Delta x)^2(\Delta t)/4k\Delta\theta$$

or

$$bd = [\rho c_p(\Delta x)^2/4k\Delta\theta](\Delta t) \qquad (2.22)$$

The increments Δx and $\Delta\theta$ in the above equation can be arbitrarily selected so that the bracketed term will be equal to unity; in that event,

$$bd = \Delta t \qquad (2.23)$$

which indicates that the linear distance bd is equal (on the adopted temperature scale) to the mean change in temperature of the small wall section Δx during the time interval $\Delta\theta$. This means that by proper selection of the Δx and $\Delta\theta$ values it is possible to determine the temperature at the center of a Δx section after a $\Delta\theta$ time interval by merely connecting the points where the gradient through that section intersects the left and right walls.

Extensions[8] of the Schmidt method permit its application to problems involving compound walls and to cases involving transfer across air films and internal air spaces. The method can also be used for flow through non-plane walls.

Conduction Through a Plane Surface

Conduction from surface-to-surface through a plane solid when the area does not vary along the path.

Equation: $q = kA(t_h - t_c)/L$

Text Reference: Section 2.2, equation 2.4.

Extensions: None.

Special Conditions: The units of thermal conductivity are taken as Btu/(hr)(sq ft)(°F/ft).

Example: A six square foot sheet of a certain material has a thermal conductivity of 0.07 Btu/(hr)(sq ft)(°F/ft). The thickness of the sheet is 0.014 feet and one side is maintained at a surface temperature of 375 F when the steady-state surface temperature of the opposite surface is 50 F. Determine the rate at which heat is flowing by conduction through the sheet.

Solution: Enter the graph (Fig. 2.1) at the base scale for a hot surface temperature of 375 F, rise to intersection with the diagonal for a cold surface temperature of 50 F, then move horizontally left to intersection with the transfer line; rise vertically to intersect the radial line for six square foot area, then move horizontally to the left to intersection with the radial line for a length of 0.014 feet; rise to intersection with the radial for thermal conductivity of 0.07, then move horizontally left to intersect the transfer line and finally rise to intersection of the top scale where read the heat transfer rate as 9750 Btu per hour.

Check: $q = (0.07)(6)(375 - 50)/(0.014) = 9750$ Btu/hr

Note: For cases in which the surface area exceeds the scale values by any multiple of 10, the actual rate of heat transfer will exceed the scale values by the same multiple of ten. For cases in which the length of path exceeds the scale value by any multiple of 10, the indicated rate of heat transfer will exceed the actual value by the same multiple of ten.

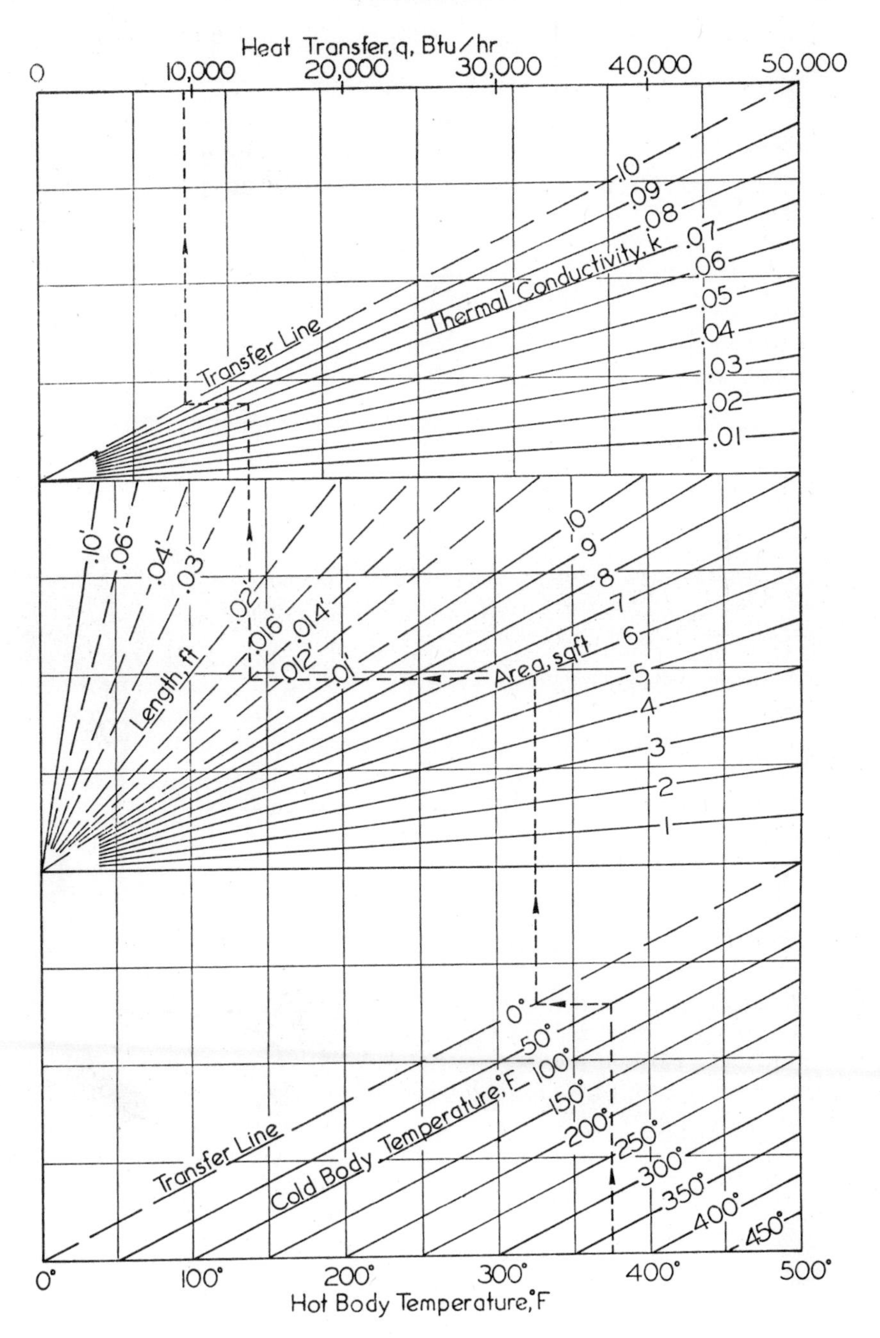
Heat Transfer, q, Btu/hr
0
10,000
20,000
30,000
40,000
50,000
Thermal Conductivity, k
.10
.09
.08
.07
.06
.05
.04
.03
.02
.01
Transfer Line
.10'
.06'
.04'
.03'
.02'
.016'
.014'
.012'
.01'
Length, ft
Area, sqft
10
9
8
7
6
5
4
3
2
1
Transfer Line
Cold Body Temperature, °F
0°
50°
100°
150°
200°
250°
300°
350°
400°
450°
0°
100°
200°
300°
400°
500°
Hot Body Temperature, °F

Figure 2.1

Logarithmic Mean Area, or Diameter, or Temperature Difference

Evaluation of logarithmic mean area (for radial heat transfer through cylinders) or evaluation of logarithmic mean temperature difference.

Equations: $A_m = \frac{A_{max} - A_{min}}{\log_e (A_{max}/A_{min})}$ $\quad \Delta t_m = \frac{\Delta t_{max} - \Delta t_{min}}{\log_e (\Delta t_{max}/\Delta t_{min})}$

Text References: Section 2.4, equation 2.9 (for area) and section 5.7, equation 5.25 (for temperature difference).

Extensions: The solution is applicable to evaluation of the logarithmic mean of any two quantities (as diameters, radii, etc.).

Special Conditions: None.

Example: The outside surface area of a length of insulated pipe is 140 sq ft and the inside surface area is 60 sq ft. Determine the mean surface area for use in evaluating the heat transfer by conduction through the pipe.

Solution: Enter the graph (Fig. 2.2) at the base scale for a value of the larger quantity of 140 and rise vertically to intersection with the line which represents a smaller quantity of 60 sq ft; from this intersection move horizontally left (in some cases *right*) to intersect the transfer line and then rise vertically to intersection of the top scale at the log mean value of 94 sq ft.

Check: $A_m = (140 - 60)/\log_e(140/60) = 80/0.848 = 94.4$ sq ft.

Note: In most cases a simpler and more rapid method of evaluating the logarithmic mean area is to use the graphical solution to determine the logarithmic mean radius or diameter and then to use this value in direct calculation of the value of A_m.

When the ratio of larger quantity to smaller quantity is less than 2 the arithmetical average will be within 4% of the logarithmic mean averages.

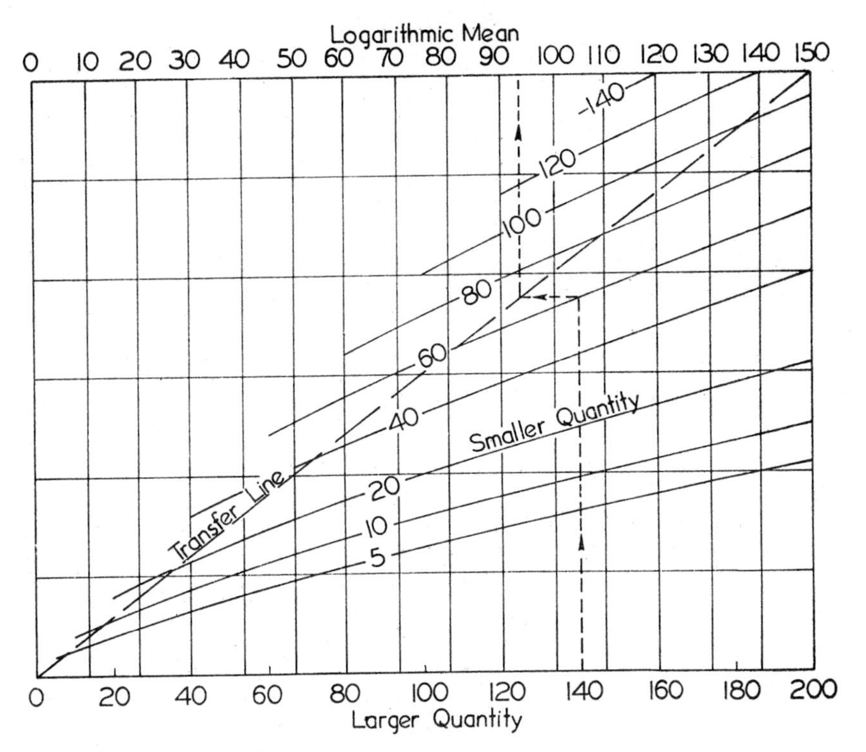
Logarithmic Mean
0 10 20 30 40 50 60 70 80 90 100 110 120 130 140 150
140
120
100
80
60
40
20
10
5
Transfer Line
Smaller Quantity
0 20 40 60 80 100 120 140 160 180 200
Larger Quantity

Figure 2.2

Geometrical Mean Area

Evaluation of geometrical mean area (for cases involving radial heat flow in a sphere).

Equation: $A_m = [(A_{max})(A_{min})]^{1/2}$

Text Reference: Section 2.4, equation 2.10.

Extension: The solution is applicable to any case requiring evaluation of the geometrical mean of two quantities.

Special Conditions: None.

Example: The inside and outside surface areas of a hollow sphere are 2 sq ft and 8 sq ft respectively. Determine the mean area for use in calculating conductive heat transfer through the wall of the sphere.

Solution. Enter the graph (Fig. 2.3) at the base scale for a value of inside surface area equal to 2 sq ft and rise to intersection with the line for outside surface area of 8 sq ft; from this intersection move horizontally right (in some cases this direction will be *left*) to intersect the transfer line and then rise to the top scale where read the value of the geometrical mean area as 4 sq ft.

Note that the solution could have been obtained equally as well by entering the graph at the value of the outside surface area and rising to intersect the inside surface area.

Check: $A_m = (2 \times 8)^{1/2} = 4$ sq ft.

Note: In most cases a simpler and more rapid method of evaluating the geometric mean area is to use the graphical solution to determine the geometric mean radius or diameter and then to use this value in direct calculation of the value of A_m.

For cases in which both the larger and smaller quantities exceed the scale values by the same multiple of 10 the geometrical average will exceed the scale value by the same multiple of 10.

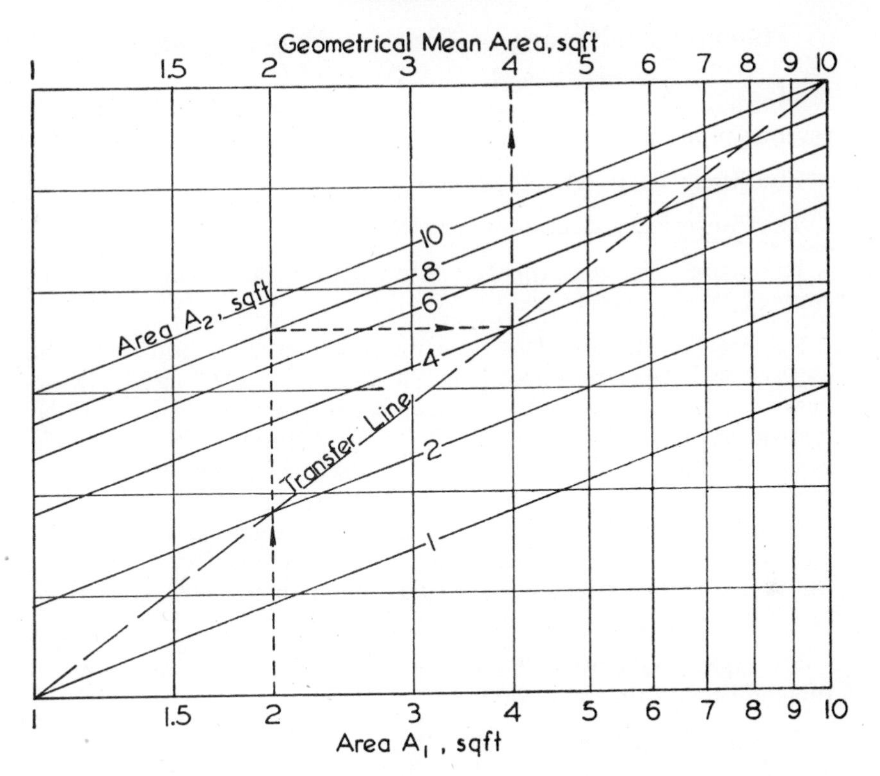
Geometrical Mean Area, sqft
1
1.5
2
3
4
5
6
7
8
9
10
Area A_2, sqft
10
8
6
4
2
1
Transfer Line
Area A_1, sqft

Figure 2.3

Thermal Resistance — Walls of Non-Ferrous Tube

Thermal resistance of non-ferrous tube (refer to Fig. 2.5 for ferrous pipe) per square foot of *outside* surface area.

Equation: $R_{co} = (A_o/A_m)(L/k)$

Text Reference: Section 2.4, equation 2.11.

Extension: Use reciprocal of result with Figs. 5.2 through 5.6 to convert to a lineal foot basis.

Special Conditions: The tube diameter (which influences the ratio of outside surface area to mean surface area for a given thickness) does not appear in the solution because most tube used in heat transmission service meets the following "standard": Wall thickness of 0.035″ is used with ⅝″ or ¾″ tube; wall thickness of 0.049″ is used with ⅝″ or ¾″ tube; wall thicknesses of 0.058″, 0.065″, 0.072″, and 0.083″ are customarily used with respective tube diameters of ⅞″, 1″, 1½″, and 2″. The error resulting from neglect of the two diameters which each correspond to wall thicknesses of 0.035″ and 0.049″ will be less than 1%.

Example: Determine the thermal resistance of a muntz metal tube having a thickness of 0.050″.

Solution: Enter the bottom of the graph (Fig. 2.4) at a thickness of 0.050″ and rise to intersect the line for muntz metal; from this point move horizontally to the right (in some cases this direction will be to the *left*) to intersection with the transfer line and from here rise to the top scale where read the thermal resistance as 0.00006 (hr)/(Btu) for each square foot of outside surface of the tube.

Check: The conductivity of muntz metal is 73 Btu/(hr) (sq ft) (°F/ft) and the mean diameter of ¾″ outside diameter tube having 0.05″ wall thickness is 0.70″. Substituting in the equation for thermal resistance,

$R_{co} = (0.75/0.70)(0.05/12)/73 = 0.000061$ based on unit area of outside surface of the tube.

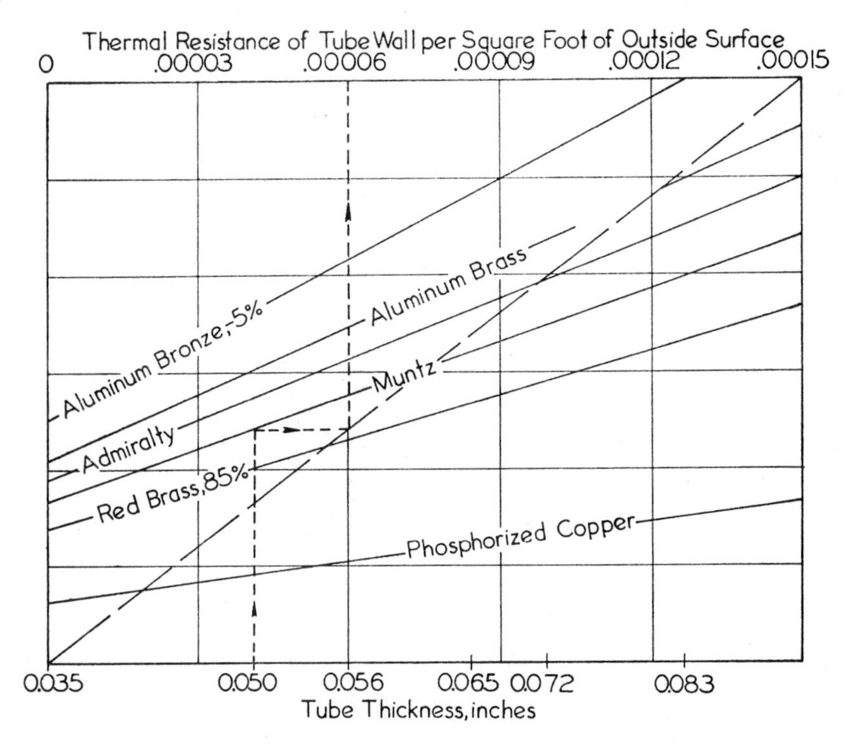
Thermal Resistance of Tube Wall per Square Foot of Outside Surface
0
.00003
.00006
.00009
.00012
.00015
Aluminum Bronze,-5%
Aluminum Brass
Admiralty
Muntz
Red Brass, 85%
Phosphorized Copper
0.035
0.050
0.056
0.065
0.072
0.083
Tube Thickness, inches

Figure 2.4

Thermal Resistance — Walls of Ferrous Tube

Thermal resistance of ferrous tube (refer to Fig. 2.4 for non-ferrous tube) per square foot of *outside* tube area.

Equation: $R_{co} = (A_o/A_m)(L/k)$

Text Reference: Section 2.4, equation 2.11.

Extension: The reciprocal of the result obtained from this graph can be used with Figs. 5.2 through 5.6 to obtain wall conductance per lineal foot of tube.

Special Conditions: The tube diameter (which influences the ratio of outside surface area to mean surface area for a given tube wall thickness) does not appear in the solution because most tube used in heat transmission service meets the following "standard": Wall thickness of 0.035″ is used with 5/8″ and 3/4″ tube; wall thickness of 0.049″ is used with 5/8″ and 3/4″ tube; wall thicknesses of 0.058″, 0.065″, 0.072″, and 0.083″ are customarily used with respective tube diameters of 7/8″, 1″, 1½″, and 2″. The error resulting from neglect of the different diameters which correspond to the same wall thickness will be less than 1%.

Example: A 1½″ tube of carbon steel (SAE 1010, 1008) with wall thickness of 0.072″ is to be used in a heat exchanger. Determine the thermal resistance of the tube wall per square foot of outside surface.

Solution: Enter the scale (Fig. 2.5) at the bottom of the graph at a value of wall thickness of 0.072″ and rise to intersect the line for carbon steel; from this intersection move horizontally left (in some cases this movement will be to the *right*) to intersection with the transfer line and from here rise to the top scale where read the thermal resistance as 0.0018 (hr)/(Btu) for each square foot of outside surface of the tube.

Check: $R_{co} = (1.5/1.43)(0.072/12)/34 = 0.00185$
(where 34 is the thermal conductivity of the carbon steel in question).

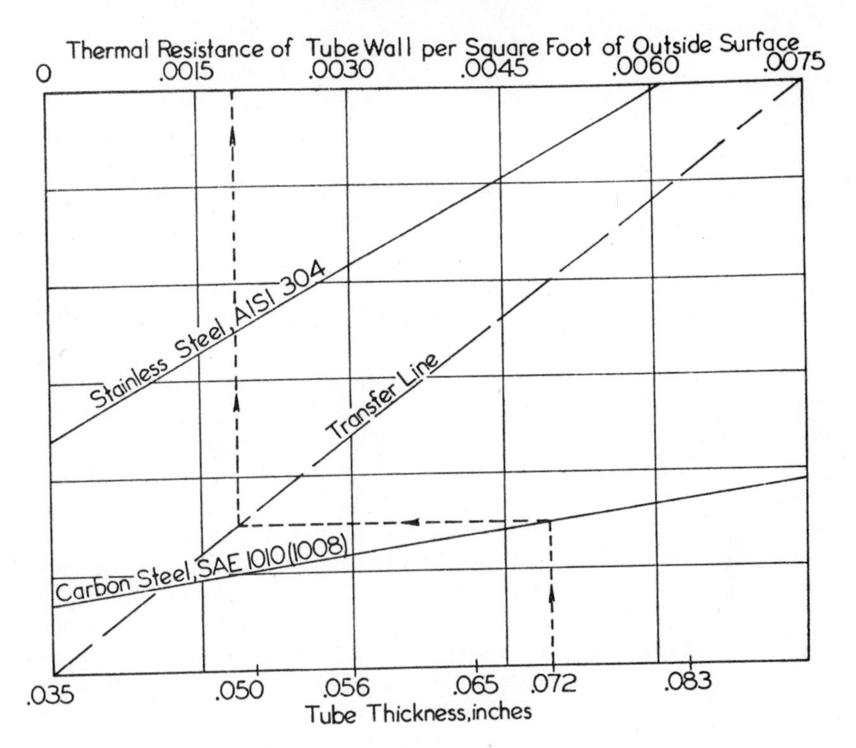
Thermal Resistance of Tube Wall per Square Foot of Outside Surface
0
.0015
.0030
.0045
.0060
.0075
Stainless Steel, AISI 304
Transfer Line
Carbon Steel, SAE 1010 (1008)
.035
.050
.056
.065
.072
.083
Tube Thickness, inches

Figure 2.5

CHAPTER III

Radiation

3.1. Heat Transfer by Radiation. The transmission of energy by the mechanism of radiation is the only case in engineering, excluding nuclear power, where one deals with energy entirely separate from mass. Radiation is sometimes discussed in terms of the wave theory and sometimes by the quantum theory; neither theory completely explains all phases of the phenomenon. The mechanism of radiation is known, however, to be based on the transfer of very small units (quanta) of pure energy (energy dissociated from mass) which move with the speed of light (186,000 miles per second) and travel through the spaces between the electron shells and the nuclei of the intervening medium. Transfer of quanta does not depend on the presence of any intervening medium and is, in fact, partially impeded by such material matter as may be present in the space between the emitting surface and the receiving surface.

In contrast with conduction and convection, radiation is a surface phenomenon, the quantity of energy leaving a heated object depending entirely on the characteristics of the object's surface (though, of course, the rate at which energy is supplied to the surface will be controlled by internal conduction and convection). Experience has shown that a perfect radiator — called a *black body* — emits radiant energy at a rate, q_s, determinable from the equation,

$$q_s = 0.172(T_s/100)^4 A_s \tag{3.1}$$

where the numerical coefficient is called the Stefan-Boltzman constant, A_s is the surface area in sq ft and T_s is the surface temperature of the black body emitter in $°F$ absolute ($°F + 460$). As is evident from equation 3.1, all black body surfaces at temperatures above absolute zero emit radiant energy, the rate increasing with the 4th power of the absolute temperature and being entirely independent of the thermal or other conditions of the surroundings. Thus, basically, radiation differs from the fundamental concept of heat which was visualized as being a flow of energy induced by a difference in temperature. No temperature difference is necessary for radiation to occur, but in order for there to be a *net* transfer of radiant energy there must be a difference in the surface temperatures of the two objects between which the exchange is taking place.

3.2. The Spectroradiometric Curve. Unlike other kinds of energy in transition, radiation varies in quality as well as quantity with the temperature of the source. At any particular temperature, radiation leaves a surface through a wide band of wave-lengths, the quantity leaving at each particular wave-length being determined jointly by the surface characteristics and by the surface temperature. At higher temperatures the amount of energy emitted at shorter wave lengths increases whereas, as the temperature is lowered, a larger fraction of the total energy is emitted in the longer thermal (infra-red) region. In the wave length range from 0.4 to 0.7 microns (1 micron being 1/25,000 of an inch) radiation affects the optic nerve as light, and, as the temperature increases, the fraction of energy emitted as light becomes greater; approximately 40% of solar radiation is in the light range whereas radiation from surfaces at temperatures of a few hundred degrees or less is too long to permit seeing the surface in the dark.

Most surfaces have emission characteristics which give spectroradiometric curves similar in form but different in magnitude from the curve for a black body. Since the shape of the curve determines the quality whereas the height determines quantity, a surface which emits radiant energy at all black body wave lengths (for the particular temperature) and at a constant fraction of black body emission at each wave length is said to be a *gray* body, and its spectroradiometric curve will have ordinates which will be a constant fraction of the black body values.

3.3. Emissivity; Absorptivity; Reflectivity; Transmissivity. For a gray body equation 3.1 takes the form,

$$q_s = 0.172 e_s (T_s/100)^4 A_s \tag{3.2}$$

where e_s is defined as the emissivity* of the surface and is equal to the ratio of emission from the actual surface to emission from a black body at the same temperature. It can be shown that the emissivity of any surface is numerically equal to its absorptivity and therefore that a gray emitter is also a gray receiver. (If this were not true, and if two surfaces at the same temperature but with different emissivities faced one another, the energy absorbed by one would exceed that emitted by the other hence a net transfer of heat would occur without a temperature difference; all experience suggests that such a situation is unlikely).

* For numerical values of the emissivity, refer to Table I in the Appendix.

All of the radiation striking a given surface must be absorbed, reflected, or transmitted, hence,

$$a + r + t = 1 \tag{3.3}$$

where a, r, and t are the absorptivity (fraction absorbed), reflectivity (fraction reflected), and the transmissivity (fraction transmitted), respectively. For opaque materials the transmissivity is zero, hence,

$$a + r = e + r = 1 \tag{3.4}$$

which says that the sum of absorbed and reflected fractions (noting that the emissivity, e, is always equal to the absorptivity) must be equal to the total incident radiation.

Clean metal surfaces usually have moderate to high values of the reflectivity, but practically all other surfaces which find use in engineering practice have emissivities in excess of 0.9 and are therefore excellent absorbers as well as emitters of radiant energy.

3.4. Directional Radiation. The energy emitted from any infinitesimal surface area leaves in all directions, hence passes through a hemispherical solid angle of 2π steradians. In evaluating radiant transfer between any two surfaces (except when one is completely enclosed by the other) it is necessary to determine the fraction of the energy leaving each surface that strikes the other surface. To develop this geometrical relationship for a pair of black bodies, equation 3.1 may be rewritten in the form,

$$dq_s = iA_s(dw) \tag{3.5}$$

where dw is any small solid angle, A_s is the area of the emitter (source), and i is the intensity of radiation leaving unit area of surface through unit solid angle in unit time. But Lambert's cosine law states that the intensity in a direction making angle ϕ_s with the normal to the emitting surface is equal to the intensity normal to the surface, i_n, multiplied by the cosine of the angle; thus

$$i = i_n \cos \phi_s \tag{3.6}$$

By substitution in equation 3.5,

$$dq_s = i_n \cos \phi_s \, (A_s) \, (dw) \tag{3.7}$$

The normal intensity, i_n, can be shown to be equal to $1/\pi$ of the total hemispherical radiation, so that on substitution into equation 3.7

$$dq_s = 0.172 (T_s/100)^4 A_s \cos \phi_s \, (dw/\pi) \tag{3.8}$$

But $(\cos \phi_s)$ (A_s) is equal to the area of the emitting surface when projected on a plane normal to the direction of emission, hence the equation shows that emission in *any* direction is at an intensity (*based on unit **projected** area*) equal to the normal intensity. The energy received from A_s by any small surface, dA_r, is thus given by equation 3.8 in which dw now represents the small solid angle subtended by the receiving surface. The subtended angle is equal to the projected area of the receiving surface in the direction of the incident radiation divided by the square of the distance from emitting surface to receiving surface, or,

$$dw = \cos \phi_r \, (dA_r)/r^2 \qquad (3.9)$$

where dA_r is the area of the small receiving surface, ϕ_r is the angle between a normal to this surface and the direction of the incident radiation and r is the distance between the source and the receiver. Then substituting into equation 3.8,

$$dq_s = 0.172 A_s (T_s/100)^4 \left[\frac{\cos \phi_s \cos \phi_r \, dA_r}{\pi r^2} \right] \qquad (3.10)$$

where the term in the bracket is equal to the fraction of energy leaving the source area, A_s, that strikes the small receiving area, dA_r. Since this term is dependent only on the geometry of the system, it is defined as the shape factor, F_a, and can be written for a receiving surface of area A_r as,

$$F_a = F_{A_r A_s} = \frac{1}{A_s} \int_{A_s} \int_{A_r} \frac{\cos \phi_s \cos \phi_r \, dA_s \, dA_r}{\pi r^2} \qquad (3.11)$$

Substitution of the shape factor into equation 3.10 gives, for receiving area A_r,

$$q_s = 0.172 \, A_s \, F_{A_r A_s} (T_s/100)^4 \qquad (3.12)$$

By analogy, the radiant energy leaving the area A_r and striking the area A_s is,

$$q_r = 0.172 \, A_r \, F_{A_s A_r} (T_r/100)^4 \qquad (3.13)$$

so the net radiant transfer from A_s to A_r must be,

$$q = 0.172 \, [F_{A_r A_s} A_s (T_s/100)^4 - F_{A_s A_r} A_r (T_r/100)^4] \qquad (3.14)$$

But evaluation of the shape factor would show that

$$F_{A_s A_r} A_r = F_{A_r A_s} A_s \qquad (3.15)$$

which is the reciprocity theorem. Then using this relationship to simplify equation 3.14 we have a final equation for evaluating net radiant transfer from black body source to black body receiver,

$$q = 0.172 \, F_{A_r A_s} A_s [(T_s/100)^4 - (T_r/100)^4] \qquad (3.16)$$

Equation 3.16 is exact for black bodies, but for gray bodies considerable difficulty arises because the interchange of reflected energy between the source and receiver will alter the net transfer rate. To account for reflected energy the reflectivities of the two surfaces must be included in the evaluation of the exchange coefficient and the simple equation for shape factor (3.11) is no longer adequate. As an approximation to the correct solution the geometry effects, as given by the simple shape factor, are sometimes treated separately from the reflection effects and two coefficients are then used,

$$q = 0.172\, F_e F_{A_r A_s} A_s[(T_s/100)^4 - (T_r/100)^4] \tag{3.17}$$

(For graphical solution refer to Fig. 3.10, p. 59)

where the coefficient, F_e, is defined as the emissivity factor. For some types of relatively simple systems equation 3.17 gives an exact solution, but for more complex cases it is necessary to develop a true combined factor; fortunately, the thermal systems important in industrial application can almost always be treated by use of coefficients for equation 3.17.

3.5. Evaluation of Shape Factors. Equation 3.11 is difficult to integrate for any but the most simple geometrical arrangements. Fortunately, however, experimental determinations of shape factors are available for some of the more important complex cases and graphical presentations are available for the cases of major industrial importance. Figures 3.1 through 3.4 give experimental shape factors for the human body with respect to energy reception from infinitesimal areas in floor, wall, or ceiling. Human shape factors are needed in the design of radiant heating and cooling systems, and of greater industrial importance, in the investigation of physiological hazard associated with certain radiologically significant industrial processes. Figures 3.5 and 3.6 are for the common cases of parallel or normal planes whereas Figures 3.7 and 3.8 give basic shape factors which can be extended (as shown by the examples with the graphs) to cover almost all cases of industrial importance.

For any body entirely enclosed by another body (including such cases as concentric cylinders) the shape factor is unity.

3.6. Evaluation of Emissivity Factors. For a small body enclosed by a large body the value of F_e is equal to the emissivity of the small body. For an enclosed body which is large with respect to the enclosing body the F_e term is given by

$$F_e = \frac{1}{1/e_1 + 1/e_2 - 1} \tag{3.18}$$

Equation 3.18 is also approximately applicable to concentric cylinders and to infinite parallel planes. For finite or for infinitesimal flat areas in parallel planes or in normal planes the approximate value of F_e is equal to the product of the two emissivities.

3.7. The Equivalent Radiant Conductance. As stated earlier (refer to section 1.4) it is desirable to establish equations for all forms of heat transfer in a standard form, thereby facilitating the analysis of cases in which series and parallel transfer occur by more than one mechanism. The accepted standard form is based on a conductance for use with the first power of the temperature difference; in order to express transfer by radiation in such form an equivalent conductance must be established for use in the equation,

$$q = C_r'(t_h - t_c) \tag{3.19}$$

Such an equation would obviously require use of an irrational coefficient since radiation is known to be proportional to the fourth rather than the first power of the temperature difference. A value of C_r' can, however, be determined by equating the rate of heat transfer, q, as given by equations 3.17 and 3.19 and solving for C_r',

$$C_r' = 0.172\, F_e F_{A_r A_s} A_s[(T_h/100)^4 - (T_c/100)^4]/(t_h - t_c) \tag{3.20}$$

Since the emissivity factor, F_e, and the generalized shape factor, F_a, depend on surface and geometry characteristics which are independent of temperature difference, it is frequently advantageous to define an equivalent radiation coefficient, h_r, by the equation,

$$C_r' = F_a F_e h_r A_s \tag{3.21}$$

Then, substituting in equation 3.19,

$$q = F_a F_e h_r (t_h - t_c) A_s \tag{3.22}$$

where F_a and F_e are evaluable by the methods discussed in sections 3.5 and 3.6, and h_r is calculable from the equation,

$$h_r = 0.172\left[\left(\frac{T_h}{100}\right)^4 - \left(\frac{T_c}{100}\right)^4\right]/(t_h - t_c) \tag{3.23}$$

(For graphical solution refer to Fig. 3.9, p. 57)

The value of h_r is very close to unity for radiant transfer occurring at room temperatures, but at higher temperatures the h_r value increases rapidly; for this reason the importance of radiant transfer relative to convective transfer becomes rapidly greater as the temperature level increases.

3.8. Gaseous and Luminous Radiation. Since radiant transfer increases as the fourth power of the temperature, the effectiveness of this mechanism of energy exchange is very much greater at high, rather than at low, temperatures. Advantage of this fact is taken in furnace construction by placing refractory materials in the firebox; such materials are heated to incandescence by the passing gases and they then transfer energy by radiation to the water tubes or other heat receiving surface. In this way the effective surface for convective transfer is materially increased. In effect, the use of such refractories provides a supplementary path for heat flow from the products of combustion to the heating surfaces of the unit. Additional refractories are provided by the inside surfaces of the firebox itself since these surfaces are raised (unless water cooled, in which case they become part of the primary heating surface) to a temperature well above that of the heating surface but less than that of the gases, the amount depending on the degree of insulation.

An extension of the above method of increasing heat transfer rate is represented in luminous flames where finely divided particles are heated to incandescence and thus radiate energy from the mass of the flame itself to refractories and to the heating surface. Since the particulate matter in the flame reaches its high temperature during the process of combustion it can be considered a primary heat source in contrast to refractories which reach a high temperature only after receiving energy by convection from the gases in the firebox or by radiation from the flame. Luminous flames thus serve to increase the transfer rate to the heating surfaces and thereby improve the thermal effectiveness of the system as a whole.

Two types of luminosity occur in the usual types of fireboxes. The first is that due to opaque particles of carbon such as are found when powdered coal is used as the fuel whereas the second type is represented by the minute semi-translucent particles of heavy hydrocarbons formed during the incomplete combustion of gaseous and, to a lesser extent, of liquid fuels. In either event the method of analysis involves consideration of a "cloud" of material, effective radiation depending to a greater extent on the effective "surface" of the cloud than on its volume. Thus, in a qualitative sense, it is evident that incomplete combustion in the early sections of a firebox may, contrary to the general opinion of a few years ago, be extremely helpful as a means of achieving a greater "yield" of energy from the fuel. Care is necessary, however, to maintain radiant transfer from the flame at a rate less than that critical value at which the luminous particles would cool to a temperature so low that combustion would not continue. The overall design problem is one of establishing a luminous flame by having initially incomplete combustion, but maintaining conditions within the combustion chamber such that energy will continue to be liberated by combustion of the particles during the same period that the incompletely burned products give off radiant energy. An ideal situation would be one in which combustion would be complete just as, or shortly before, the products leave the combustion chamber.

3.9. Gaseous Absorption. As usually written, the equations for radiant exchange are based on the assumption that transfer of radiation from source to receiver occurs through a non-absorbing atmosphere. Actually, however, both the carbon dioxide and the water vapor in the normal atmosphere absorb (and also emit) radiant energy. For most problems of industrial importance the influence of gaseous absorption can be safely neglected, but in cases where radiant transfer takes place between one or more surfaces of high reflectivity the influence of such absorption may be of great importance.

Equations for the emission of radiation from either carbon dioxide or water vapor can be written in the form,

$$q = aT^bA \tag{3.24}$$

where a is a coefficient which varies with the kind of gas or vapor and is functionally related to the absolute pressure and to the length of radiant path through the gas or vapor, T is the absolute temperature of the gas or vapor, b is an exponent which depends on the kind of gas or vapor and is somewhat influenced by the temperature range. By defining an equivalent coefficient, h_g, for gaseous radiation the transfer rate for exchange between a gas or vapor and a surface can be expressed as,

$$q = h_gA(t_h - t_c) \tag{3.25}$$

where

$$h_g = a(T_h^b - T_c^b)/(t_h - t_c) \tag{3.26}$$

(For graphical solution refer to Fig. 3.11, p. 61)

For an ordinary room under conditions of occupancy the h_g value for carbon dioxide can conservatively be taken as 0.02 Btu/(hr) (sq ft) (°F) and the value of h_g for water vapor (of the order of 0.10) can be determined by graphical means (refer Fig. 3.11); the total h_g for the atmosphere will then be equal to the sum of these two values.

Shape Factor of Standing Human — With Respect to Floor Element

Shape factor of a standing subject with respect to radiant energy received from an element of floor area.

Equation: $F_a = \frac{1}{A_s}\int_{A_s}\int_{A_r} \frac{\cos\phi_s \cos\phi_r \, dA_s \, dA_r}{\pi r^2}$

Text Reference: Sections 3.4 and 3.5, equation 3.11

Extension: To obtain the shape factor of a standing subject with respect to radiant energy reception from a finite area, as an entire floor, read point shape factors from the figure for center-points of small divisions of the large area and average the point values to obtain the overall shape factor.

Special Conditions: Data presented in this figure are from an experimental evaluation of the stated equation. Results were obtained from a mechanical integrator.

Example: A small heated area of floor surface is located 4 feet directly in front of a standing subject. Determine the fraction of radiation leaving the small area which is intercepted by the subject.

Solution: Enter the graph (Fig. 3.1) at 4 feet on the bottom scale and rise to Curve A for a full-face subject; from this intersection move right (in some cases *left*) to the transfer line then rise to read the answer as 0.03 at the top scale. Thus 3% of the energy emitted by the small area will strike the subject.

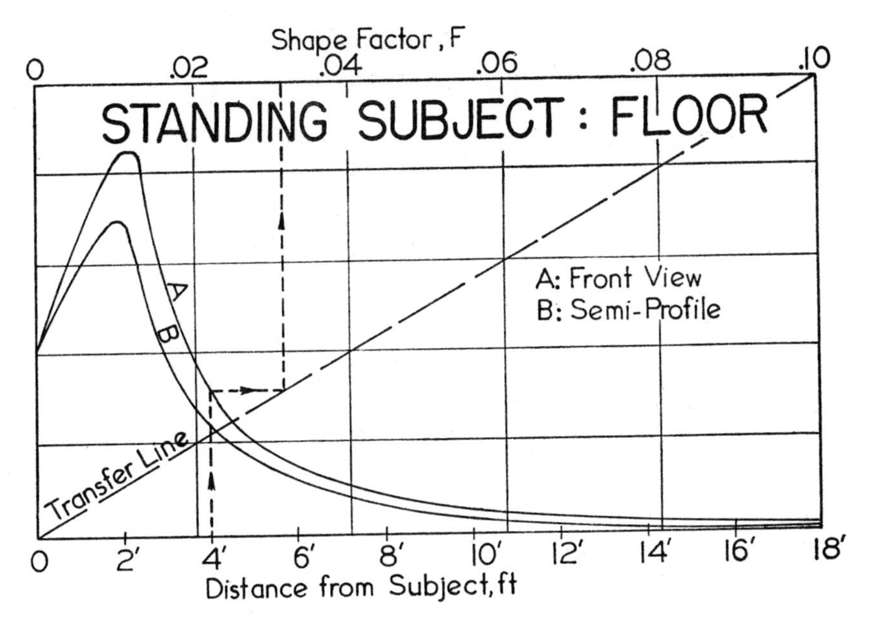
Shape Factor, F
0
.02
.04
.06
.08
.10
STANDING SUBJECT : FLOOR
A
B
A: Front View
B: Semi-Profile
Transfer Line
0
2′
4′
6′
8′
10′
12′
14′
16′
18′
Distance from Subject, ft

Figure 3.1

Shape Factor of Standing Human — With Respect to Wall Element

Shape factor of a standing subject with respect to radiant energy received from an element of wall area.

Equation: $F_a = \frac{1}{A_s}\int_{A_s}\int_{A_r}\frac{\cos\phi_s \cos\phi_r \, dA_s \, dA_r}{\pi r^2}$

Text Reference: Sections 3.4 and 3.5, equation 3.11.

Extension: To obtain the shape factor of a standing subject with respect to radiant energy reception from a finite area, as an entire wall,* read point shape factors from the figure for center-points of small divisions of the large area and average the point values to obtain the overall shape factor.

Special Conditions: Data presented in this figure are from an experimental, rather than analytical, evaluation of the stated equation. Results were obtained through use of a dummy and a mechanical integrator.

Example: A subject is standing 2 feet out from a wall on a line which is normal to the wall; he is standing so that he is in profile with respect to the normal. A small heated area is located on the wall 4 feet 6 inches directly above the point where the normal intersects the wall at the floor level. Determine the fraction of energy intercepted by the subject of that emitted by the small wall area.

Solution: Enter the graph (Fig. 3.2) at 4 feet 6 inches on the bottom scale and rise to the upper section (for a subject in profile) where intersect the curve for 2 feet distance out from the wall; from this intersection move horizontally to the right (in some cases this direction will be to the *left*) to intersect the transfer line and from this point rise to read the shape factor at the top scale as approximately 0.19. This means that 19% of the radiant energy emitted by the small wall area will be intercepted by the subject.

***Note:** In determining an average shape factor for the wall as a whole, it is necessary to interpolate between the curves for profile and for full-face.

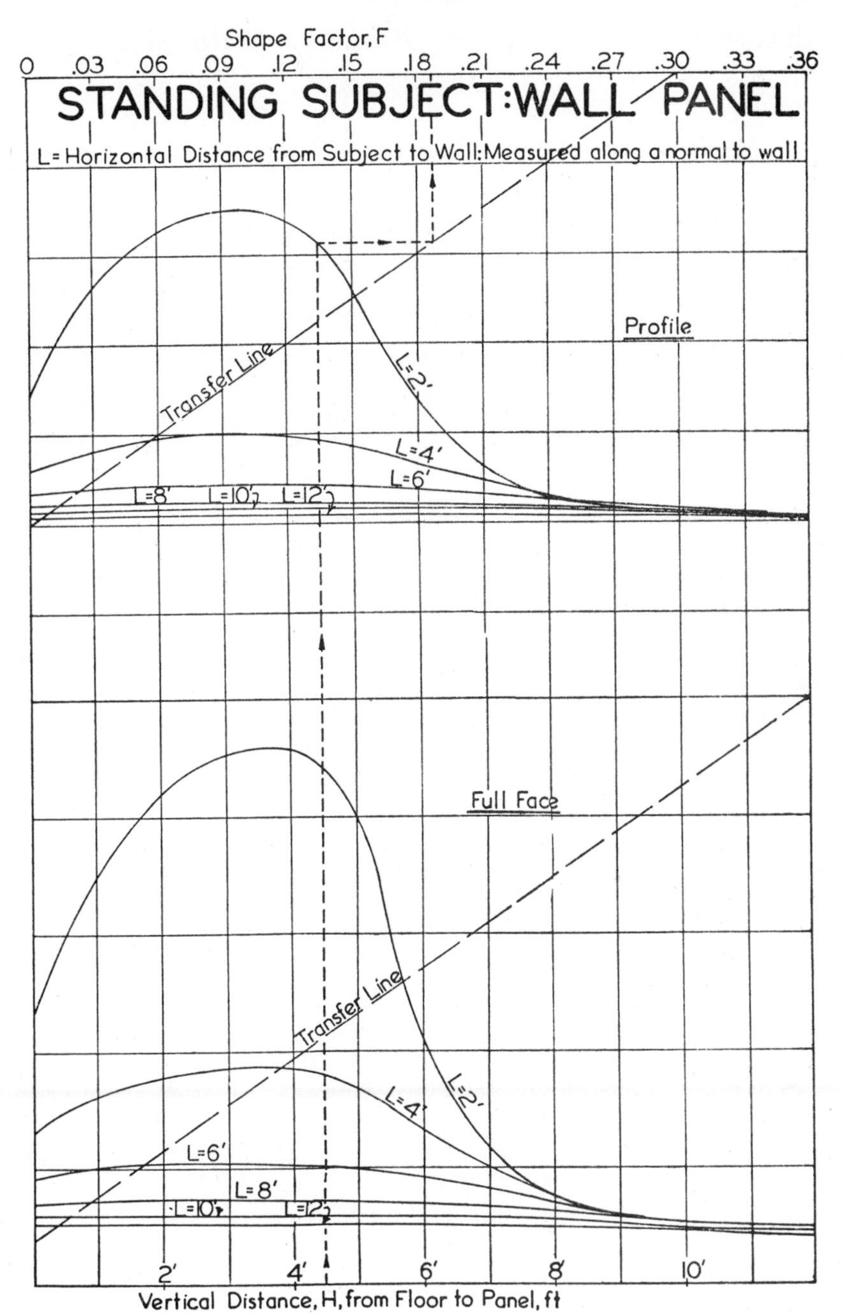
Shape Factor, F
0 .03 .06 .09 .12 .15 .18 .21 .24 .27 .30 .33 .36
STANDING SUBJECT: WALL PANEL
L = Horizontal Distance from Subject to Wall: Measured along a normal to wall
Profile
Transfer Line
L=2'
L=4'
L=6'
L=8'
L=10'
L=12'
Full Face
Transfer Line
L=2'
L=4'
L=6'
L=8'
L=10'
L=12'
2'
4'
6'
8'
10'
Vertical Distance, H, from Floor to Panel, ft

Figure 3.2

Shape Factor of Standing Human — With Respect to Ceiling Element

Shape factor of a standing subject with respect to radiant energy received from an element of ceiling area.

Equation: $F_a = \frac{1}{A_s} \int_{A_s} \int_{A_r} \frac{\cos \phi_s \cos \phi_r \, dA_s \, dA_r}{\pi r^2}$

Text Reference: Sections 3.4 and 3.5, equation 3.11.

Extension: To obtain the shape factor of a standing subject with respect to radiant energy reception from a finite ceiling area, as an entire ceiling, read point shape factors from the graphical solution for center-points of small divisions of the larger area and average the point values to obtain the overall shape factor.

Special Conditions: Data presented in the graphical solution are from an experimental rather than analytical solution of the stated equation. Results were obtained through use of a dummy and a mechanical integrator.

Example: A subject is standing in a room with a ceiling 12 feet high. It is desired to determine his shape factor with respect to radiant energy received from a narrow ring of heated ceiling area. The ring is 12 feet in diameter and the position of the subject is directly below the center of the annular ring.

Solution: The distance out from the subject to the heated annular ring is uniformly 6 feet. Enter the graph (Fig. 3.3) at 6 feet on the lower scale and rise to the upper section for a ceiling height of 12 feet. From intersection with curve A (for full-face) move horizontally to the left (in some cases this would be to the *right*) to intersection with the transfer line and then rise to read the shape factor at the top scale as 0.012. This shape factor is applicable to those parts of the annular ring which are directly in front of or directly behind the subject. If an exact overall shape factor is required individual point values can be determined by interpolation among the curves for full-face, semi-profile, and full-profile, but in most practical cases the overall shape factor can be taken (for an annular ring) as equal to the point value for semi-profile; in this case the shape factor, from curve B, would be 0.01.

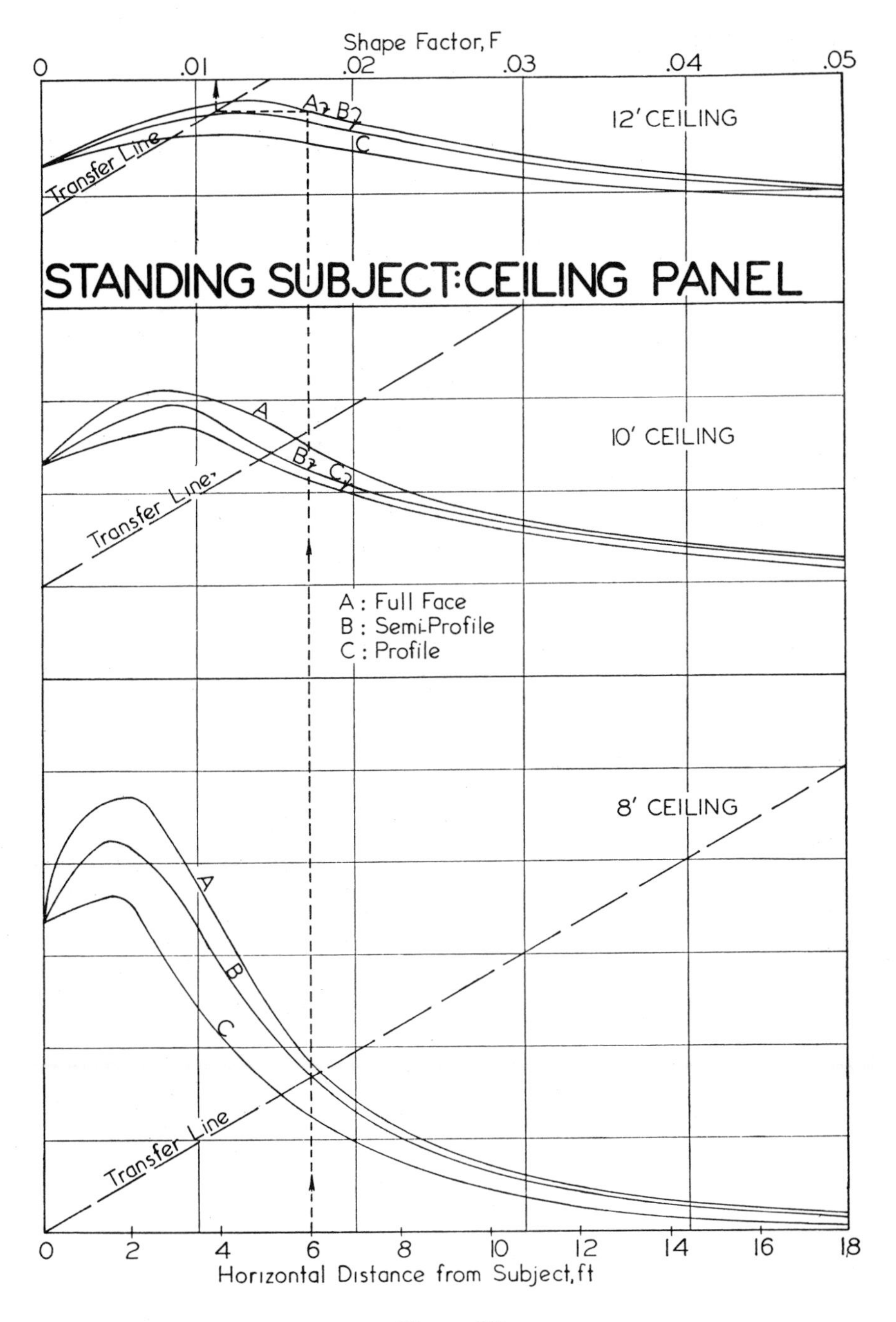
Shape Factor, F
0
.01
.02
.03
.04
.05
12' CEILING
Transfer Line
A
B
C
STANDING SUBJECT: CEILING PANEL
10' CEILING
Transfer Line
A : Full Face
B : Semi-Profile
C : Profile
8' CEILING
Transfer Line
0
2
4
6
8
10
12
14
16
18
Horizontal Distance from Subject, ft

Figure 3.3

Shape Factor of Sitting Human — With Respect to Ceiling

Shape factor of a sitting subject with respect to radiant energy received from an element of ceiling area.

Equation: $F_a = \frac{1}{A_s} \int_{A_s} \int_{A_r} \frac{\cos \phi_s \cos \phi_r \, dA_s \, dA_r}{\pi r^2}$

Text Reference: Section 3.4, section 3.5, and equation 3.11.

Extension: To obtain the shape factor of a seated subject with respect to radiant energy emitted by a large area, as the entire ceiling, read point shape factors from the graphical solution for center-points of small divisions of the larger area and average the point values to obtain the overall shape factor.

Special Conditions: Data presented in this graphical solution are from an experimental rather than analytical solution of the stated equation. Results were obtained through use of a dummy and a mechanical integrator.

Example: A subject is seated 4 feet out from the normal to a small heated ceiling area. The room ceiling height is 10 feet and the subject is in front semi-profile with respect to the normal to the heated area. Determine the percentage of energy emitted by the small area which is intercepted by the seated subject.

Solution: Enter the graph (Fig. 3.4) at 4 feet on the bottom scale and rise to the center section (which is for the stated 10′ ceiling height). Intersect curve *B*, for front semi-profile, and from the intersection move horizontally right (in some cases this will be *left*) to intersect the transfer line. From this point rise to read the point shape factor from the top scale; for the problem illustrated the shape factor is read as approximately 0.155 indicating that something more than 15½% of the radiation leaving the small ceiling area strikes the subject.

Note: For a seated subject it will be noted that shape factors for front and back full-face positions differ. This is due to the fact that for a front view some energy interception occurs at the thighs of the subject.

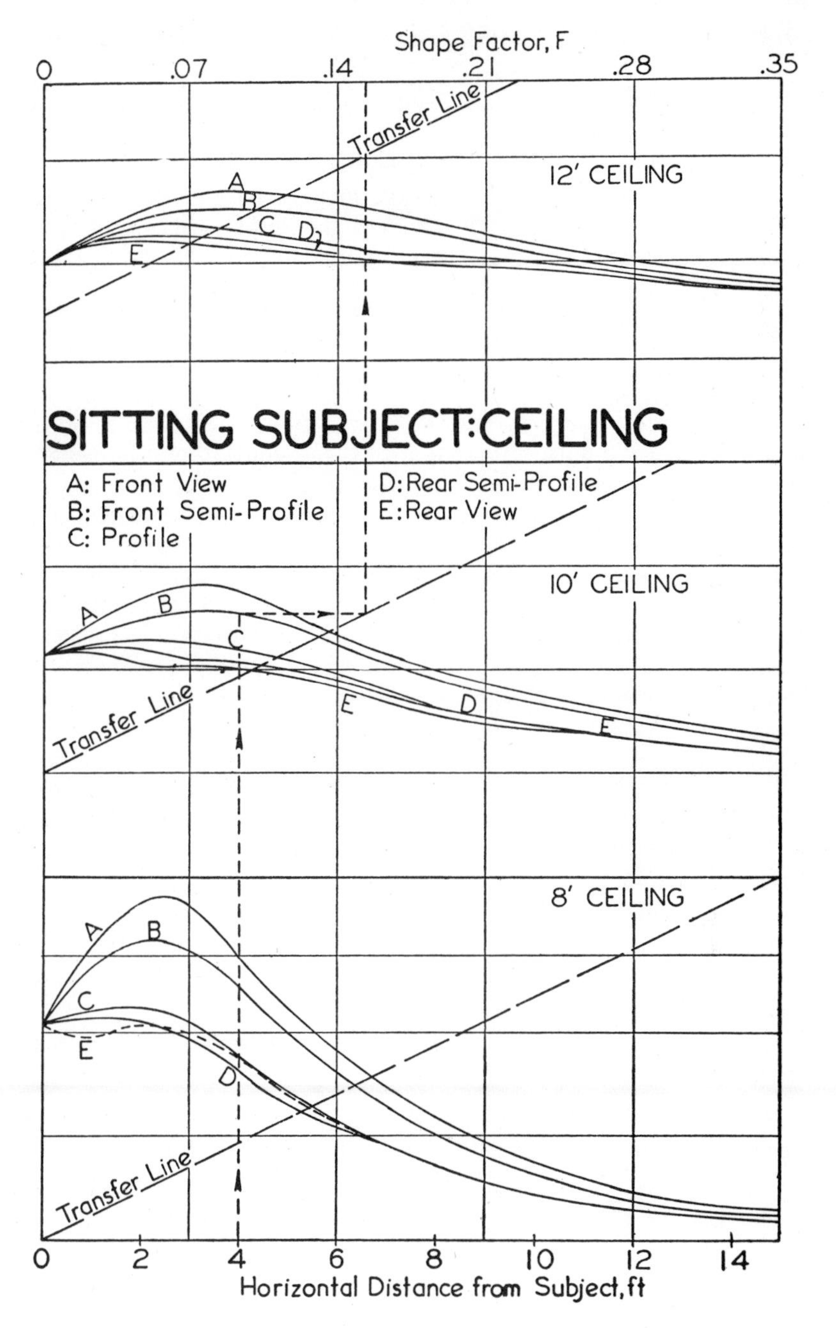
Shape Factor, F
0
.07
.14
.21
.28
.35
Transfer Line
12' CEILING
A
B
C
D
E
SITTING SUBJECT:CEILING
A: Front View
B: Front Semi-Profile
C: Profile
D: Rear Semi-Profile
E: Rear View
10' CEILING
Transfer Line
8' CEILING
Transfer Line
0
2
4
6
8
10
12
14
Horizontal Distance from Subject, ft

Figure 3.4

Shape Factors of Parallel Opposed Planes — Rectangular

Shape factor for radiant energy transfer between equal rectangular areas located directly opposite one another, and with sides parallel, in parallel planes. Let Z equal the ratio of the length of one side (of each rectangle) to the normal distance between the two planes and let Y equal the ratio of the length of the other side (of each rectangle) to the normal distance between the two planes.

Equation: Not stated because of its complexity, but an integrated form of 3.11.

Text Reference: Sections 3.4 and 3.5.

Extension: By simple arithmetical additions and subtractions of shape factors the data from the graphical solution can be readily extended* to determine the shape factor of *any* rectangle, regardless of size and shape, with respect to any other rectangle of different size and shape provided only that the two rectangles are in parallel planes and are so oriented that their sides are respectively parallel. This extension permits use of the graphical solution in evaluation of the shape factor of a window with respect to a section of opposite wall, or evaluation of the shape factor of a floor with respect to a heating or cooling panel in the ceiling.

Special Conditions: None.

Example: A room is 40 feet long and 15 feet wide; its ceiling height is 10 feet. Determine the shape factor for radiant exchange between a heating panel which occupies the entire ceiling area and the unheated floor.

Solution: The ratios Z and Y are $40/10 = 4.0$ and $15/10 = 1.5$. Enter the graph (Fig. 3.5) at the bottom scale for a Z value of 4.0 and rise to intersection with the transfer line. From this point move horizontally left (in some cases this direction will be *right*) to intersect the Y curve for 1.5, then rise to the top scale where read the shape factor as 0.46.

Note: Unlike the procedure with most graphical solutions, in this case the *first* intersection is with the transfer line.

* Raber and Hutchinson, *Panel Heating and Cooling Analysis*, John Wiley & Sons, Chapter VIII, 1947.

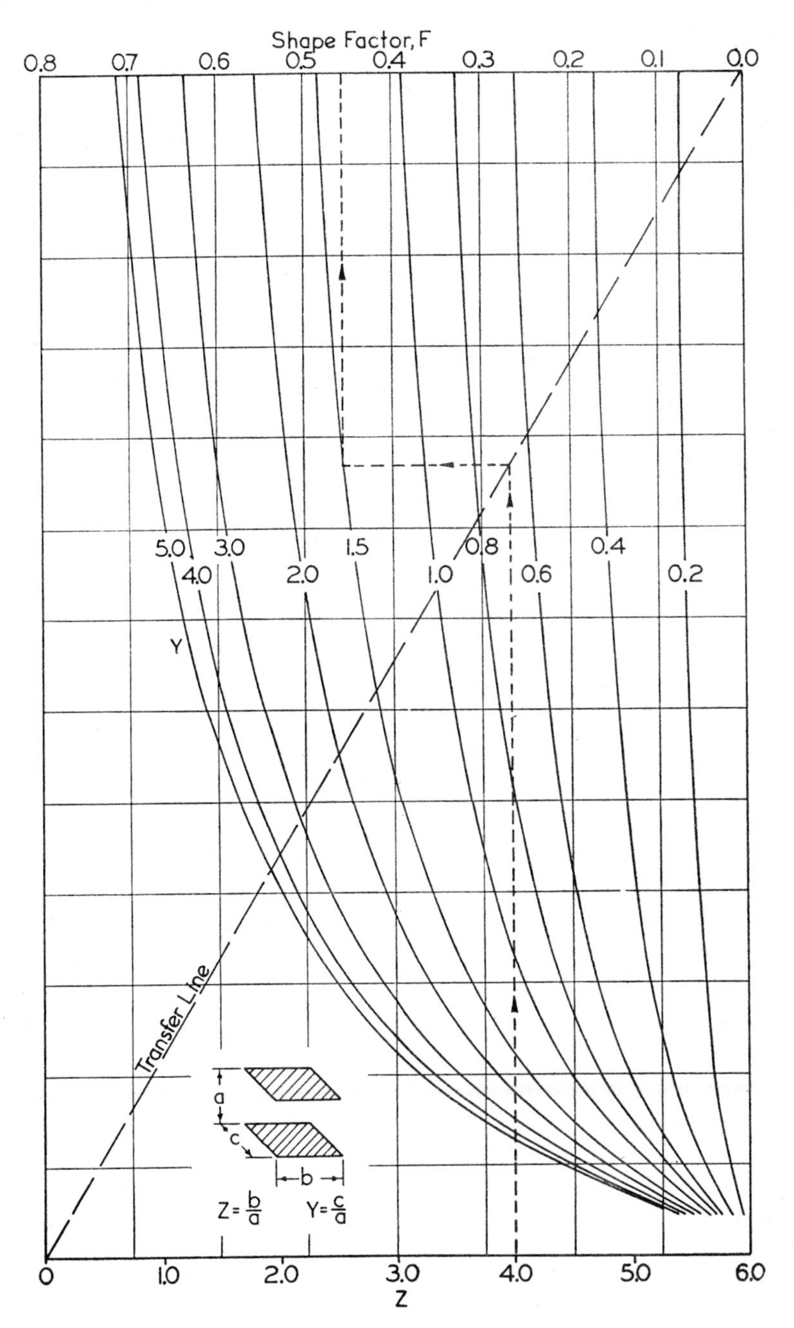
Shape Factor, F
0.8
0.7
0.6
0.5
0.4
0.3
0.2
0.1
0.0
5.0
4.0
3.0
2.0
1.5
1.0
0.8
0.6
0.4
0.2
Y
Transfer Line
a
c
b
Z = b/a
Y = c/a
0
1.0
2.0
3.0
4.0
5.0
6.0
Z

Figure 3.5

Shape Factors of Normal Rectangular Planes Having a Common Side

Shape factor for radiant energy transfer between rectangular areas (not necessarily equal areas) in planes normal to one another, the rectangles having one common side. Let Z equal the ratio of the non-common side of one rectangle to the common side and let Y equal the ratio of the non-common side of the other rectangle to the common side.

Equation: Because of its complexity the specific equation is not stated, but it is an integrated form of equation 3.11.

Text Reference: Sections 3.4 and 3.5.

Extension: By simple arithmetical addition and subtraction of shape factors the data from the graphical solution can be readily extended* to permit determination of the shape factor of *any* rectangle, regardless of size, shape, or position, with respect to any other rectangle provided only that the two rectangles are in normal planes and are so oriented that one pair of sides of one rectangle is parallel to one pair of sides of the other rectangle. This extension permits use of the graph in determining the shape factor of such a system as that represented by a window with respect to a floor or ceiling.

Special Conditions: The shape factor obtained from the graph is based on the rectangle for which the Y ratio is written. Note, therefore, that it is important to select the Y and Z ratio in terms of the rectangle whose area is to be used with the resultant shape factor. Having determined the shape factor based on the Y ratio area from the graph, the shape factor based on Z ratio area could be obtained from the reciprocity theorem (equation 3.15) if it is needed.

Example: A room 35 feet by 12 feet has a ceiling 10 feet high. Determine the shape factor of the wall which is 35 feet long with respect to the wall which is 12 feet long.

Solution: $Y = 12/10 = 1.2$ and $Z = 35/10 = 3.5$. Enter Fig. 3.6 at $Z = 3.5$, rise to the transfer line then move left to intersect $Y = 1.2$. Rise from this intersection to the top scale where read the shape factor (with respect to the wall 12 feet long) as 0.23.

* Raber and Hutchinson, *Panel Heating and Cooling Analysis*, John Wiley & Sons, Chapter VIII, 1947.

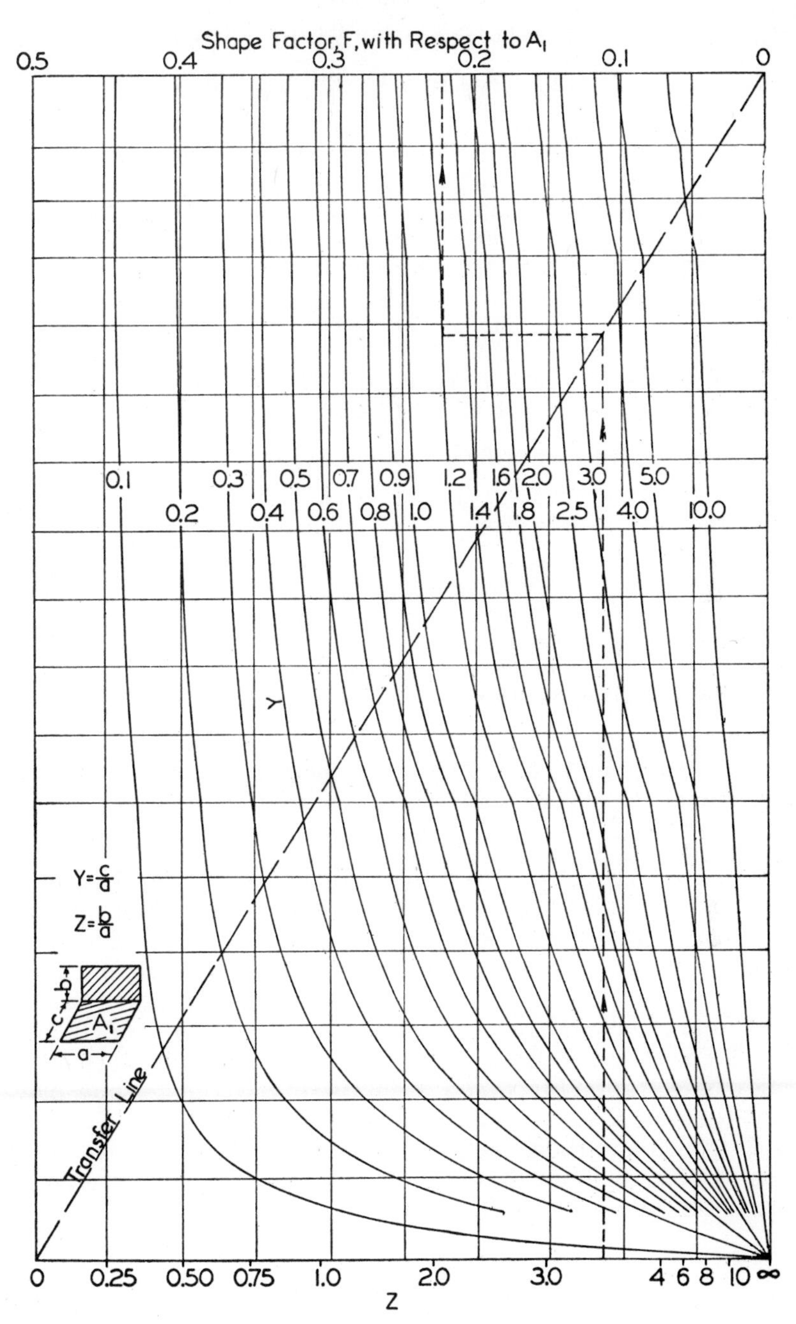
Shape Factor, F, with Respect to A_1
0.5
0.4
0.3
0.2
0.1
0
0.1
0.2
0.3
0.4
0.5
0.6
0.7
0.8
0.9
1.0
1.2
1.4
1.6
1.8
2.0
2.5
3.0
4.0
5.0
10.0
Y
$Y=\frac{c}{a}$
$Z=\frac{b}{a}$
b
c
A_1
a
Transfer Line
0
0.25
0.50
0.75
1.0
2.0
3.0
4
6
8
10
∞
Z

Figure 3.6

Shape Factor of a Rectangular Plane with Respect to a Small Area in a Parallel Plane

Shape factor of a rectangular area with respect to a small finite area which is located in a plane parallel to the rectangular area and on a line normal to and through one corner of the rectangle. Let Z equal the ratio of one side of the rectangle to the normal distance from rectangle to small area and let Y equal the ratio of length of the other side of the rectangle to the same normal distance.

Equation: Because of its complexity the specific equation is not stated, but it is an integrated form of equation 3.11.

Text Reference: Sections 3.4 and 3.5.

Extension: By simple arithmetical addition and subtraction of shape factors the data from this graphical solution can be readily extended to determine the shape factor of any rectangular area with respect to any area (not necessarily rectangular) of any size and in any position subject only to the condition that it is in a plane parallel to the rectangular area.

Special Conditions: None.

Example: A room 13 feet on one side by 27 feet on the other has a ceiling height of 10 feet. Determine the shape factor of the floor with respect to energy emitted from a small area located in the center of the ceiling.

Solution: Divide the floor into four equal rectangles 6.5 feet by 13.5 feet each. Each rectangle then meets the conditions of this graphical solution and the shape factor of the entire floor with respect to the small central ceiling area will therefore be four times as great as the shape factor of one of the quarters. For each quarter the Y and Z values are, respectively, $6.5/10 = 0.65$ and $13.5/10 = 1.35$. To obtain the shape factor for any quarter enter the bottom scale of the graph (Fig. 3.7) at 1.35, rise to the transfer line, move right (in some cases this will be *left*) to intersection with the curve for $Y = 0.65$ and then rise to read the shape factor from the top scale as slightly more than 0.12. The shape factor for the entire floor is then $4 \times 0.12 = 0.48$.

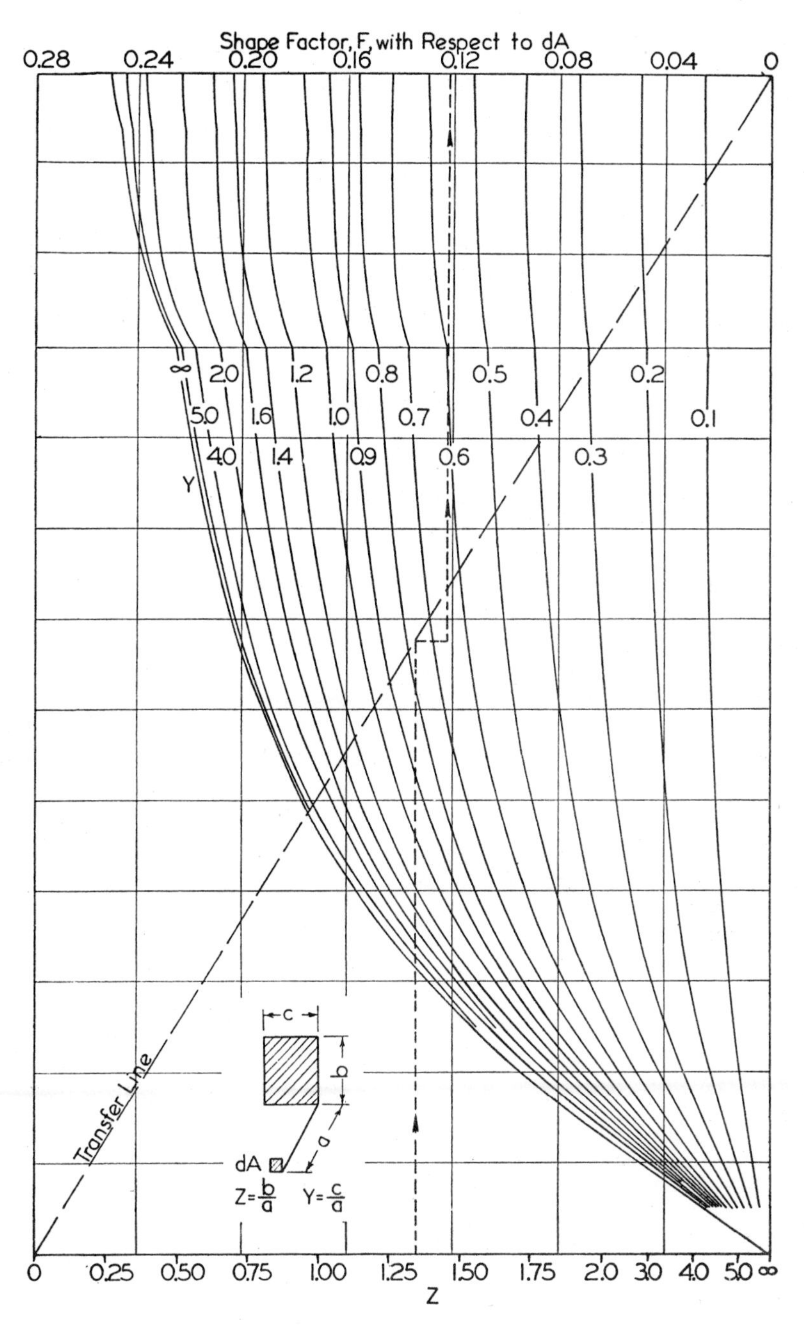
Shape Factor, F, with Respect to dA
0.28
0.24
0.20
0.16
0.12
0.08
0.04
0
∞
2.0
1.2
0.8
0.5
0.2
5.0
1.6
1.0
0.7
0.4
0.1
4.0
1.4
0.9
0.6
0.3
Y
Transfer Line
c
b
a
dA
Z = b/a
Y = c/a
0
0.25
0.50
0.75
1.00
1.25
1.50
1.75
2.0
3.0
4.0
5.0
∞
Z

Figure 3.7

Shape Factor of a Rectangular Plane with Respect to a Small Area in a Normal Plane

Shape factor of a rectangular area with respect to a small finite area which is located in a plane normal to the rectangular area and on a line normal to and through one corner of the rectangle. Let Z equal the ratio of the length of one side of the rectangle to the normal distance from the rectangle to the small area and let Y equal the ratio of length of the other side of the rectangle to the same normal distance.

Equation: Because of its complexity the specific equation is not stated, but it is an integrated form of equation 3.11.

Text Reference: Sections 3.4 and 3.5.

Extension: By simple arithmetical addition and subtraction of shape factors the data from this graphical solution can be readily extended to determine the shape factor of any rectangular area with respect to any area (not necessarily rectangular) subject only to the condition that it is in a plane normal to the rectangular area and that *one* side is "seen" from all points in the rectangular area.

Special Conditions: The ratio Z uses the side of the rectangle which is *normal* to the small area and the ratio Y the side of the rectangle which is *parallel* to the plane of the small area; ratios Y and Z *are not interchangeable.*

Example: It is desired to determine the shape factor of a wall 10 feet high by 8 feet long with respect to a point on the floor which is 10 feet out along a normal that passes through the lower right hand corner of the wall.

Solution: The value of Z is $10/10 = 1.0$ and the value of Y is $8/10 = 0.8$. Enter the bottom scale of the graph (Fig. 3.8) at $Z = 1.0$ and rise to intersect the transfer line then move horizontally right (in some cases this will be horizontally *left*) to intersection with the curve for Y equal 0.8. From this point rise to the top scale where read the shape factor as 0.05.

Note: Unlike most graphs, this one is so constructed that risers from the bottom scale go directly to the transfer line.

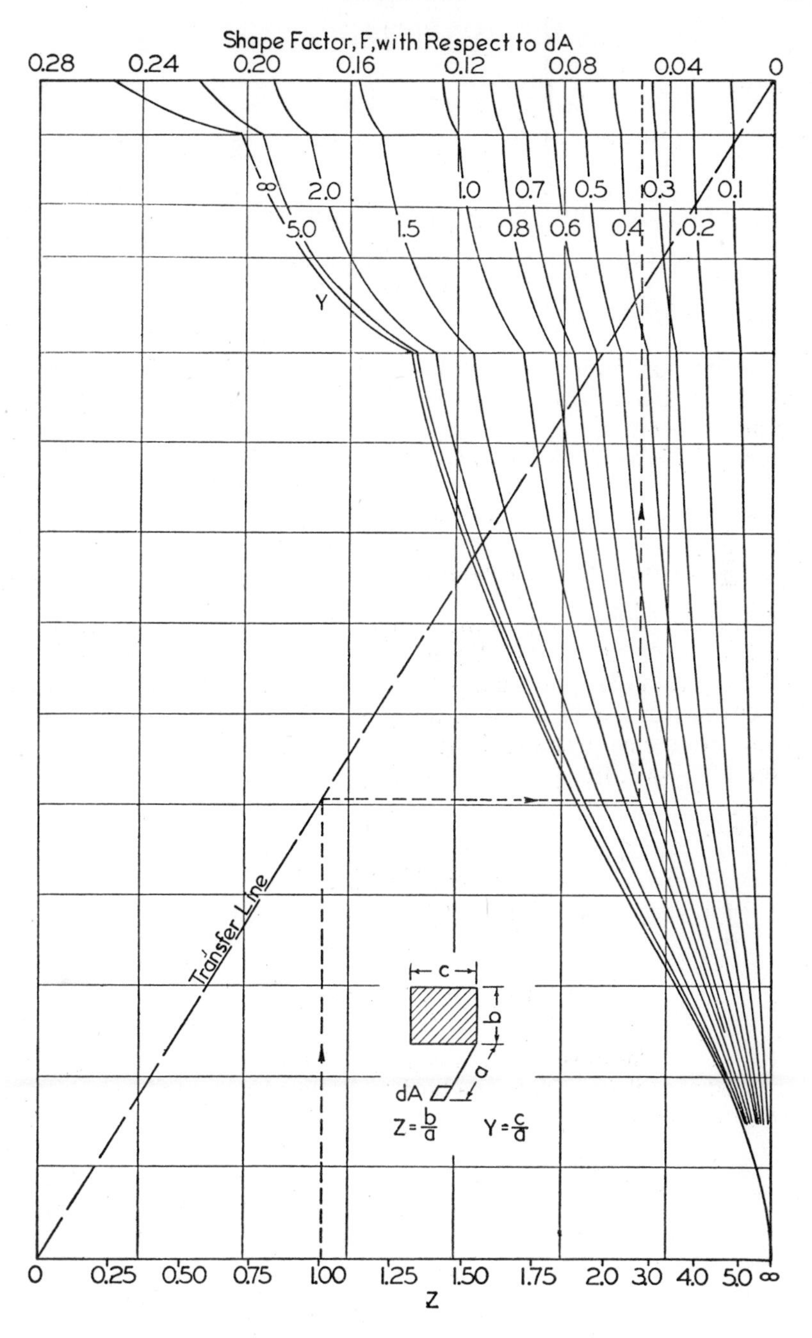
Shape Factor, F, with Respect to dA
0.28
0.24
0.20
0.16
0.12
0.08
0.04
0
∞
2.0
1.0
0.7
0.5
0.3
0.1
5.0
1.5
0.8
0.6
0.4
0.2
Y
Transfer Line
c
b
a
dA
Z = b/a
Y = c/a
0
0.25
0.50
0.75
1.00
1.25
1.50
1.75
2.0
3.0
4.0
5.0
∞
Z

Figure 3.8

Equivalent Film Coefficient, h_r, for Radiation

Evaluation of an equivalent radiation coefficient for use in expressing radiant exchange in terms of the first-power temperature difference.

Equation: $h_r = 0.172[(T_h/100)^4 - (T_c/100)^4]/(t_h - t_c)$

Text Reference: Section 3.7, equation 3.23.

Extension: None.

Special Conditions: The value of h_r is approximately unity for surfaces which are at temperatures close to those which are usually found in occupied spaces. At higher temperatures h_r increases whereas at lower temperatures it is less than unity.

Example: Radiant exchange is to be evaluated between a surface at a temperature of 83 F and another surface at a temperature of 50 F. Determine the equivalent radiation coefficient.

Solution: Enter the bottom scale of the graph (Fig. 3.9) at a hot surface temperature of 83 F and rise to intersection with the transfer line; from this point move horizontally to the right to intersect the curve for a cold surface temperature of 50 F and from this intersection rise to the scale at the top of the graph where read the value of h_r as 1.01.

Check:

$$h_r = \frac{0.172\left[\left(\frac{460+83}{100}\right)^4 - \left(\frac{460+50}{100}\right)^4\right]}{83-50}$$

$$= 1.01 \text{ Btu/(hr) (sq ft) (°F)}$$

Note: Unlike most of the graphical solutions this one is so constructed that risers from the bottom scale of the graph go directly to the transfer line.

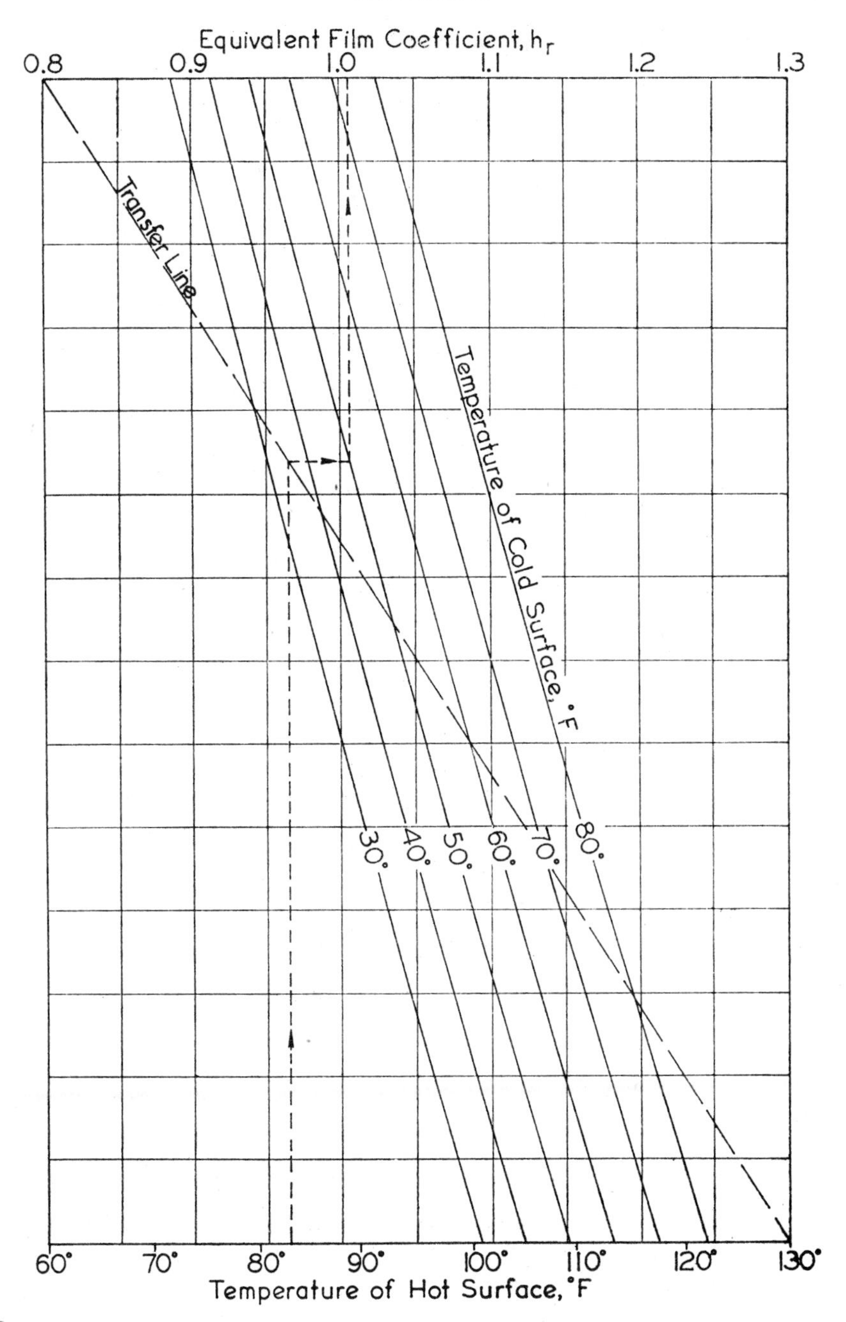
Equivalent Film Coefficient, h_r
0.8
0.9
1.0
1.1
1.2
1.3
Transfer Line
Temperature of Cold Surface, °F
30°
40°
50°
60°
70°
80°
60°
70°
80°
90°
100°
110°
120°
130°
Temperature of Hot Surface, °F

Figure 3.9

Net Radiant Transfer Between any Two Surfaces

Net radiant transfer between any two surfaces when surface temperatures, shape factor, and emissivity factor are known.

Equation: $q = 0.172\, F_e\, F_a\, A_s[(T_s/100)^4 - (T_r/100)^4]$

Text Reference: Section 3.4, equation 3.17.

Extensions: None.

Special Conditions: None.

Example: A small hot surface at 100 F is so located with respect to a small cold surface at 0 F that the shape factor F_a, based on area of the cold surface, is 0.63. The arrangement is such that the emissivity factor, F_e, is equal to the product of the emissivities of the two surfaces and has been evaluated at 0.76. Determine the net rate of radiant exchange between the two surfaces in Btu per hour per square foot of area of the colder surface.

Solution: Enter the graph (Fig. 3.10) at the bottom scale at a hot body surface temperature of 100 F and rise to intersection with the curve for a cold body surface temperature of 0 F. From this point move horizontally to the right (in some cases this will be to the *left*) to an interpolated intersection with the radial line for a shape factor of 0.63; from this intersection rise vertically to intersection with the line for an emissivity factor of 0.76 and from this point move horizontally to the right (in some cases this will be to the *left*) to intersect the transfer line. From this point rise to the top of the graph and read the answer from the scale which bears the same number as the group of emissivity lines in which intersection occurred. Thus, for the problem illustrated, the emissivity intersection took place in group I so the number I scale is therefore used in determining the answer of 44 Btu/(hr) (square foot of cold surface).

Check:

$$q = (0.172)\,(0.76)\,(0.63)\left[\left(\frac{460+100}{100}\right)^4 - \left(\frac{460+0}{100}\right)^4\right]$$

$$= 44 \text{ Btu/(hr) (square foot of cold surface)}$$

Note: If F_a were evaluated in terms of the hot surface area the answer would likewise be in terms of hot surface area.

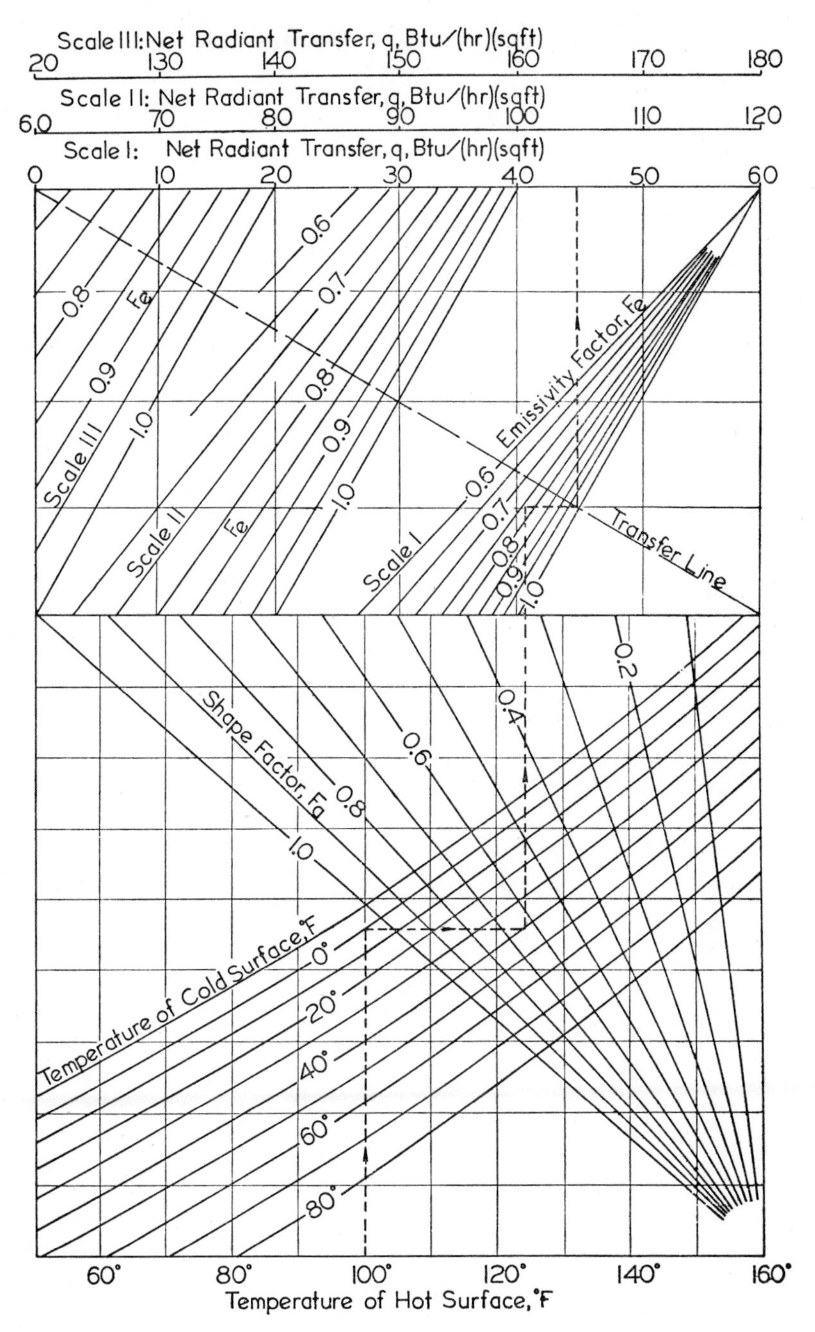
Scale III: Net Radiant Transfer, q, Btu/(hr)(sqft)
120 130 140 150 160 170 180
Scale II: Net Radiant Transfer, q, Btu/(hr)(sqft)
60 70 80 90 100 110 120
Scale I: Net Radiant Transfer, q, Btu/(hr)(sqft)
0 10 20 30 40 50 60
Scale III
Scale II
Scale I
Fe
0.6
0.7
0.8
0.9
1.0
Emissivity Factor, Fe
Transfer Line
Shape Factor, Fa
0.2
0.4
0.6
0.8
1.0
Temperature of Cold Surface, °F
0°
20°
40°
60°
80°
60° 80° 100° 120° 140° 160°
Temperature of Hot Surface, °F

Figure 3.10

Equivalent Gaseous Radiation Coefficient, h_w, for Water Vapor

Evaluation of the equivalent coefficient for gaseous radiation between a surface and a mass of water vapor.

Equation: $h_g = a(T_h^b - T_c^b)/(t_h - t_c)$

Text Reference: Section 3.9, equation 3.26.

Extensions: For ordinary room conditions an equivalent coefficient for gaseous radiation between a surface and a mass of carbon dioxide can be taken as approximately constant at 0.02 Btu/(hr)(sq ft)(°F). Thus by adding 0.02 to the coefficient obtained from this graphical solution a combined gaseous coefficient will be obtained for evaluating radiant transfer between a surface and the two principal absorbing (and radiating) gases in the normal atmosphere.

Special Conditions: The actual determination of the equivalent gaseous coefficient requires precise knowledge of the length of path through the mass of gaseous material. The graphical solution presented here is based on the assumption (which is reasonable and accurate for rooms of average size) that the average path length (strictly, the beam length) is equal to the ceiling height.

Example: A room having a ceiling 9 feet high contains air at a dry-bulb temperature of 70 F and with a relative humidity of 54%. A ceiling panel in this room operates at a surface temperature of 86 F and it is desired to determine the equivalent gaseous coefficient for radiant exchange between the panel and the water vapor in the room.

Solution: Enter the graph (Fig. 3.11) in the lower left quadrant along the bottom scale at a panel surface temperature of 86 F. Rise vertically to intersect the transfer line then move horizontally to the right (in some cases this will be to the *left*) to intersect the curve for a gas temperature of 70 F. From this point rise vertically through the upper left quadrant. Now re-enter the graph in the lower right quadrant at a base scale value of 70 F, rise to intersect the curve for 54% relative humidity and then move horizontally to intersection with the curve for 9′ ceiling height. From this point rise to the transfer line, move left to intersect the first determined dashed line and read the coefficient as 0.086 for water vapor.

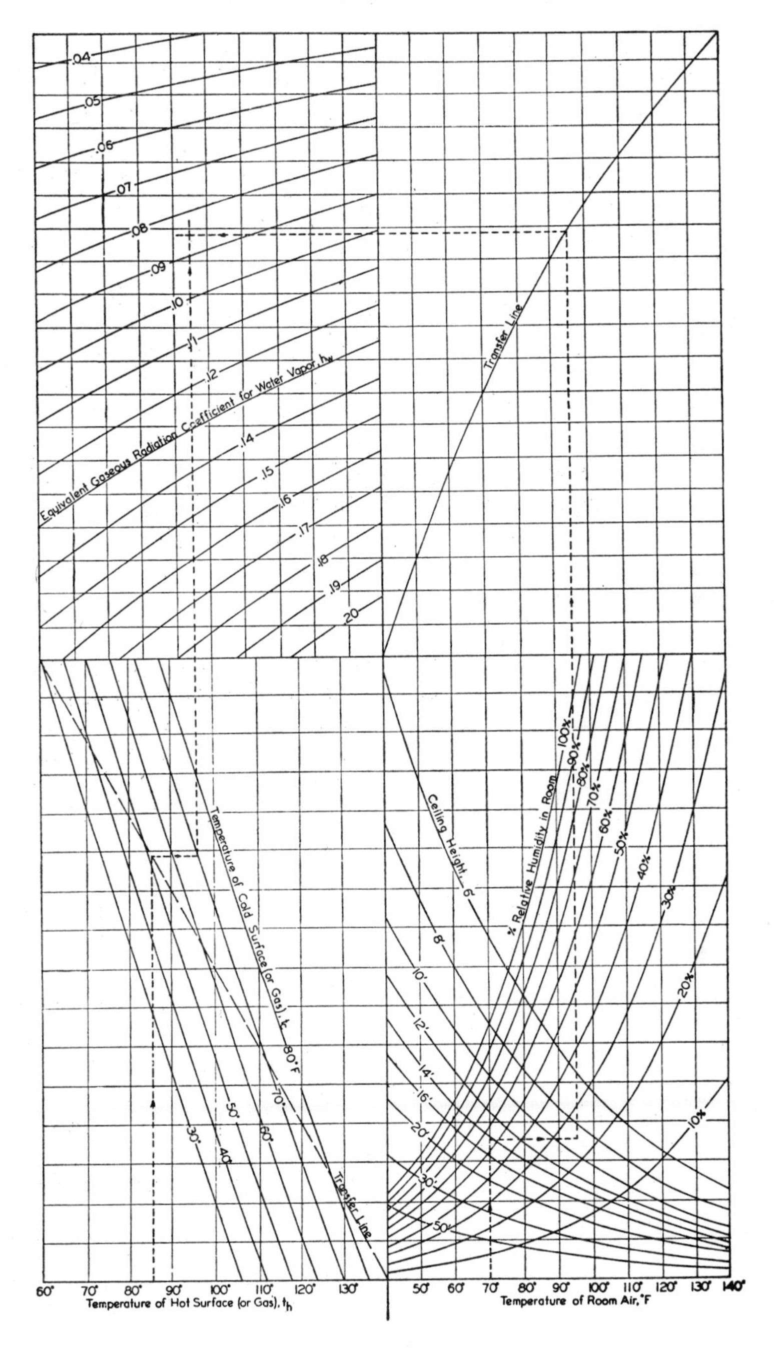
Equivalent Gaseous Radiation Coefficient for Water Vapor, h_w
Transfer Line
Temperature of Cold Surface (or Gas), t_c
Ceiling Height
% Relative Humidity in Room
Transfer Line
Temperature of Hot Surface (or Gas), t_h
Temperature of Room Air, °F

Figure 3.11

CHAPTER IV

Convection: Basic Relationships

4.1. Newton's Law of Cooling. The rate of heat transfer between a surface and the main body of the passing fluid is given by an equation originally formulated by Newton,

$$q = hA\,(t_h - t_c) \tag{4.1}$$

(For graphical solution refer to Fig. 4.1, p. 73)

where h is defined as the film coefficient of heat transfer and is related to the convective conductance, C_v', by the equation,

$$C_v' = hA \tag{4.2}$$

Evaluation of the film coefficient is difficult since convection is a complex phenomenon which is determined in part from the hydrodynamic as well as the thermal characteristics of the particular system. Three separate processes enter into the transfer of energy by convection:

(1) Directional mass transfer of fluid from a warmer to a colder region.

(2) Mechanical mixing of adjacent fluid volumes.

(3) Conductive transfer of heat between adjacent fluid elements.

The first two of these processes are directly related to the velocity distribution in the main body of the fluid whereas the third process is determined by the temperature distribution. Another influencing factor is the relationship between the temperature gradients at the fluid boundary and in the main fluid mass.

4.2. Dimensionless Parameters for Similarity of Velocity and Temperature Distribution. Any effective attempt to establish equations for the evaluation of the film coefficient must necessarily be based on establishing similarities between the few systems on which experiments have been conducted and the many systems to which the experimental results are to be applied. Experience has shown that generalization of experimental data for convection is possible provided four conditions exist:

(1) The two systems must be geometrically similar. Geometrical

similarity exists when the shapes, surface characteristics (roughness), and the relative positions of objects in both systems are the same.

(2) The two systems must have similar velocity fields. Similarity of velocity fields exists when the velocities at the boundaries of the two systems are similar and when the ratio of inertia forces to viscous forces is the same in the main masses of the two fluids. The inertia force is the product of tangential stress times area. Dimensionally, inertia force is,

$$F = ma = D^3\rho(V/\theta) = D^3\rho V(V/D) = D^3\rho V^2/D = D^2V^2\rho \quad (4.3)$$

where m is mass, a is acceleration, ρ density, V velocity, θ time, and D length. Viscous force is dimensionally equal to,

$$F = \mu(dV/dD)\ D^2 = \mu VD \quad (4.4)$$

where μ is the viscosity. The ratio of these two forces is a dimensionless parameter, called Reynolds number, *Re*, and given by,

$$Re = (D^2V^2\rho)/(\mu VD) = DV\rho/\mu \quad (4.5)$$

(For graphical solution refer to Fig. 4.2, p. 75)

Any consistent set of units can be used in evaluation of the Reynolds number, but for most engineering calculations the units of greatest convenience will be,

- V in feet
- D in feet per second
- ρ in pounds per cubic foot
- μ in pounds per second per foot. When values of viscosity are given in centipoises they can be converted to lb/(sec) (ft) by multiplying by 0.000672.

Constancy of Reynolds number, when associated with similarity of the boundary velocities, is a sufficient criterion of similarity between velocity patterns in two fluid systems. For all systems in which forced convection occurs, whether with streamline or with turbulent flow, there is a determinable characteristic velocity and hence an opportunity to use Reynolds number as a criterion of flow.

With free convection, however, the flow pattern is established without a directly measurable characteristic velocity hence a need exists for the establishment of an "equivalent" velocity that can be used in determining a value of Reynolds number. Fluid movement in free convection occurs as a result of gravitational forces induced by variations in fluid density. When a temperature difference exists in a fluid, the buoyant force resulting from thermal expansion can be readily evaluated. The product of this force and the distance L through which it acts gives $\rho\beta\Delta tL/2$ as the approximate work done by the force. In this expression, β is the coefficient of thermal expansion, Δt is the temperature difference, and the other symbols are as previously identified. By equating this work to the external kinetic energy, $\rho V^2/2g$, an equivalent characteristic velocity for free convection can be evaluated as,

$$V = (g\beta\Delta tL)^{1/2} \tag{4.6}$$

By substitution of this equivalent velocity in the Reynolds number equation, a new dimensionless parameter, called Grashof's number, Gr, which is numerically equal to the square of the equivalent Reynolds number for free convection, may be established,

$$Gr = L^3\rho^2\beta g(\Delta t)/\mu^2 \tag{4.7}$$

(For graphical solution refer to Fig. 4.3, p. 77)

Summarizing, Reynolds number is the criterion for similarity of flow in all systems which involve forced convection except when the characteristic velocity approaches or exceeds the velocity of sound. The Grashof number is the criterion for similarity of flow in all systems which involve free convection.

(3) The two systems must have similar temperature fields. Similarity of temperature fields exists when the boundary temperatures are similar and when the ratio of thermal diffusivity, $k/\rho c_p$, to kinematic viscosity, μ/ρ, is the same in the main masses of the two fluids. Since both thermal diffusivity and kinematic viscosity have dimensions of square feet per second, the resultant ratio is a dimensionless parameter and is known as the Prandtl number, Pr, as given by the equation,

$$Pr = c_p\mu/k \tag{4.8}$$

(For graphical solution refer to Fig. 4.4, p. 79)

For many gases and vapors the Prandtl number has an almost constant value of approximately 0.8. For liquids, however, the range of variation is very great. In many systems which have a Prandtl number of unity, the velocity field and the temperature field will superimpose. Although it is applied to systems, the Prandtl number is a relationship among the physical properties of the fluid; it is, therefore, a property of the fluid.

4.3. Dimensionless Thermal Parameters. In order to utilize the three parameters of the preceding section in dimensionless equations, an additional thermal parameter must be established which will relate the film coefficient, in a dimensionless way, to the other characteristics of the system. The group used for this purpose is known as the Nusselt number, Nu, and is given by,

$$Nu = hD/k \tag{4.9}$$

(For graphical solution refer to Figs. 4.5 & 4.6, pp. 81 & 83)

By graphical means[2] it can be demonstrated that the Nusselt number has physical significance as the ratio of the temperature gradient at a bounding surface to the average gradient in the fluid.

4.4. Dimensionless Equations for Convection. Both analysis and experiment have shown that a great many effective correlations of data for convective heat transfer can be obtained by use of two fundamental dimensionless equations:

(1) For forced convection,

$$Nu = \phi(Re, Pr) \tag{4.10}$$

and for the greater number of cases,

$$Nu = a(Re)^x(Pr)^y \tag{4.11}$$

where a is an experimentally determined coefficient and x and y are experimentally determined exponents.

(2) For free convection,

$$Nu = \phi(Re, Gr) \tag{4.12}$$

and for the greater number of cases,

$$Nu = a(Pr)^x(Gr)^y \tag{4.13}$$

Common procedure in the solution of convection problems is to evaluate the Nusselt number from the applicable dimensionless equation and then to calculate the film coefficient from the equation,

$$h = (Nu)(k/D) \tag{4.14}$$

(For graphical solution refer to Figs. 4.7 & 4.8, pp. 85 & 87)

The remaining sections of this chapter are devoted to explicit forms of the equations for free convection and for forced convection under conditions of streamline flow or of gravity flow; chapter VI takes up forced convection under conditions of turbulent flow.

4.5. Streamline Flow of Liquids and Gases. When flow occurs with a Reynolds number lower than a critical value of approximately 2100, the mixing and eddy effects associated with turbulence disappear; each element of fluid within a pipe then travels parallel to the axis and the flow is defined as laminar or streamline. For the heating or cooling of gases or liquids in streamline flow Colburn proposed the equation,

$$Nu = 1.62[(\mu/\mu_f)^{1/3}(1 + 0.015\,Gr^{1/3})](4wc_p/\pi kL)^{1/3} \tag{4.15}$$

where μ is the viscosity at the bulk temperature of the fluid and μ_f is the viscosity at the film temperature; w is the flow rate in lbs/hr, c_p is the specific heat at constant pressure, and L is a characteristic length.

For the special case of viscous liquids heating or cooling inside horizontal or vertical pipes, McAdams[1] recommends a simplified form of equation 4.15,

$$Nu = 1.86\,(\mu/\mu_s)^{0.14}[(Re)\,(Pr)\,(D/L)]^{1/3} \tag{4.16}$$

(For graphical solution refer to Fig. 4.9, p. 89)

where μ_s is the viscosity evaluated at the temperature of the transfer surface and L is the length of tube along which heat transfer is taking place.

4.6. Streamline Flow: Water in Vertical Pipes. When flow occurs at less than the critical Reynolds number (2100) the buoyant effects accounted for by Grashof's number become controlling with respect to rate of heat transfer. In special cases, however, less complex dimensional correlations can be used to obtain expressions which are satisfactory over a limited range. Thus for water being heated while flowing upward in a vertical pipe, McAdams [1] recommends the simplified equation,

$$h = 0.42t\,(\Delta t)^{1/3} \tag{4.17}$$

(For graphical solution refer to Fig. 4.10, p. 91)

whereas for downward flow the recommended equation retains the same form but has an altered coefficient,

$$h = 0.49t\,(\Delta t)^{1/3} \tag{4.18}$$

(For graphical solution refer to Fig. 4.10, p. 91)

where t is the average water temperature and Δt is the average temperature difference between tube wall and fluid.

4.7. Gravity Flow of Water. In large vertical shell-and-tube condensers and in other kinds of industrial equipment water sometimes flows down through tubes at a rate which is insufficient to fill the tube. In such cases the film coefficient for heating or cooling water will usually be substantially greater than the value that would exist if the flow were reversed and the tube completely filled. For layer flow of water down through a vertical tube the recommended equation is,

$$h = 120\,(w/\pi D_i)^{1/3} \tag{4.19}$$

(For graphical solution refer to Fig. 4.11, p. 93)

where w is the flow rate in pounds per hour.

For gravity flow of water over the outside of horizontal pipes in a sinuous coil or "trombone" cooler the recommended equation is,

$$h = 65\,(w/2LD_o)^{1/3} \tag{4.20}$$

(For graphical solution refer to Fig. 4.12, p. 95)

4.8. Free Convection: Liquids and Gases. Although excellent correlations have been obtained for convective heat transfer under the influence of buoyant forces, the constants applicable to the dimensionless equations have been found to vary rather widely as a function of various dimensionless groups. For this reason it is convenient to show the general free convection correlations graphically rather than analytically. The most widely applicable correlation is a special form of equation 4.13,

$$Nu = a[(Gr)(Pr)]^{x} \tag{4.21}$$

Figure 4.13 gives an explicit evaluation of equation 4.21 for free convection from single horizontal cylinders to liquids or to gases. For values of the Grashof-Prandtl product greater than 1,000 the correlation shows a straight line and McAdams[1] suggests use of the equation,

$$Nu = 0.525[(Gr)(Pr)]^{0.25} \tag{4.22}$$

where the physical properties of the fluid (density, specific heat, viscosity, and thermal conductivity) are all to be evaluated at the arithmetical average of mean fluid and cylinder surface temperatures. For large cylinders the recommended correlation retains the form of equation 4.22, but the coefficient decreases to 0.47.

4.9. Free Convection: Air over Flat Plates. The film coefficient for air being heated or cooled during flow by natural convection over a flat plate depends on the temperature difference between the air and the surface and on the orientation of the system. Since buoyant effects are largely responsible for free convection, it is evident that the film coefficient will be greater for those orientations which permit gravitational effects to induce an air velocity over the transfer surface. Thus, cool air in contact with a heated horizontal surface which is facing down, such as a panel heated ceiling, will receive heat from the surface but will not tend to move across the surface since the gravitational effect will tend to prevent, rather than induce, fluid movement. In exactly the same way, warm air coming in contact with a cooled horizontal surface which is facing up, as in the case of a panel cooled floor, will have minimum tendency toward movement and therefore will have a minimum film coefficient for convective heat transfer. For a vertical surface, whether heated or cooled, the change in density of the adjacent air stream will tend to establish flow and thereby provide a "sweeping" of the transfer surface and an increase in the value of the film coefficient. For a heating surface facing up or for a cooling surface facing down, the tendency would be for the heated or cooled air to "fall away" from the surface and hence to establish a maximum approach to turbulent conditions and a consequent maximum value of the film coefficient. For flat plates of moderate to large size the following empirical equations are recommended:

(1) For heating plates facing up or for cooling plates facing down,

$$h = 0.38\,(\Delta t)^{1/4} \tag{4.23}$$

(For graphical solution refer to Fig. 4.14, p. 99)

(2) For vertical plates higher than 1 ft whether heating or cooling,

$$h = 0.27\,(\Delta t)^{1/4} \tag{4.24}$$

(For graphical solution refer to Fig. 4.14, p. 99)

(3) For heated plates facing down or for cooling plates facing up,

$$h = 0.20\,(\Delta t)^{1/4} \tag{4.25}$$

(For graphical solution refer to Fig. 4.14, p. 99)

4.10. Free Convection: Air Spaces. A special case of free convection over flat plates is represented by the type of structural air space that frequently occurs in the walls of buildings. In vertical air spaces of this type the only air motion occurring across the surface is that due to natural convection. The air near the inner surface of the space increases in temperature and accordingly, due to reduced density, tends to move upward; the air adjacent to the outer surface loses heat, increases in density, and tends to move downward. Thus, if there is no barrier to prevent flow within the space, an induced circulation will be set up causing an upward movement across the inner surface and a downward movement across the outer surface. The convective film coefficient will obviously depend on the extent of the circulation and would be expected to increase with the temperature difference across the air space. However, air space temperature difference will vary widely, as a function of type of construction, even when the temperature difference between room air and outside air remains the same. This complication stands in the way of establishing rational generalized relationships. For most cases which occur in practice, empirical equations give results of adequate accuracy. Figure 4.15 presents in graphical form the convective air-space conductances commonly used in the evaluation of overall coefficients for building construction.

4.11. Free Convection: Air over Pipes. The film coefficient for natural convection of air, whether heating or cooling, over vertical or horizontal pipes is given by the equation,

$$h = 0.27\,(\Delta t/D_o)^{1/4} \tag{4.26}$$

(For graphical solution refer to Fig. 4.16, p. 103)

where D_o is the outside diameter. The length of pipe, provided it is greater than 1 foot, does not appreciably influence the value of the film coefficient.

4.12. Heat Transfer During Phase Change: Boiling Liquids. When heat transfer occurs to-or-from a fluid which is not undergoing change of phase, the process is usually one of steady-state. In such cases the instantaneous value of the convective film coefficient at a given point in the system does not differ from the mean value at the same point. When heat transfer is accompanied by phase change from liquid to vapor, as in boiling, the condition is no longer one of steady-state. In this case there is an irregular periodicity due to formation, growth, and liberation of bubbles from the heating surface. A number of empirical relationships have been used to evaluate film coefficients for boiling and some semi-rational equations have been proposed. However, this phenomenon is so complex that a generalized solution of acceptable accuracy has yet to be obtained.

Qualitatively, it is known that a smooth surface, and one that is easily wetted, will contribute to a greater value of the film coefficient. When boiling occurs within horizontal or vertical tubes, the resultant film coefficients do not differ greatly from those for a flat plate except that if the fluid is flowing through the tube under conditions of high velocity the usual forced convection relationships will control and the film coefficient will be approximately equal to the value for transfer without phase change. Boiling processes which occur under most industrial conditions are classified as "*nucleate* boiling," but under special conditions of very high transfer rate, as is the case when drops of liquid strike a very hot plate, the spheroidal state will exist and *film* boiling will occur. Except for unusually high loads or such special applications as the quenching of metals, film boiling does not occur in industrial processes.

For nucleate boiling of a liquid on a clean flat plate a general equation has been proposed by Jakob[2] and is recommended here in the following modified form,

$$h = \left(\frac{\sigma}{\rho' - \rho''}\right)^{1.5} \left(\frac{\Delta t}{\sigma_a}\right)^4 \left(\frac{0.0023k}{\nu_a}\right)^5 \tag{4.27}$$

(For graphical solution refer to Fig. 4.17, p. 105)

where σ is the surface tension (lb/ft), ν is kinematic viscosity (sq ft/hr), the prime indicates saturated liquid, the double prime indicates saturated vapor, subscript a denotes atmospheric pressure, and other symbols are as previously used.

For boiling within a tube, unless under conditions of forced convection, the flat plate values can be increased by about 25%.

4.13. Heat Transfer during Phase Change: Condensation. For most transfer surfaces, condensation occurs as a film and then flows with streamline motion from the surface. In such cases the major resistance to heat transmission is in conduction through the film. An analysis by Nusselt, in which it was assumed that all resistance was localized in the film, gave results which correspond closely with those which have been found in practice. Film condensation occurs whenever the transfer surface is wetted by the condensate. Because such wetting usually occurs with all normal surfaces, this mechanism of condensation is applicable to most practical industrial problems. In rare instances, as with unusually clean transfer surfaces, condensation may occur dropwise with resultant film coefficients many times larger than for filmwise transfer; however, since continuance of dropwise condensation can seldom be depended on, it is preferable in industrial designs to assume that the surface will be wetted and to use the more conservative film coefficients which are obtained for filmwise condensation. The equations most commonly used in the evaluation of condensation film coefficients are those proposed by Nusselt:

(1) For a pure vapor condensing on horizontal tubes, with Reynolds number greater than 2100,

$$Nu = 0.651D\left(\frac{\rho^2 g}{n\mu D w}\right)^{1/3} \tag{4.28}$$

where n is the number of tubes over one another and w is the condensation rate. Solving for h,

$$h = 0.651k\left(\frac{\rho^2 g}{n\mu D w}\right)^{1/3} \tag{4.29}$$

(For graphical solution for *steam*, refer to Fig. 4.18, p. 107)

where all physical properties are evaluated at the film temperature.

(2) For pure vapor condensing on a vertical tube with Reynolds number greater than 2100 and tube length greater than 20 feet, the criterion of streamline flow must be checked; for tube lengths between 10 and 20 feet, the calculated value of the film coefficient can be increased by 20%,

$$h = 0.925\rho k(g/N\mu\, w')^{1/3} \tag{4.30}$$

(For graphical solution for *steam*, refer to Fig. 4.19, p. 109)

where N is the length of tube, and w' is the flow rate, lb/(hr)(tube). All physical properties are evaluated at the film temperature.

When the ratio of condensate flow rate in (lb)/(hr) (tube) to the product of viscosity and diameter is greater than 1,020 Stoever[3] recommends the following equation in place of equation 4.30,

$$h = 0.0084 \left(\frac{w'}{\mu D}\right)^{0.4} \left(\frac{k^3\rho^2 g}{\mu^2}\right)^{1/3} \qquad (4.31)$$

(For graphical solution for *steam*, refer to Fig. 4.20, p. 111)

where the physical properties are evaluated at the film temperature.

Newton's Law of Cooling

Evaluation of the rate of heat transfer as given by Newton's Law of Cooling.

Equation: $q = hA(t_h - t_c)$

Text Reference: Section 4.1, equation 4.1.

Extensions: None.

Special Conditions: None.

Example: Air at 375 F is losing heat to a flat surface at a temperature of 50 F. The surface area is 6 square feet and the film coefficient of heat transfer is known to be 4 Btu/(hr) (sq ft) (°F). Determine the rate at which heat transfer is occurring between air and surface.

Solution: Enter the bottom scale (Fig. 4.1) at a temperature of 375 F and rise to intersection with the diagonal for a cold body temperature of 50 F. From this point move horizontally left to intersect the transfer line and then rise to meet the radial line for an area of 6 square feet. From this intersection move horizontally left to the transfer line and then rise to the radial line for a film coefficient of 4. Now move horizontally left to the transfer line and from the intersection rise to the scale at the top of the graph where read the rate of heat transfer as 7800 Btu/hour.

Check: By direct substitution in the stated equation,

$$q = (4)(6)(375 - 50) = 7800 \text{ Btu/hour}$$

Note: For problems in which the area of transfer surface or the film coefficient exceeds the scale value by any multiple of 10 the actual rate of heat transfer will exceed the scale value by the same multiple of 10. If both area and film coefficient exceed scale values by multiples of 10 the rate will exceed the scale value by the product of the two multiples of 10. (Note also that the transfer line in the center section of the graph coincides with the radial line for an area of 8 square feet.)

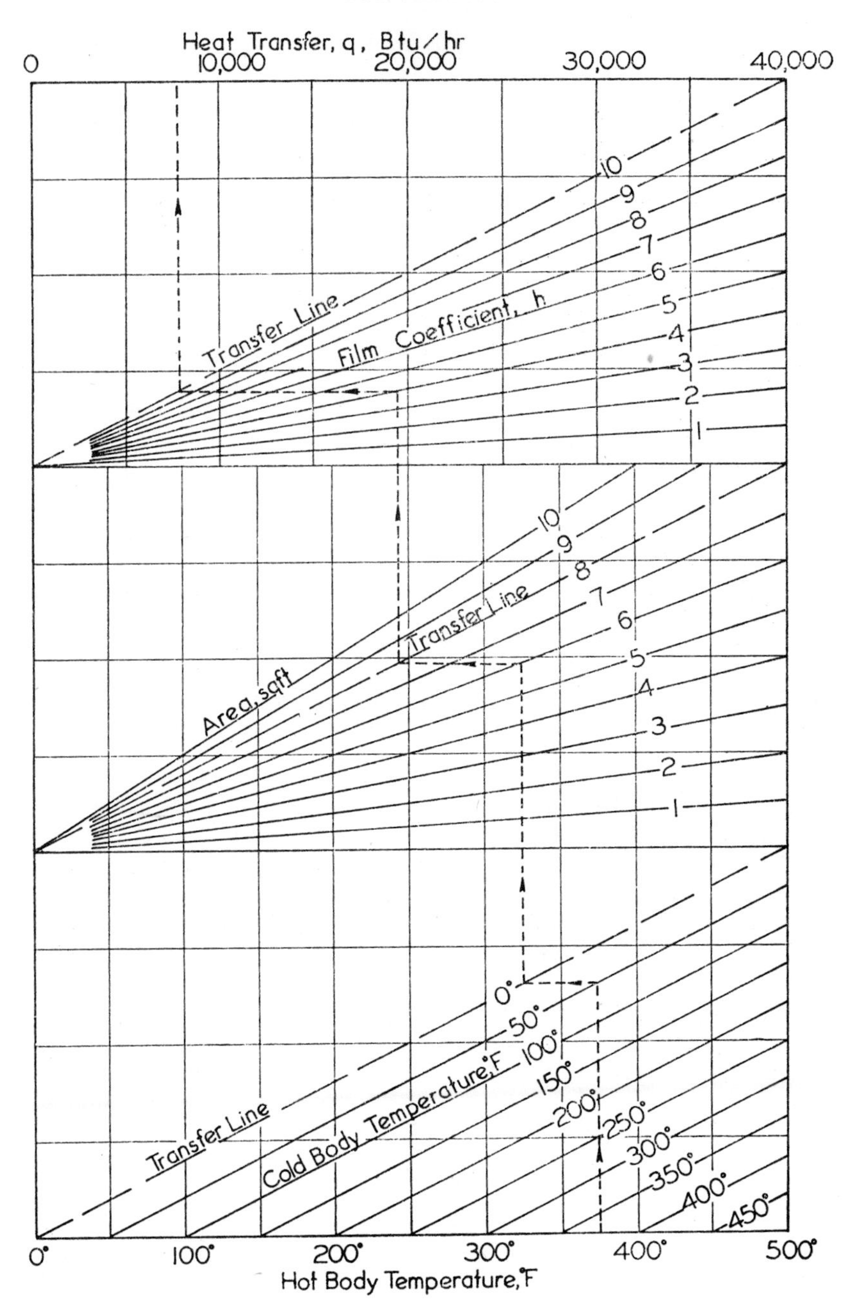
Heat Transfer, q, Btu/hr
0
10,000
20,000
30,000
40,000
Transfer Line
Film Coefficient, h
10
9
8
7
6
5
4
3
2
1
Transfer Line
Area, sqft
10
9
8
7
6
5
4
3
2
1
Transfer Line
Cold Body Temperature, °F
0°
50°
100°
150°
200°
250°
300°
350°
400°
450°
0°
100°
200°
300°
400°
500°
Hot Body Temperature, °F

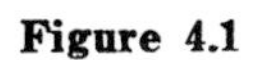

Figure 4.1

Reynolds Number

Evaluation of Reynolds number.

Equation: $Re = DV\rho/\mu$

Text Reference: Section 4.2, equation 4.5.

Extensions: None.

Special Conditions: Reynolds number is a dimensionless parameter and may be evaluated in any set of consistent units. For some engineering calculations it is convenient to use D in feet, V in feet per hour, ρ in pounds per cubic foot, and μ in pounds per hour per foot. For convenience in using the graph the D values are given in inches, V in ft/sec, and the μ values are given in the common units of centipoises; conversion of D, V, and μ to acceptably consistent units is accomplished in the construction of the graph hence the value of Re obtained from the graph is, as indicated on the scale, dimensionless. (When the user has μ in centipoises he can convert to lb/(hr) (ft) by multiplying the centipoises by 2.42.)

Example: Flow is occurring through a pipe having an inside diameter of 0.5 inches. The fluid has a density of 10 lbs/cu ft, and a viscosity of 0.20 centipoises. The velocity is 5 ft/sec. Determine the Reynolds number.

Solution: Enter the bottom scale (Fig. 4.2) at a velocity of 5 ft/sec and rise to the line for 0.5 inch inside diameter. From this point move horizontally left to the transfer line and then rise to the center section of the chart where intersect the line for a density of 10 lbs/cu ft. From this point move horizontally right to the transfer line and then rise to intersection with the line (in upper section of the chart) for a viscosity of 0.2 centipoises. From this intersection move horizontally left to the transfer line and then rise to the scale at the top of the graph where read the value of the Reynolds number as approximately 16,000.

Check: $Re = (0.5/12)\,(5 \times 3600)\,(10)/(0.2 \times 2.42) = 15{,}580$

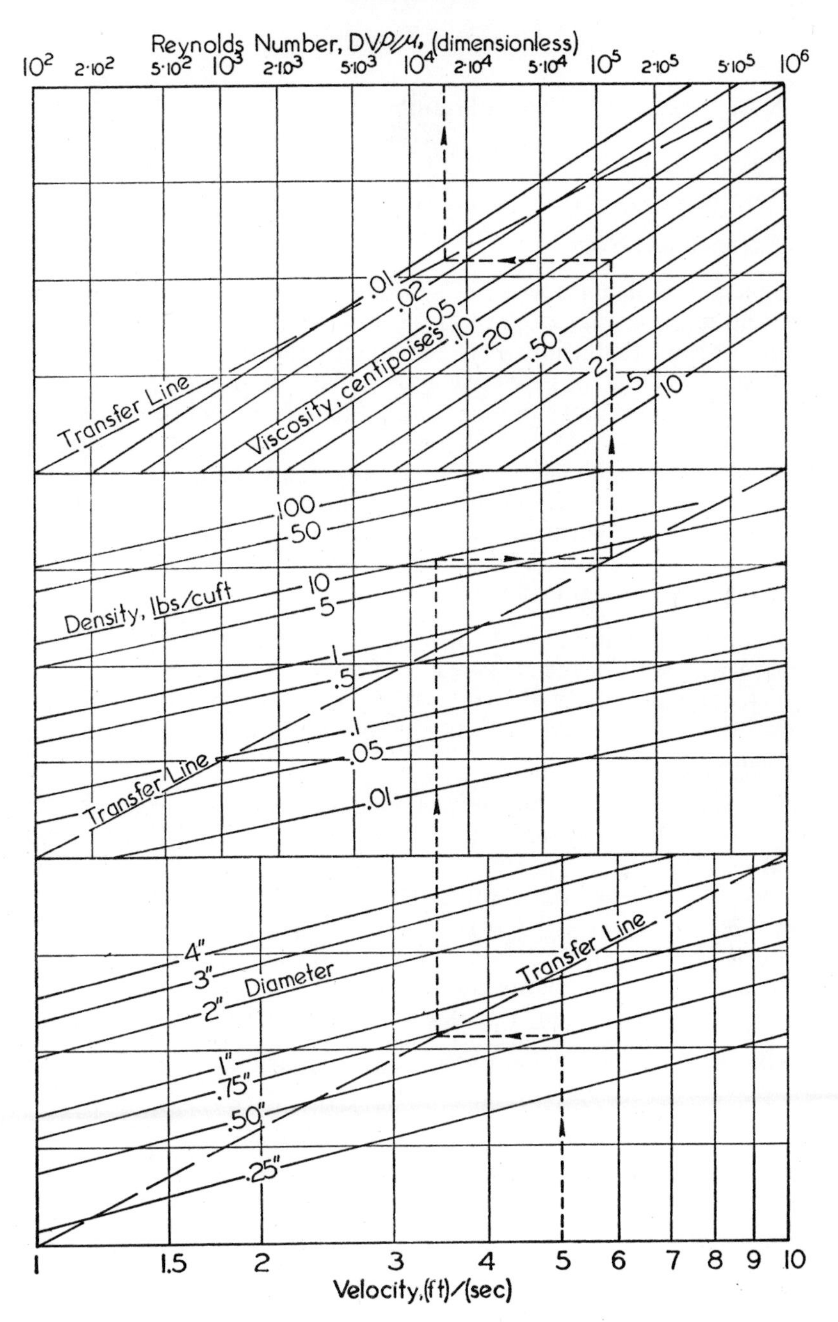
Reynolds Number, DVρ/μ, (dimensionless)
10^2 2·10^2 5·10^2 10^3 2·10^3 5·10^3 10^4 2·10^4 5·10^4 10^5 2·10^5 5·10^5 10^6
Transfer Line
Viscosity, centipoises
.01 .02 .05 .10 .20 .50 1 2 5 10
Density, lbs/cuft
100 50 10 5 1 .5 .1 .05 .01
Transfer Line
Diameter
4" 3" 2" 1" .75" .50" .25"
Transfer Line
1 1.5 2 3 4 5 6 7 8 9 10
Velocity, (ft)/(sec)

Figure 4.2

Grashof Number

Evaluation of the Grashof number.

Equation: $Gr = L^3 \rho^2 \beta g (\Delta t) / \mu^2$

Text Reference: Section 4.2, equation 4.7.

Extensions: None.

Special Conditions: Grashof's number is a dimensionless parameter and may be evaluated in any set of consistent units. For most engineering calculations it is convenient to use L in feet, and μ in lb/(hr) (ft), but for greater convenience in using the graph, the D values are given there in inches and μ in centipoises; conversion to acceptably consistent units is accomplished in the construction of the graph hence the value of Gr obtained from the graph is, as indicated on the scale, dimensionless. (The dimensionally consistent value of the acceleration due to gravity, g, is not the customary 32.2 ft/(sec) (sec), but 4.17×10^8 ft/(hr) (hr); this value is built into the graphical solution.)

Example: A fluid is being heated under conditions such that the temperature difference is 250 F and the coefficient of expansion is 0.004. It has a density of 1 lb/cu ft and a viscosity of 10 centipoises. For flow through a 4 inch diameter tube, determine the value of the Grashof number.

Solution: Enter the bottom scale of the graph (Fig. 4.3) at 250 F and rise to intersection with the line corresponding to a viscosity of 10 centipoises. From this point move horizontally left to the line for a coefficient of expansion of 0.004 and then rise to intersect the line for density of 1 lb/cu ft. From this point move horizontally right to the transfer line and then rise to the line for 4-inch diameter pipe. From this point move right to the transfer line and then rise to read the Grashof number as approximately 25,000.

Check: By substitution in the stated equation,

$$Gr = (4/12)^3 (1.0)^2 (0.004) (4.17 \times 10^8) (250) / (2.42 \times 10)^2$$
$$= 26{,}350$$

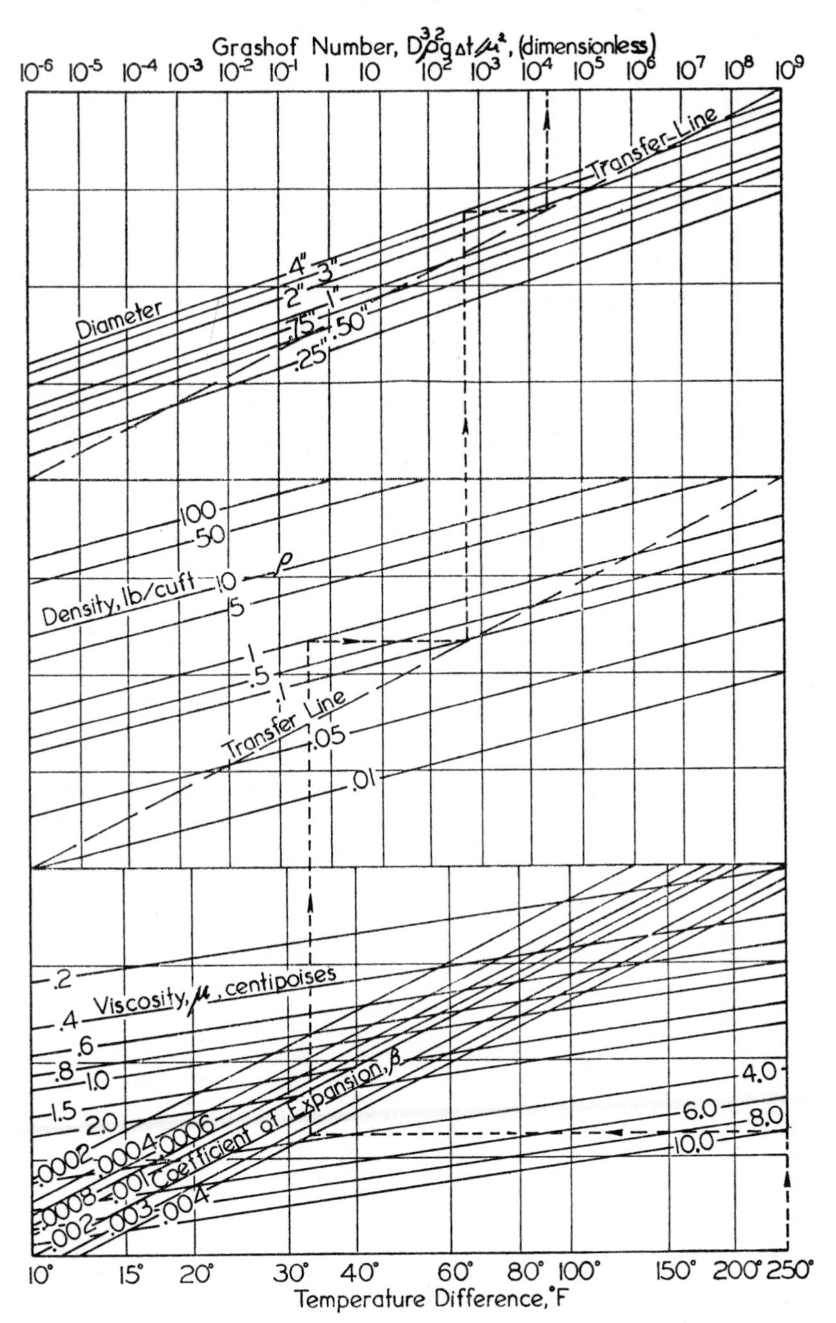
Grashof Number, $D^3\rho^2 g\Delta t/\mu^2$, (dimensionless)
10⁻⁶ 10⁻⁵ 10⁻⁴ 10⁻³ 10⁻² 10⁻¹ 1 10 10² 10³ 10⁴ 10⁵ 10⁶ 10⁷ 10⁸ 10⁹
Transfer-Line
Diameter
4" 3" 2" 1" .75" .50" .25"
100 50 10 5 1 .5 .1 .05 .01
Density, lb/cuft
ρ
Transfer Line
.2 .4 .6 .8 1.0 1.5 2.0
Viscosity, μ, centipoises
4.0 6.0 8.0 10.0
.0002 .0004 .0006 .0008 .001 .002 .003 .004
Coefficient of Expansion, β
10° 15° 20° 30° 40° 60° 80° 100° 150° 200° 250°
Temperature Difference, °F

Figure 4.3

Prandtl Number

Evaluation of the Prandtl number.

Equation: $Pr = c_p\mu/k$

Text Reference: Section 4.2, equation 4.8.

Extensions: None.

Special Conditions: The Prandtl number is a dimensionless parameter and may be evaluated in any set of consistent units. For most engineering calculations c_p would be in Btu/(lb) (°F), k in Btu/(hr) (sq ft) (°F/ft), and μ in lb/(hr) (ft). For convenience in using the graph the μ values are there given in the common units of centipoises; conversion of μ from centipoises to consistent units is accomplished in the construction of the graph hence the graph value of the Prandtl number is, as indicated on the scale, a dimensionless quantity. (Viscosity in centipoises can be converted to units of lb/(hr) (ft) by multiplying by 2.42.)

Example: A fluid having a specific heat of 0.28 Btu/(lb) (°F) and a viscosity of 1.5 centipoises has a thermal conductivity of 0.05 Btu/(hr) (sq ft) (°F/ft). Determine the value of the Prandtl number.

Solution: Enter the bottom scale of the graph (Fig. 4.4) at specific heat of 0.28 and rise to intersect the radial line for a thermal conductivity of 0.05. From this point move horizontally right to intersect the transfer line and then rise to the radial line in the upper section of the graph for a viscosity of 1.5 centipoises. From here move horizontally left to the transfer line and then rise to the top scale where read the value of the Prandtl number for this fluid as approximately 20.

Check: $Pr = (0.28)(1.5 \times 2.42)/(0.05) = 20.3$

Note: The graphical construction of this figure differs from that of most of the graphs in that the transfer line in the lower half is reversed, running diagonally upward from right to left instead of left to right.

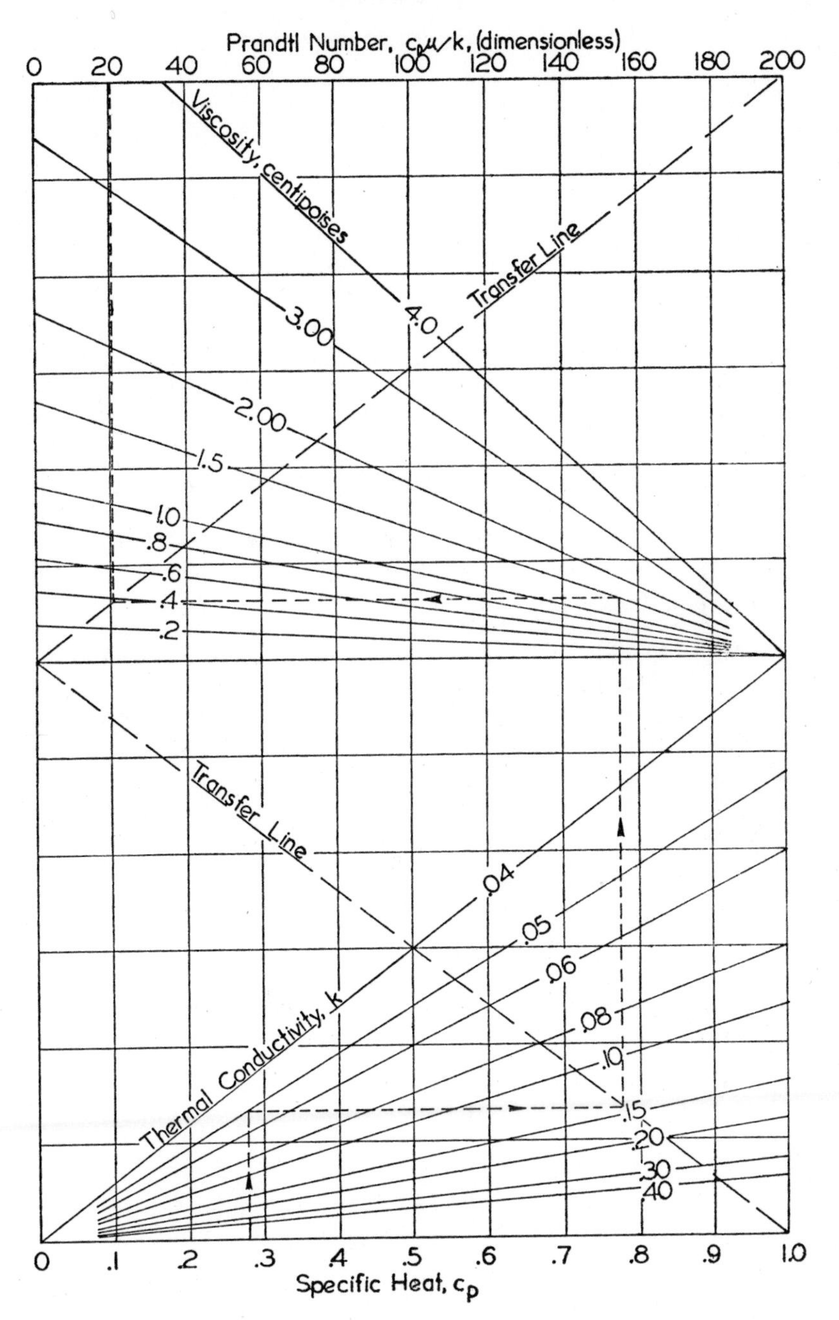
Prandtl Number, $c_p\mu/k$, (dimensionless)
0 20 40 60 80 100 120 140 160 180 200
Viscosity, centipoises
4.0
3.00
2.00
1.5
1.0
.8
.6
.4
.2
Transfer Line
Transfer Line
Thermal Conductivity, k
.04
.05
.06
.08
.10
.15
.20
.30
.40
0 .1 .2 .3 .4 .5 .6 .7 .8 .9 1.0
Specific Heat, c_p

Figure 4.4

Nusselt Number — Range: 0 to 1000

Evaluation of the Nusselt number: Range from 0 to 1000 (for larger range refer to Fig. 4.6; for evaluation of h from Nu refer to Figs. 4.7 and 4.8).

Equation: $Nu = hD/k$

Text Reference: Section 4.3, equation 4.9.

Extensions: None.

Special Conditions: The Nusselt number is a dimensionless parameter hence may be evaluated in any set of consistent units. For the customary units of thermal conductivity, Btu/(hr) (sq ft) (°F/ft), the corresponding units of diameter should be in feet. However, for convenience in using the graph, diameter lines on the graph are marked in inches and the necessary conversion to consistent units is taken care of in the construction of the graph. The Nusselt number obtained from the graph is therefore, as indicated on the scale, dimensionless.

Example: A fluid is being cooled while flowing through a pipe of 2 inches inside diameter. The film coefficient is 50 Btu/(hr) (sq ft) (°F) and the thermal conductivity of the fluid is 0.06 Btu/(hr) (sq ft) (°F/ft). Evaluate the Nusselt number.

Solution: Enter the bottom scale of the graph (Fig. 4.5) at an h value of 50 and rise to intersection with the radial for a thermal conductivity of 0.06. From this point move horizontally right (in some problems the direction will be to the *left*) to intersect the transfer line and then rise to the upper section of the graph where intersect the radial line for 2-inches diameter. From this point move horizontally left (in some problems the direction will be *right*) to intersect the transfer line and then rise to the top scale where read the value of the Nusselt number as 140.

Check: $Nu = (50)(2/12)/(0.06) = 139$

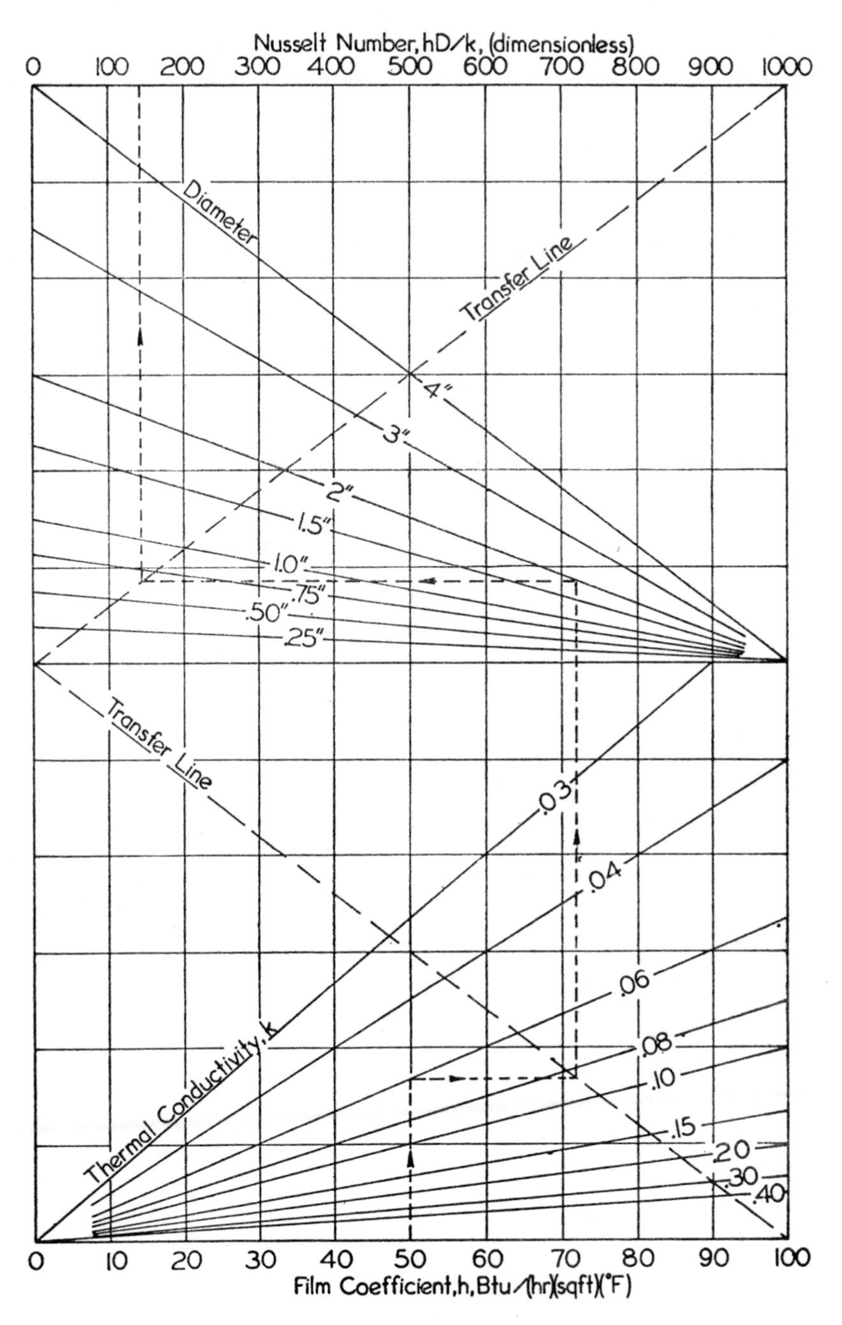
Nusselt Number, hD/k, (dimensionless)
0 100 200 300 400 500 600 700 800 900 1000
Diameter
Transfer Line
4"
3"
2"
1.5"
1.0"
.75"
.50"
.25"
Transfer Line
.03
.04
.06
.08
.10
.15
.20
.30
.40
Thermal Conductivity, k
0 10 20 30 40 50 60 70 80 90 100
Film Coefficient, h, Btu/(hr)(sqft)(°F)

Figure 4.5

Nusselt Number — Range: 0 to 5000

Evaluation of the Nusselt number: Range from 0 to 5000 (for smaller range refer to Fig. 4.5; for evaluation of h from Nu refer to Figs. 4.7 and 4.8).

Equation: $Nu = hD/k$

Text Reference: Section 4.3, equation 4.9.

Extensions: None.

Special Conditions: The Nusselt number is a dimensionless parameter hence may be evaluated in any set of consistent units. For the customary units of thermal conductivity, Btu/(hr) (sq ft) (°F/ft), the corresponding units of diameter should be in feet. However, for convenience in using the graph, the diameter lines on the graph are marked in inches and the necessary conversion to consistent units is taken care of in the construction of the graph. The Nusselt number obtained from the graph is therefore, as stated on the scale, dimensionless.

Example: A fluid is being cooled while flowing through a pipe of 3 inches inside diameter. The film coefficient is 1100 Btu/(hr) (sq ft) (°F) and the thermal conductivity of the fluid is 0.10 Btu/(hr) (sq ft) (°F/ft). Evaluate the Nusselt number.

Solution: Enter the bottom scale of the graph (Fig. 4.6) at an h value of 1100 and rise to intersection with the radial line for a thermal conductivity of 0.10. From this point move to the left (in some cases the direction will be to the *right*) to intersect the transfer line and then rise to the upper section of the graph where intersect the radial line for 3-inches diameter. From this point move horizontally to the right (in some problems the direction will be to the *left*) to intersection with the transfer line and then rise to the top scale where read the value of Nu as 2750.

Check: $Nu = (1100)\,(3/12)\,/\,(0.10) = 2750$

Note: The reverse solution, that is, for h, under the same conditions as given in the above example, is given in Fig. 4.8.

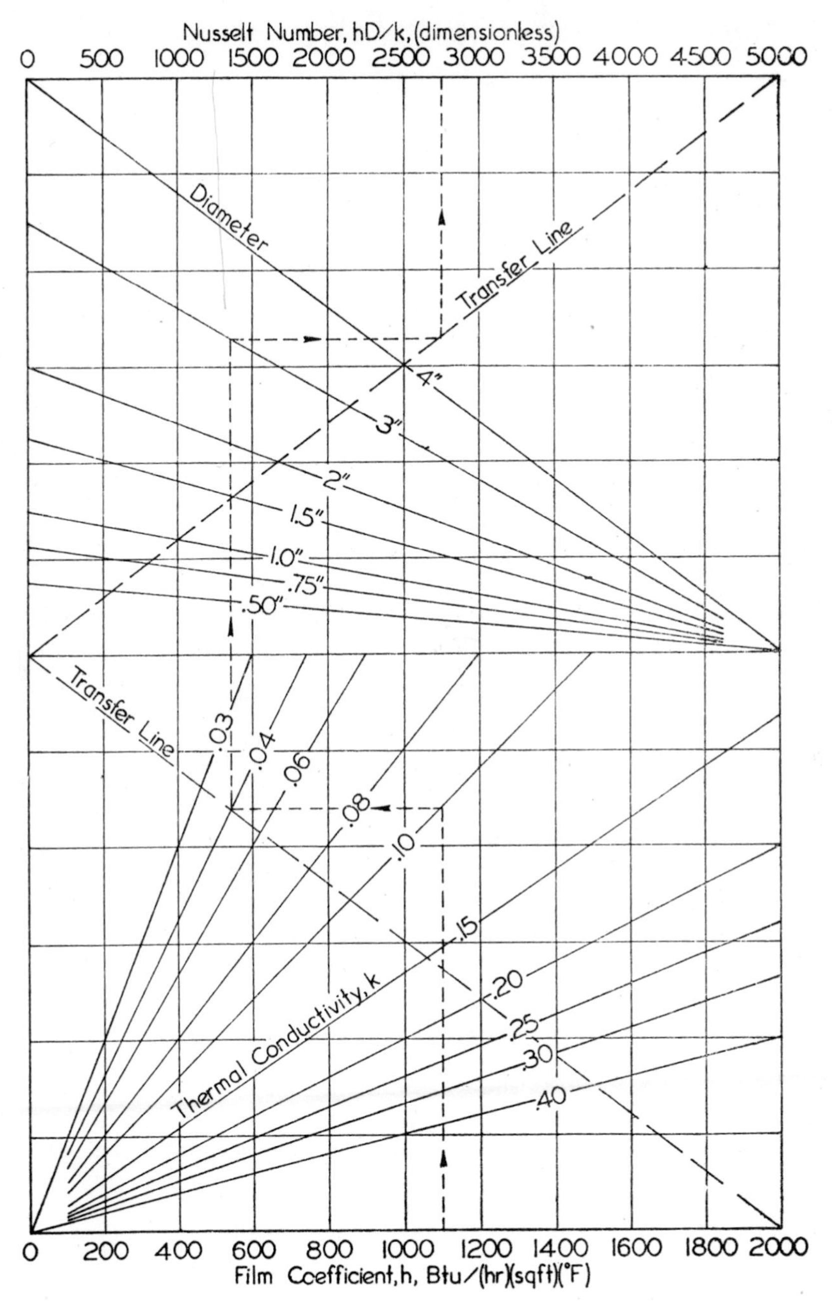
Nusselt Number, hD/k, (dimensionless)
0 500 1000 1500 2000 2500 3000 3500 4000 4500 5000
Diameter
Transfer Line
4"
3"
2"
1.5"
1.0"
.75"
.50"
Transfer Line
.03
.04
.06
.08
.10
.15
.20
.25
.30
.40
Thermal Conductivity, k
0 200 400 600 800 1000 1200 1400 1600 1800 2000
Film Coefficient, h, Btu/(hr)(sqft)(°F)

Figure 4.6

Film Coefficient, h, from Nusselt Number — Range: 0 to 100

Evaluation of the film coefficient from the Nusselt number: Range 0 to 100 (for larger range refer to Fig. 4.8; for evaluation of *Nu* when the film coefficient is known, refer to Figs. 4.5 and 4.6).

Equation: $h = (Nu)(k/D)$

Text Reference: Section 4.4, equation 4.14.

Extensions: None.

Special Conditions: The Nusselt number is a dimensionless parameter hence the dimensions of h and of D, in the above stated equation, must be dimensionally consistent. Since h is in Btu/(hr)(sq ft)(°F) it is evident that D must be in feet. However, for convenience in using the graph, the diameter lines on the graph are identified in units of inches. The necessary conversion to consistent units is taken care of in the construction of the graph.

Example: A fluid is being heated while it flows in a pipe of 2 inches inside diameter. Conditions are such that the Nusselt number has a value of 140 (note that graphical evaluations of *Nu* for various types of thermal systems are given in Figs. 4.9, 4.13, 6.1, 6.2, and 6.4). The thermal conductivity of the fluid is 0.06 Btu/(hr)(sq ft)(°F/ft). Determine the inside-film coefficient.

Solution: Enter the bottom scale of the graph (Fig. 4.7) at a *Nu* of 140, rise to intersect the transfer line, then move horizontally right to intersect the radial line for 2-inches diameter. From this point rise to the transfer line in the upper section of the graph then move left to intersect the radial line for a thermal conductivity of 0.06. From this point rise to the top scale where read the value of the film coefficient as 50 Btu/(hr)(sq ft)(°F).

Check: $h = (140)(0.06)/(2/12) = 50$.

Note: Unlike most of the graphical solutions this one requires rising first to a transfer line and then moving horizontally to intersect a radial line for a given property of the system. (The usual construction involves rising to a radial line and then moving horizontally to intersect a transfer line.)

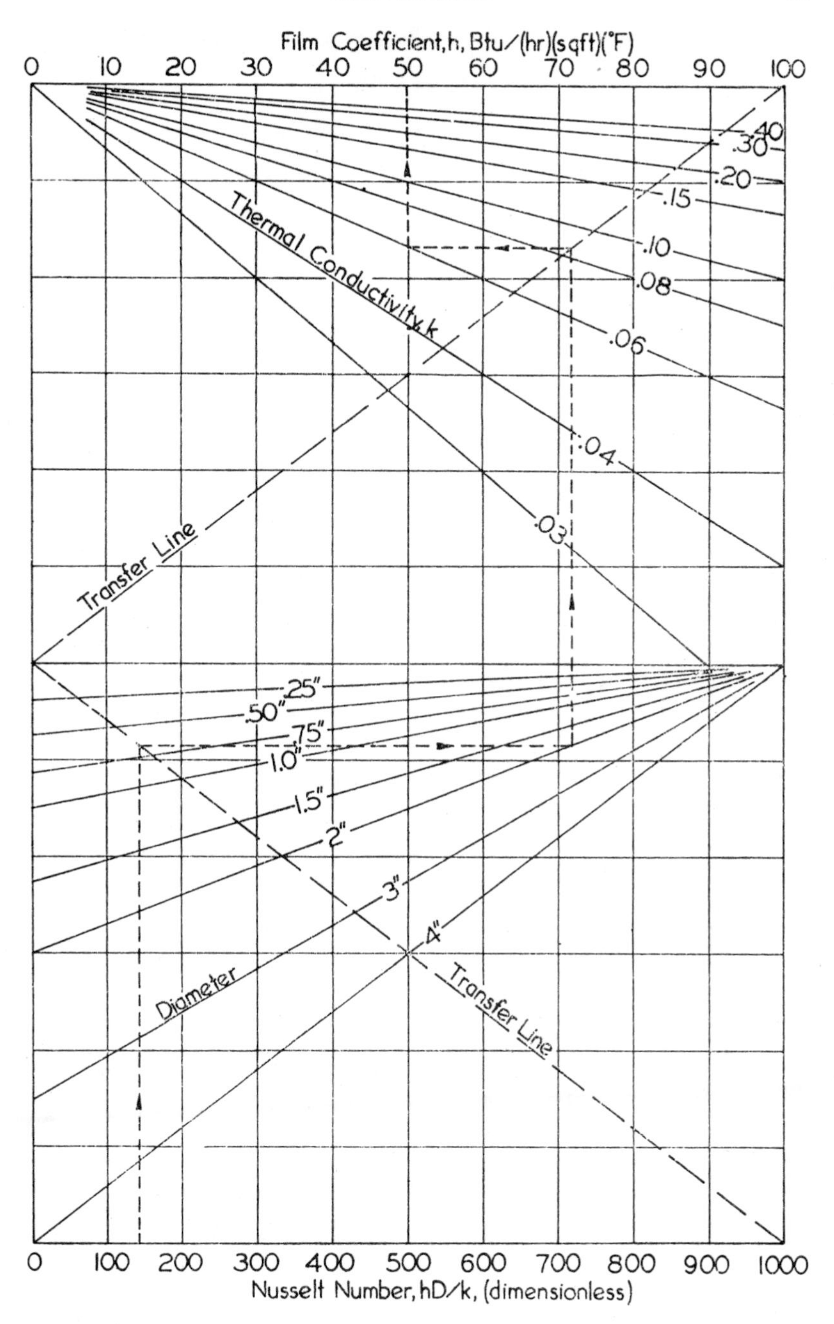

Film Coefficient, h, Btu/(hr)(sqft)(°F)
0
10
20
30
40
50
60
70
80
90
100
.40
.30
.20
.15
.10
.08
.06
.04
.03
Thermal Conductivity, k
Transfer Line
.25"
.50"
.75"
1.0"
1.5"
2"
3"
4"
Diameter
Transfer Line
0
100
200
300
400
500
600
700
800
900
1000
Nusselt Number, hD/k, (dimensionless)

Figure 4.7

Film Coefficient, h, from Nusselt Number — Range: 0 to 2000

Evaluation of the film coefficient from the Nusselt number: Range from 0 to 2000 (for smaller range refer to Fig. 4.7; for evaluation of Nu when the film coefficient is known, refer to Figs. 4.5 and 4.6).

Equation: $h = (Nu)(k/D)$

Text Reference: Section 4.4, equation 4.14.

Extensions: None.

Special Conditions: The Nusselt number is a dimensionless parameter hence the dimensions of h and D, in the above stated equation, must be dimensionally consistent. Since h is in Btu/(hr)(sq ft)(°F) it is evident that D must be in feet. However, for convenience in using the graph, diameter lines on the graph are identified in units of inches. The necessary conversion to consistent units is taken care of in the construction of the graph.

Example: A fluid is being heated while flowing in a pipe of 3 inches inside diameter. Conditions are such that the Nusselt number has a value of 2750 (note that graphical evaluations of Nu for various types of thermal systems are given in Figs. 4.9, 4.13, 6.1, 6.2, and 6.4). The thermal conductivity of the fluid is 0.10 Btu/(hr)(sq ft)(°F/ft). Determine the inside film coefficient.

Solution: Enter the bottom scale of the graph (Fig. 4.8) at a Nu of 2750, rise to intersect the transfer line, then move horizontally left to intersect the radial line for 3 inches diameter. From this point rise to the transfer line in the upper section of the graph (noting that, by coincidence, this intersection is also an intersection with the radial for 0.04 conductivity), then move right to intersect the radial line for a thermal conductivity of 0.10 and from this point rise to the top scale where read the value of the film coefficient as 1100 Btu/(hr)(sq ft)(°F).

Check: $h = (2750)(0.10)/(3/12) = 1100$

Note: Unlike most of the graphical solutions, this one requires rising first to a transfer line and then moving over to a radial line; with most graphs the opposite procedure is followed.

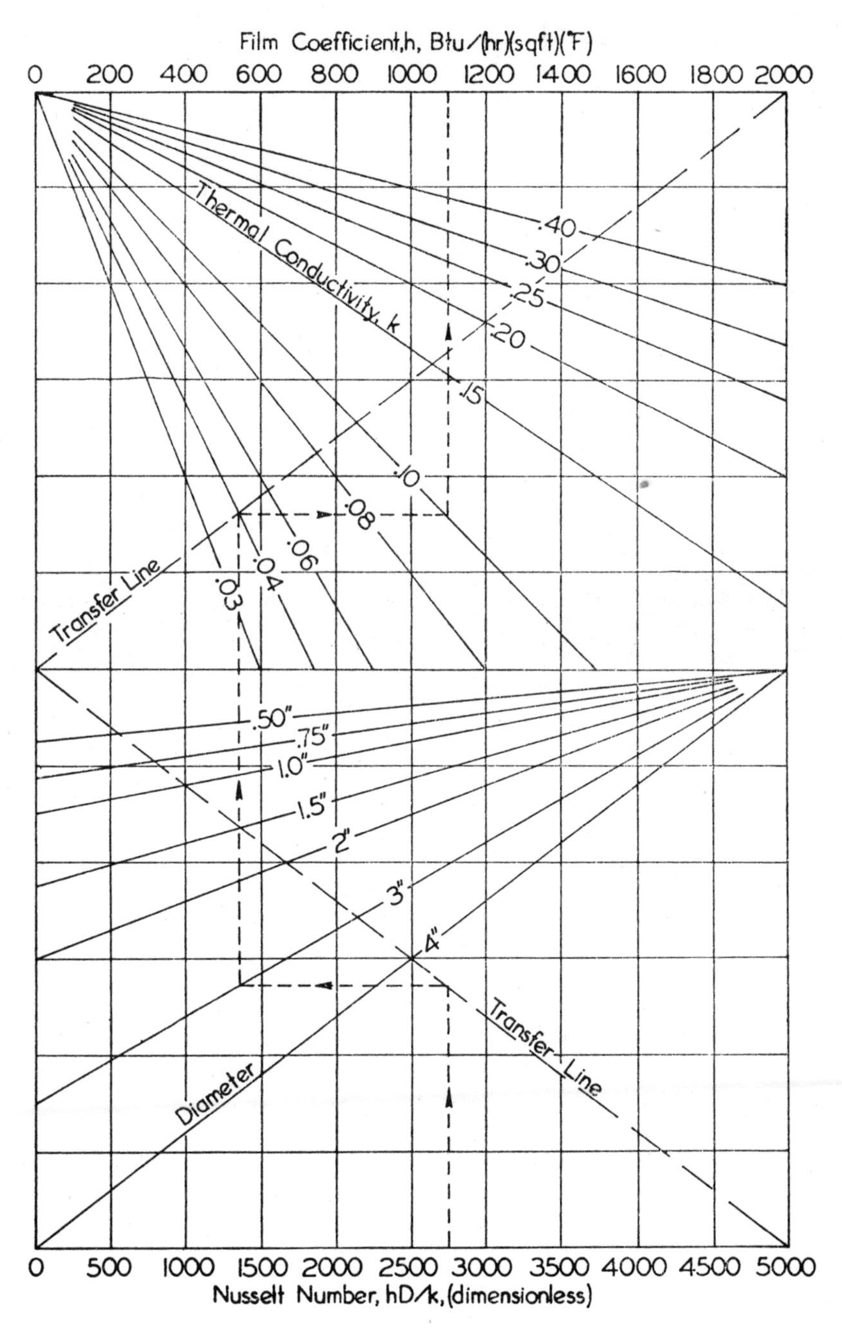
Film Coefficient,h, Btu/(hr)(sqft)(°F)
0 200 400 600 800 1000 1200 1400 1600 1800 2000
Thermal Conductivity, k
.40
.30
.25
.20
.15
.10
.08
.06
.04
.03
Transfer Line
.50"
.75"
1.0"
1.5"
2"
3"
4"
Transfer Line
Diameter
0 500 1000 1500 2000 2500 3000 3500 4000 4500 5000
Nusselt Number, hD/k, (dimensionless)

Figure 4.8

Film Coefficients for Viscous Liquids Heating or Cooling Inside Pipes

Evaluation of the film coefficient for a viscous liquid (*Re* less than 2100) heating or cooling inside horizontal or vertical pipes.

Equation: $Nu = 1.86\,(\mu/\mu_s)^{0.14}[(Re)\,(Pr)\,(D/L)]^{1/3}$

Text Reference: Section 4.5, equation 4.16.

Extensions: None.

Special Conditions: The value of μ is taken at the bulk temperature of the fluid whereas μ_s is taken at the approximate temperature of the film. The D/L ratio in the stated equation is dimensionless, but for greater convenience in using the graph, the values of the D/L ratios shown on the graph are for the diameter, D, in inches and the characteristic length, L, in feet. The solution gives the value of *Nu* in terms of known values of the Reynolds and Prandtl numbers, each of which is evaluable from other graphical solutions.

Example: A fluid is heating within a pipe under conditions such that the Prandtl number (graphically evaluated from Fig. 4.4) is 200 and the Reynolds number (graphically evaluated from Fig. 4.2) is 2000. The inside diameter of the pipe is 2 inches and the length of the section in which heating takes place is 10 feet. The ratio of the viscosity in the main bulk of fluid to that in the fluid film is approximately 0.32. Determine the inside-film coefficient if the thermal conductivity of the fluid is 0.1 Btu/(hr) (sq ft) (°F/ft).

Solution: Enter the bottom scale of the graph (Fig. 4.9) at a *Pr* of 200 and rise to intersect the line for a *Re* of 2000. From this point move horizontally left to intersect the transfer line then rise to the center section of the graph where intersect the line for a diameter-length ratio of 0.2. From this point move horizontally left to the transfer line and then rise to the upper section of the graph where intersect the line for a viscosity ratio of 0.32. From this point move horizontally left to the transfer line and rise from this intersection to the scale at the top of the graph where read the value of *Nu* as 30. The film coefficient is then,

$$h = (k/D)\,(Nu) = [(0.1)/(2/12)]\,(30)$$
$$= 18 \text{ Btu/(hr) (sq ft) (°F)}$$

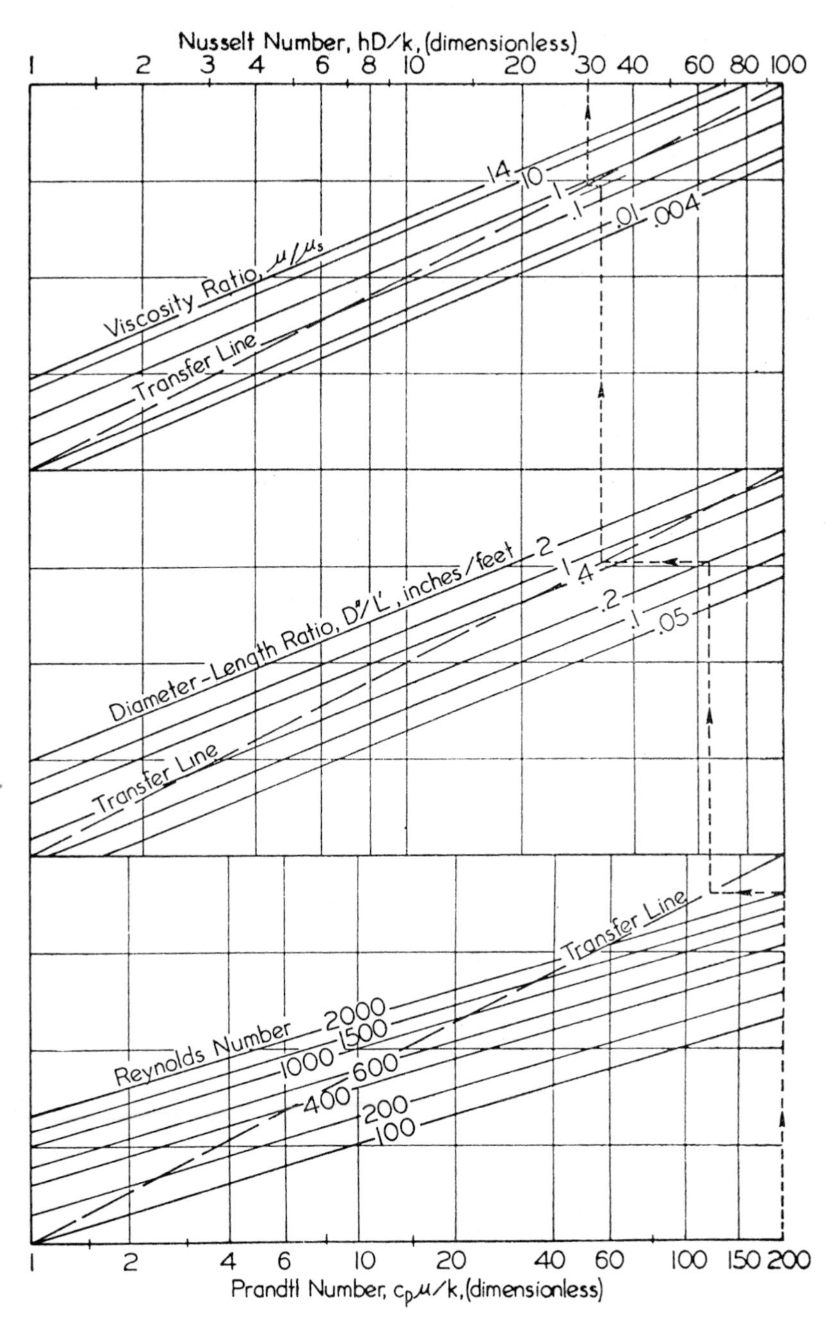
Nusselt Number, hD/k, (dimensionless)
1 2 3 4 6 8 10 20 30 40 60 80 100
Viscosity Ratio, μ/μs
14
10
1
.1
.01
.004
Transfer Line
Diameter-Length Ratio, D"/L', inches/feet
2
1
.4
.2
.1
.05
Transfer Line
Transfer Line
Reynolds Number
2000
1500
1000
600
400
200
100
1 2 4 6 10 20 40 60 100 150 200
Prandtl Number, cpμ/k, (dimensionless)

Figure 4.9

Film Coefficient for Water Heating during Streamline Flow in a Vertical Pipe

Evaluation of the film coefficient for *water* that is being heated during streamline flow upward or downward in a vertical pipe.

Equations: For upward flow: $h = 0.42(t)(\Delta t)^{1/3}$

For downward flow: $h = 0.49(t)(\Delta t)^{1/3}$

Text Reference: Section 4.6, equations 4.17 and 4.18.

Extensions: None.

Special Conditions: The graphical solution is applicable only when the value of the Reynolds number is *less* than the critical value of 2100; for cases where the *Re* exceeds this critical value, refer to Fig. 6.49 for water heating or cooling within, or outside and normal to, a single tube.

Example: Water at an average temperature of 150 F is being heated while in streamline flow through a vertical tube. The average temperature difference between the tube wall and the passing fluid is 20 F. Determine the value of the film coefficient: (1) For downward flow; (2) For upward flow.

Solution: Enter the bottom scale of the graph (Fig. 4.10) at a temperature of 150 F and rise to the line for a temperature difference of 20 F. From the point of intersection move horizontally left (for some problems this direction will be to the *right*) to the transfer line and then rise to one or the other of the scales at the top of the graph: (1) For downward flow the inside film coefficient is read from the upper of the top scales as approximately 200 Btu/(hr) (sq ft) (°F); (2) For upward flow the inside film coefficient is read from the lower of the top scales as approximately 170 Btu/(hr) (sq ft) (°F).

Check: Downward flow: $h = 0.42(150)(20)^{1/3} = 199$

Upward flow: $h = 0.49(150)(20)^{1/3} = 171$

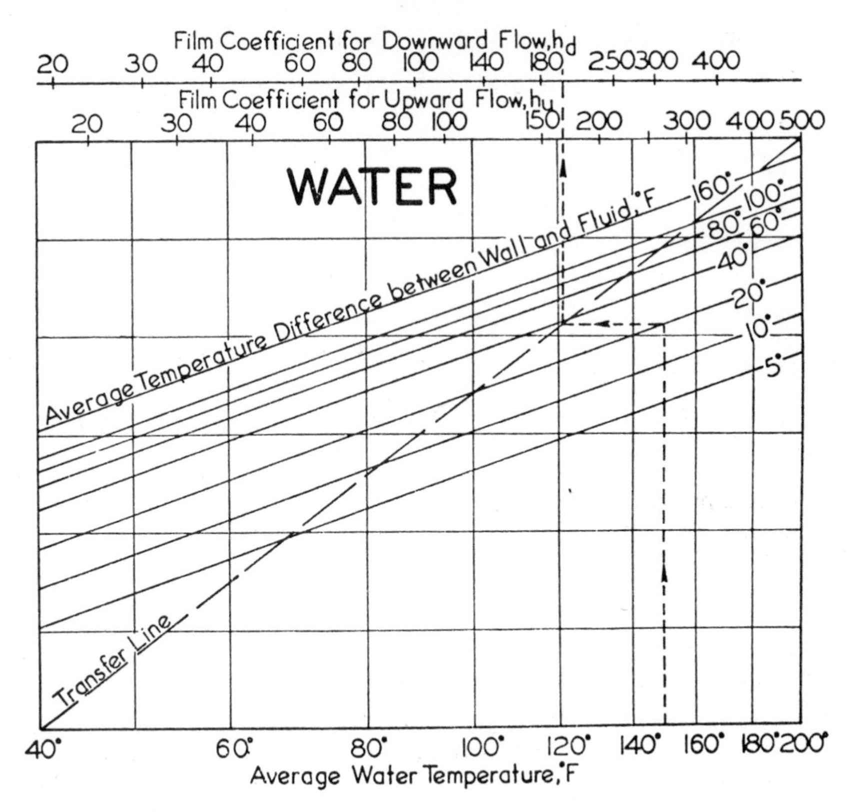
Film Coefficient for Downward Flow, h_d
20 30 40 60 80 100 140 180 250 300 400
Film Coefficient for Upward Flow, h_u
20 30 40 60 80 100 150 200 300 400 500
WATER
Average Temperature Difference between Wall and Fluid, °F
160° 100° 80° 60° 40° 20° 10° 5°
Transfer Line
40° 60° 80° 100° 120° 140° 160° 180° 200°
Average Water Temperature, °F

Figure 4.10

Film Coefficient for Water Flowing by Gravity Down Through a Vertical Tube

Evaluation of the film coefficient for *water* flowing by gravity down through a vertical tube.

Equation: $h = 120\left(\frac{w}{\pi D_i}\right)^{1/3}$

Text Reference: Section 4.7, equation 4.19.

Extensions: None.

Special Conditions: This graphical solution is applicable only when the flow rate is less than that necessary to fill the pipe.

Example: The mass flow rate of water down through a ¼-inch inside diameter condenser tube is 200 lb/hr. Determine the film coefficient.

Solution: Enter the bottom scale of the graph (Fig. 4.11) at a mass flow rate of 200 and rise to intersection with the line for a tube of ¼-inch diameter. From this point move horizontally right (in some problems this direction will be to the *left*) to intersect the transfer line, then rise to the top scale where read the film coefficient as approximately 1750 Btu/(hr) (sq ft) (°F).

Check: By substitution in the stated equation,

$$h = (120)(200)^{1/3}/(0.25\pi/12)^{1/3} = 1740$$

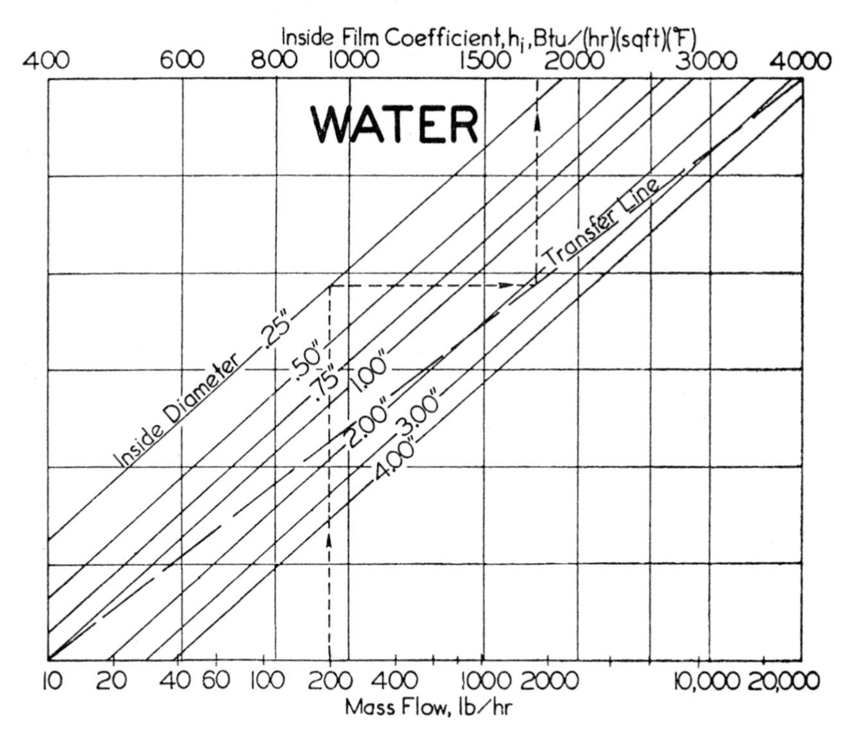
Inside Film Coefficient, h_i, Btu/(hr)(sqft)(°F)
400
600
800
1000
1500
2000
3000
4000
WATER
Transfer Line
Inside Diameter .25"
.50"
.75"
1.00"
2.00"
3.00"
4.00"
10
20
40
60
100
200
400
1000
2000
10,000
20,000
Mass Flow, lb/hr

Figure 4.11

Film Coefficient for Water Trickling by Gravity over the Outside of Horizontal Pipes

Evaluation of the film coefficient for *water* trickling by gravity over the outside of horizontal pipes.

Equation: $h = 65 \left[\frac{w}{2LD_o}\right]^{1/3}$

Text Reference: Section 4.7, equation 4.20.

Extensions: None.

Special Conditions: In the stated equation the flow rate w is that which occurs over each tube of length L in the sinuous coil or "trombone" type heat exchanger.

Example: Water is flowing by gravity over the outside of a series of slightly inclined tubes which are placed vertically over one another in a "trombone" type cooler. The flow rate is 200 lb/hr. Determine the outside film coefficient if each tube is ¾ inch outside diameter and 4 feet long.

Solution: Enter the bottom scale of the graph (Fig. 4.12) at a flow rate of 200 lb/hr and rise to the diagonal for a ¾-inch tube. From this point move horizontally right (for some problems this direction would be to the *left*) to intersection with the transfer line, then rise to intersect the diagonal for a tube length of 4 feet. From this latter intersection move horizontally left (in some cases this direction will be to the *right*) to the transfer line and from there rise vertically to the scale at the top of the graph where read the value of the outside film coefficient as approximately 500 Btu/(hr) (sq ft) (°F). For a system in which the average temperature difference (fluid-to-fluid) is known and for which the inside film coefficient has been determined, the overall coefficient can be calculated and the necessary number of tube lengths determined.

Check: By substitution in the stated equation,

$$h = (65)\,[(200)/(2)\,(4)\,(0.75/12)]^{1/3} = 479$$

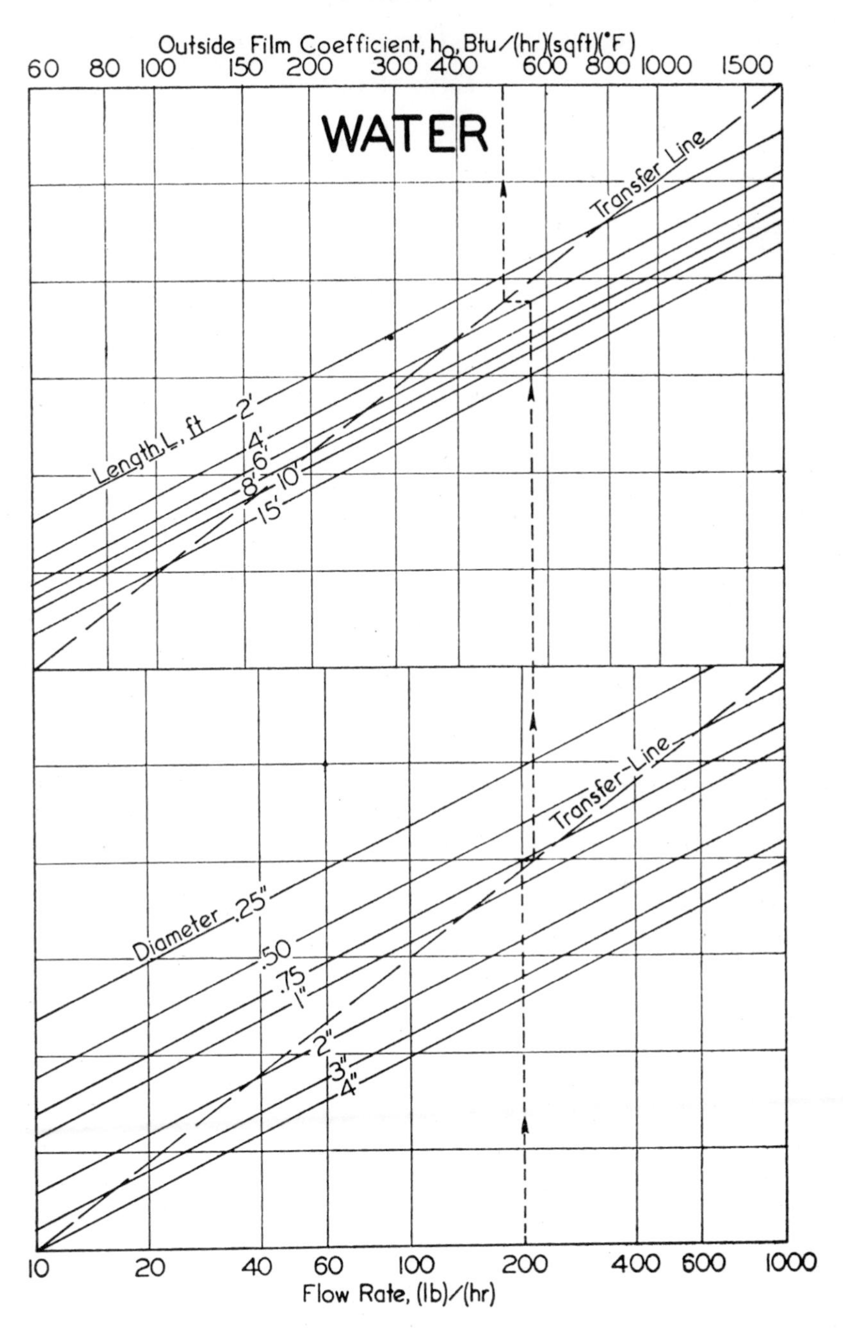
Outside Film Coefficient, h_o, Btu/(hr)(sqft)(°F)
60 80 100 150 200 300 400 600 800 1000 1500
WATER
Transfer Line
Length, L, ft 2' 4' 6' 8' 10' 15'
Transfer-Line
Diameter .25" .50 .75 1" 2" 3" 4"
10 20 40 60 100 200 400 600 1000
Flow Rate, (lb)/(hr)

Figure 4.12

Film Coefficient for Free Convection from a Horizontal Pipe to Liquids or Gases

Evaluation of the film coefficient for free convection from single horizontal cylinders to liquids or to gases.

Equation: $Nu = a[(Gr)(Pr)]^x$

Text Reference: Section 4.8, equations 4.21 and 4.22.

Extensions: None.

Special Conditions: The graphical solution is to be used in determining the Nusselt number when values of the Prandtl and Grashof numbers are known. From the properties of the fluid and of the system the Prandtl number can be evaluated graphically by using Fig. 4.4 and the Grashof number by using Fig. 4.3. Once the Nusselt number has been determined from this graph the value of the film coefficient can be determined either by calculation or graphically from Figs. 4.7 or 4.8.

In evaluating the dimensionless parameters for this case, the values of the fluid properties used should be those corresponding to the arithmetical average of mean fluid and cylinder surface temperatures.

Example: A fluid is being heated while passing over a cylinder under conditions of free convection. The Prandtl-Grashof product is 100. If the thermal conductivity is 0.1 Btu/(hr) (sq ft) (°F/ft) and the cylinder outside diameter is 0.25 inch, determine the outside film coefficient.

Solution: Enter the bottom scale of the graph (Fig. 4.13) at a $(Pr)(Gr)$ value of 100 and rise to intersect the solid curve. From this point move horizontally left (in some problems this direction will be to the *right*) to the transfer line and then rise to the scale at the top of the graph where read the value of the Nusselt number as approximately 2.1. The film coefficient for this system is then,

$$h = (k/D)(Nu) = [(0.1)/(0.25/12)](2.1)$$

$$= 10 \text{ Btu/(hr) (sq ft) (°F)}$$

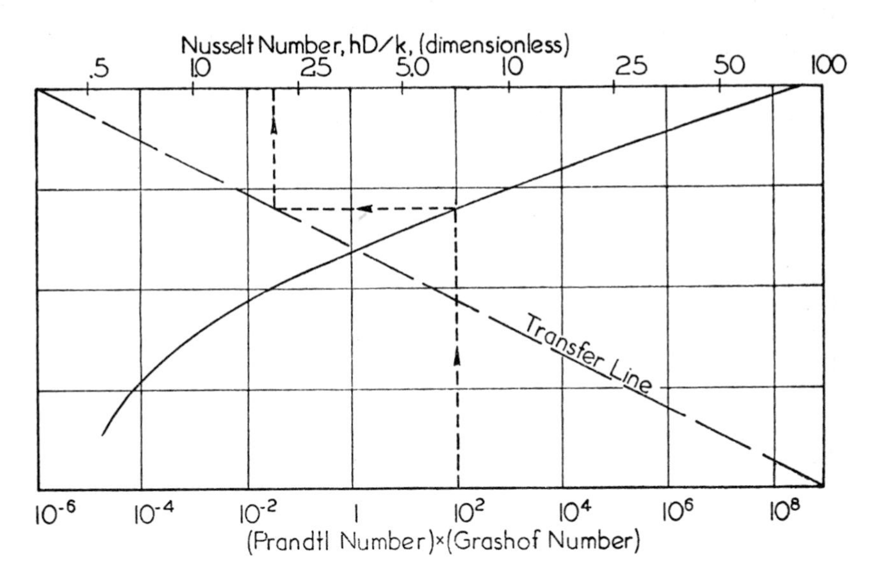
Nusselt Number, hD/k, (dimensionless)
.5
1.0
2.5
5.0
10
25
50
100
Transfer Line
10^{-6}
10^{-4}
10^{-2}
1
10^{2}
10^{4}
10^{6}
10^{8}
(Prandtl Number)×(Grashof Number)

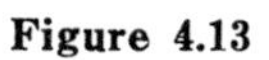

Figure 4.13

Film Coefficient for Air Heating by Natural Convection While Passing over Flat Plates

Evaluation of the film coefficient for the heating of air by natural convection while passing over a flat plate (for the cooling of air refer to the discussion under "Extensions").

Equations: $h = 0.38\,(\Delta t)^{1/4}$ for heating plate facing up.

$h = 0.27\,(\Delta t)^{1/4}$ for heating plate vertical.

$h = 0.20\,(\Delta t)^{1/4}$ for heating plate facing down.

Text Reference: Section 4.9, equations 4.23, 4.24, and 4.25.

Extensions: For air *cooling* while flowing by natural convection over a flat plate *facing down,* use the curve for air heating while passing over a plate facing up. For air *cooling* while flowing by natural convection over a flat plate *facing up,* use the curve for air heating while passing over a heating plate facing down. (Thus note that in an installation for panel heating or cooling, a ceiling panel for heating will have the same capacity, for a given temperature difference, as a floor panel will have for cooling.)

Special Conditions: The curve for vertical plates is limited to plates which are higher than 1 foot.

Example: An occupied industrial space is to be heated by a floor panel designed for a surface temperature of 85 F. If the room air temperature is to be held at 65 F, determine the panel rating.

Solution: Enter the bottom scale of the graph (Fig. 4.14) at a floor-to-air temperature difference of $85 - 65 = 20$ F, and rise to intersection with the curve for a flat plate facing up. From this point move right to the transfer line and then rise to the top scale where read the value of the film coefficient as approximately 0.81 Btu/(hr) (sq ft) (°F). The panel rating is the product of film coefficient and temperature difference or $0.81 \times 20 = 16.2$ Btu/(hr) (sq ft).

Check: $h = 0.38\,(20)^{0.25} = 0.803$ Btu/(hr) (sq ft) (°F).

(Note, however, that the limit of accuracy of an empirical equation of this kind is insufficient to justify three-place accuracy in reporting the result.)

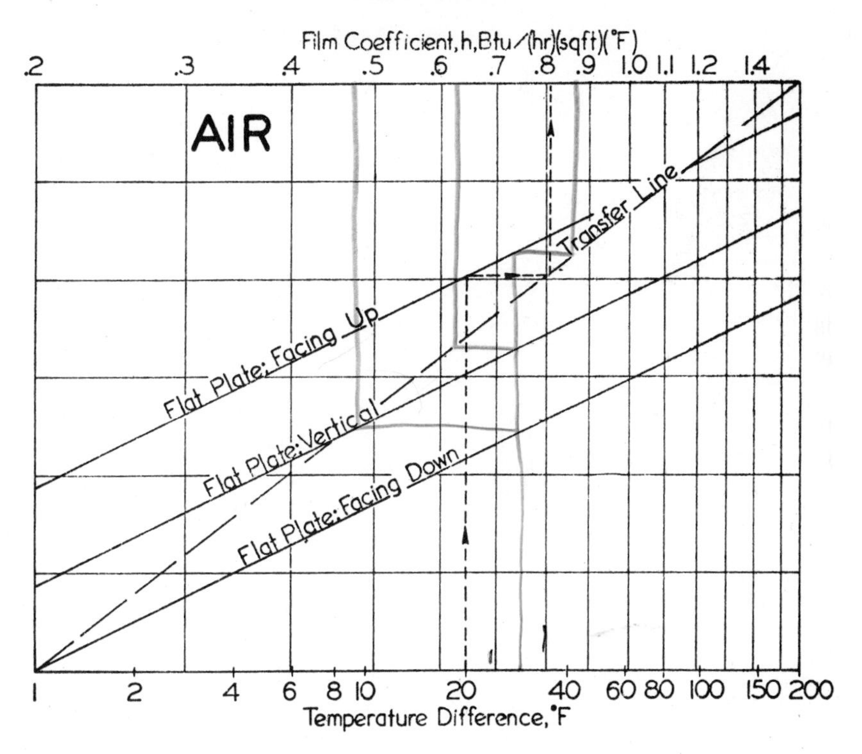
Film Coefficient, h, Btu/(hr)(sqft)(°F)
.2
.3
.4
.5
.6
.7
.8
.9
1.0
1.1
1.2
1.4
AIR
Transfer Line
Flat Plate: Facing Up
Flat Plate: Vertical
Flat Plate: Facing Down
1
2
4
6
8
10
20
40
60
80
100
150
200
Temperature Difference, °F

Figure 4.14

Conductance for Vertical Air Spaces

Evaluation of the conductance of a vertical air space.

Equation: Plot of empirical data.

Text Reference: Section 4.10.

Extensions: None.

Special Conditions: The conductance given by the graph is a combined value for transfer across the air space by the parallel mechanisms of convection and radiation. Conductances are for unobstructed air spaces (no horizontal barriers) in which the flow is entirely by free convection and is due to the temperature difference from the warm to the cool sides of the space.

For air spaces of width greater than 1½ inches, it is recommended that the conductance be taken as equal to that for a 1½ inch space.

Example: A wall has an air space 0.364 inches wide. Conditions are such that the calculated mean temperature of the space is 85 F. Determine the conductance.

Solution: Enter the bottom scale of the graph (Fig. 4.15) at a mean temperature of 85 F and rise to the line for an air space width of 0.364 inches. From this point move horizontally left (in some problems this direction will be *right*) to the transfer line, then rise to the scale at the top of the graph where read the combined conductance (convection plus radiation) as approximately 1.52 Btu/(hr) (sq ft) (°F).

Note: In most applications, the mean temperature cannot be determined until the conductance of the air space is known since this conductance, in part, determines the overall coefficient of heat transfer for the wall. A mean temperature is usually assumed, the conductance evaluated, and the overall coefficient then calculated. The mean temperature of the air space is then checked. If assumed and calculated mean temperatures differ greatly, the trial-and-error process will have to be repeated.

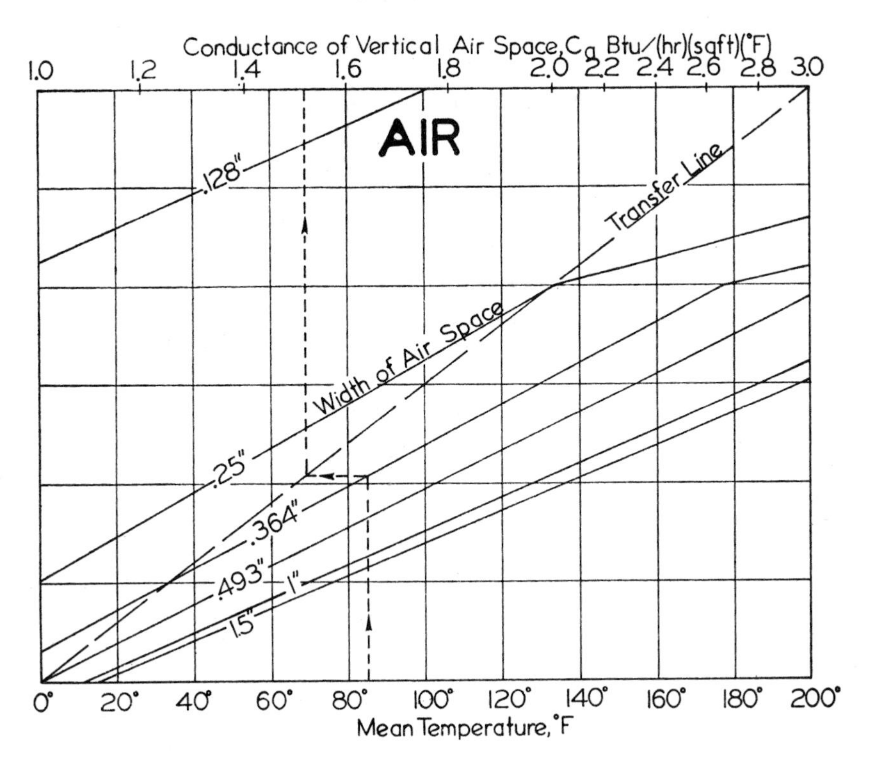
Conductance of Vertical Air Space, C_a Btu/(hr)(sqft)(°F)
1.0
1.2
1.4
1.6
1.8
2.0
2.2
2.4
2.6
2.8
3.0
AIR
.128"
Transfer Line
Width of Air Space
.25"
.364"
.493"
1"
1.5"
0°
20°
40°
60°
80°
100°
120°
140°
160°
180°
200°
Mean Temperature, °F

Figure 4.15

Film Coefficient for Air Flowing over Pipes by Natural Convection

Evaluation of the film coefficient for *air* flowing over pipes by natural convection.

Equation: $h = 0.27\,(\Delta t/D_o)^{0.25}$

Text Reference: Section 4.11, equation 4.26.

Extensions: None.

Special Conditions: The solution is applicable to air heating or cooling while flowing over either horizontal or vertical pipes. Pipe length must be in excess of one foot (to minimize end effects).

Example: A 1½ inch Type K copper tube, uninsulated, carries a refrigerant through a room in which the air temperature is 60 F. The surface temperature of the pipe is 0 F. If the length of the tube is 20 feet and if its surface temperature does not appreciably change along its length, determine the rate of heat gain of the refrigerant due to passage through the room.

Solution: The air-to-surface temperature difference is 60 F so enter the bottom scale of the graph at this value and rise to intersect the diagonal for 1½-inch tube. From this point move horizontally left (in some cases this direction would be to the *right*) to the transfer line and then rise to the top scale where read the value of the film coefficient as approximately 1.27 Btu/(hr) (sq ft) (°F). To convert this coefficient to a lineal basis, refer to Fig. 5.4 and read (by the method shown on the figure) a film coefficient of 550 Btu/(hr) (°F) (lineal foot) as corresponding to a film coefficient of 1270 Btu/(hr) (°F) (sq ft of outside surface of 1½ inch tube). Since the actual film coefficient (from Fig. 4.16) is 1.27 the actual coefficient on a lineal basis is therefore 0.55. The rate of heat gain for the tube is then equal to the product of tube length, lineal coefficient, and temperature difference or 20 x 0.55 x 60 = 660 Btu per hour.

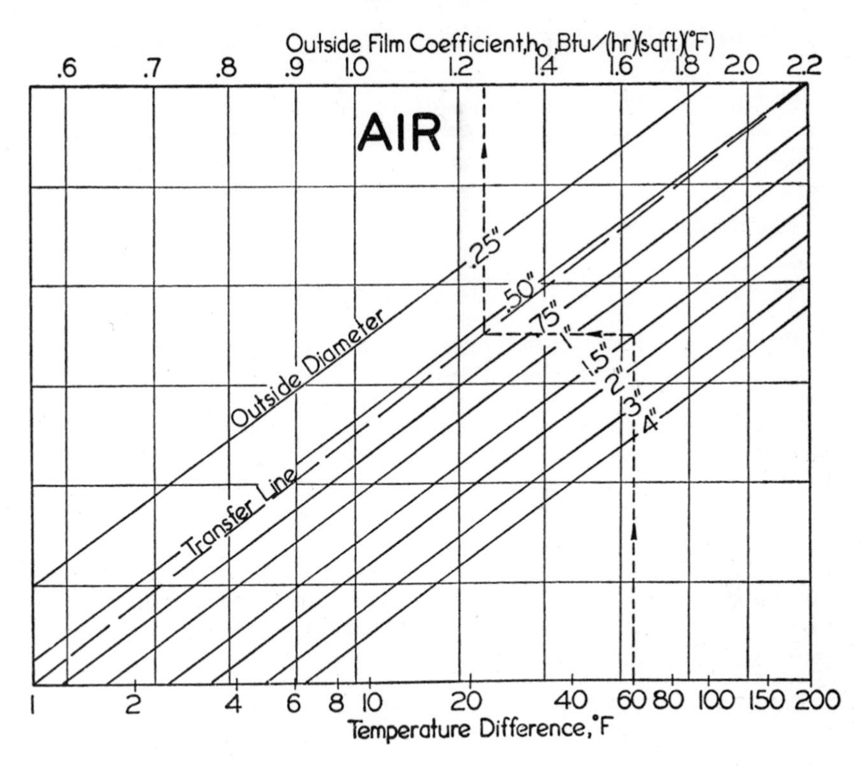
Outside Film Coefficient, h_o, Btu/(hr)(sqft)(°F)
.6
.7
.8
.9
1.0
1.2
1.4
1.6
1.8
2.0
2.2
AIR
.25"
.50"
.75"
1"
1.5"
2"
3"
4"
Outside Diameter
Transfer Line
1
2
4
6
8
10
20
40
60
80
100
150
200
Temperature Difference, °F

Figure 4.16

Film Coefficient for Water Boiling on a Flat Plate

Evaluation of the film coefficient for the nucleate boiling of water on a clean flat plate. (Refer to "Extensions" for boiling within a tube.)

Equation: $h = \left(\dfrac{\sigma}{\rho' - \rho''}\right)^{1.5} \left(\dfrac{\Delta t}{\sigma_a}\right)^{4} \left(\dfrac{0.00231k}{\nu_a}\right)^{5}$

Text Reference: Section 4.12, equation 4.27.

Extensions: For water boiling within a tube, add 25% to the value of the film coefficient obtained from the graph.

Special Conditions: For forced circulation of water at high velocity through a tube, the film coefficient for boiling will be practically the same as the film coefficient for water heating under conditions of turbulent flow (refer Fig. 6.49).

Example: Water at 35 pounds per square inch gauge pressure is boiling in a tube under conditions such that the temperature difference from the inside surface of the tube to the water is 20 F. Determine the film coefficient for nucleate boiling.

Solution: The absolute pressure of the water is 35 plus 14.7 or approximately 50 pounds per square inch. Enter the bottom scale of the graph (Fig. 4.17) at 50 and rise to intersect the curve. From this point move horizontally right to the transfer line and then rise to the upper section of the graph where intersect the diagonal for a temperature difference of 20 F. From this point move horizontally left to intersect the transfer line and then rise to the scale at the top of the graph where read the value of the film coefficient for nucleate boiling on a clean flat plate as approximately 1300 Btu/(hr) (sq ft) (°F).

But for natural convection within a tube the film coefficient is 25% greater than that for a flat plate hence the value in this case becomes 1.25 x 1300 = 1625 Btu/(hr) (sq ft) (°F).

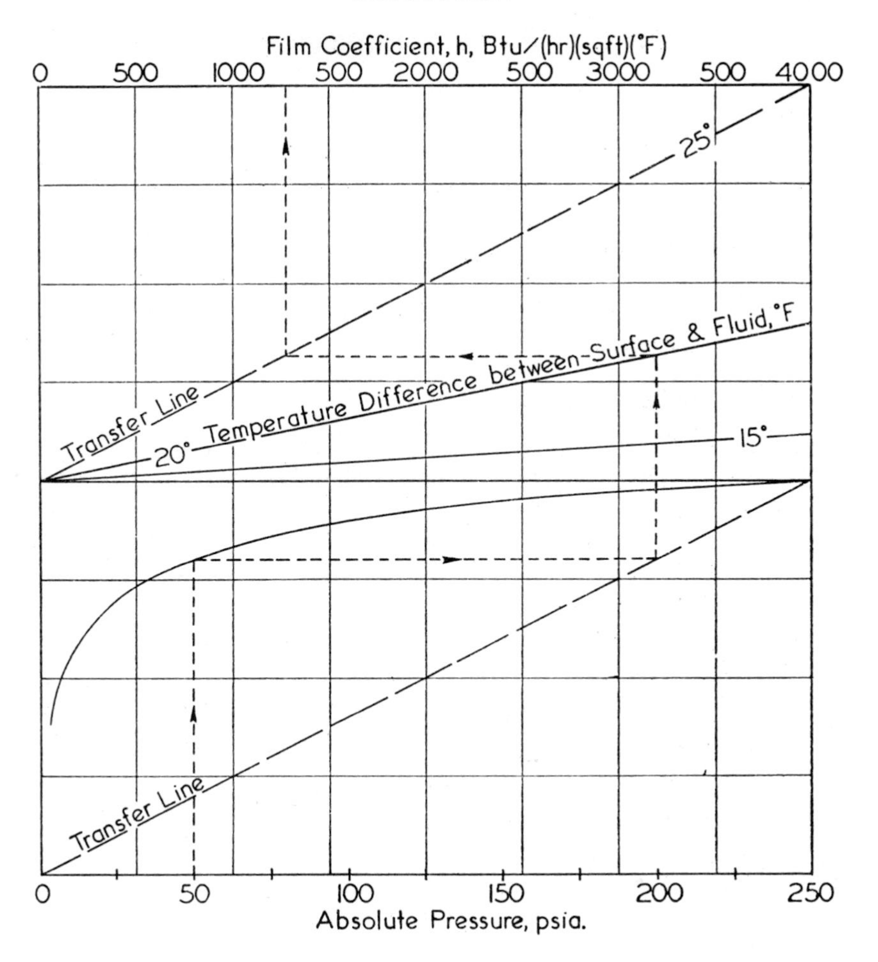
Film Coefficient, h, Btu/(hr)(sqft)(°F)
0 500 1000 500 2000 500 3000 500 4000
25°
20° Temperature Difference between Surface & Fluid, °F
15°
Transfer Line
Transfer Line
0 50 100 150 200 250
Absolute Pressure, psia.

Figure 4.17

Film Coefficient for Steam Condensing on a Horizontal Tube

Evaluation of the film coefficient for filmwise condensation of *steam* on horizontal tubes when the Reynolds number exceeds 2100.

Equation: $h = 0.651\, k \left(\frac{\rho^2 g}{n\mu D w}\right)^{1/3}$

Text Reference: Section 4.13, equation 4.29.

Extensions: None.

Special Conditions: None.

Example: Steam is condensing on 10 pipes (¾ inch outside diameter) that are lined up vertically. The condensation rate is 15 pounds per hour per square foot of outside surface (considering all 10 pipes in the calculation of the area) and the surface temperature of the pipes is known to be 250 F. Determine the film coefficient for filmwise condensation.

Solution: Enter the bottom scale of the graph (Fig. 4.18) at a condensation rate of 15 and then rise to intersect the radial line for ¾-inch pipe. From this point move horizontally right (in some problems this direction will be *left*) to the transfer line and then rise to the middle section of the graph where intersect the radial for a surface temperature of 250 F. From this point move horizontally to the left to the transfer line and then rise to the upper section of the graph where intersect the radial for 10 pipes. From this intersection move horizontally left to the transfer line and then rise to the scale at the top of the graph where read the film coefficient as slightly less than 2000 Btu/(hr) (sq ft) (°F).

Note: In using this graph it will frequently be necessary to solve the particular problem by trial-and-error since the flow rate per square foot of surface will not usually be known except by calculation from the film coefficient. Thus, in many cases, a flow rate will have to be assumed, the film coefficient evaluated, and the assumption checked. When disagreement is marked, the procedure can be repeated until the desired degree of accuracy has been attained.

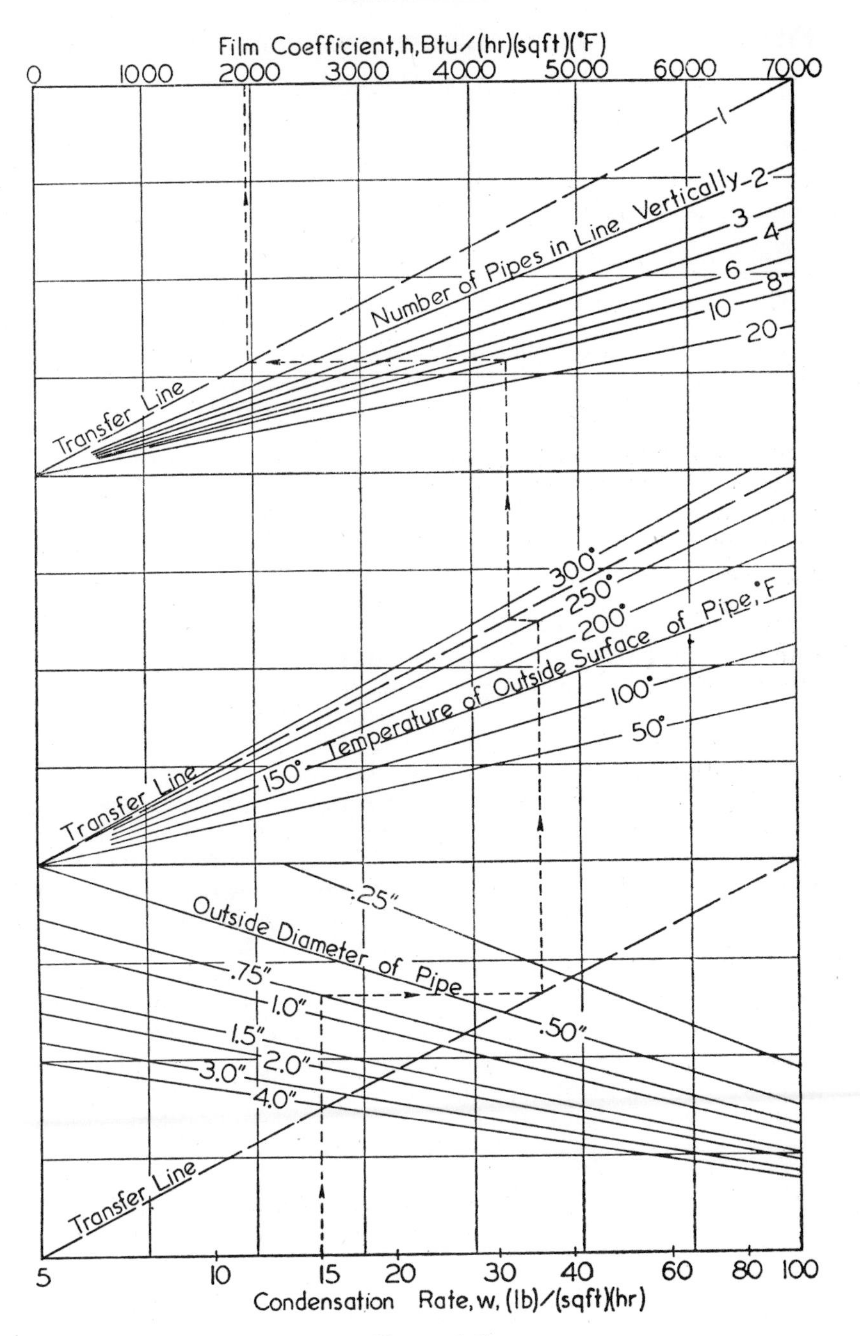
Film Coefficient, h, Btu/(hr)(sqft)(°F)
0
1000
2000
3000
4000
5000
6000
7000
Number of Pipes in Line Vertically
1
2
3
4
6
8
10
20
Transfer Line
300°
250°
200°
150°
100°
50°
Temperature of Outside Surface of Pipe, °F
Transfer Line
.25"
.50"
.75"
1.0"
1.5"
2.0"
3.0"
4.0"
Outside Diameter of Pipe
Transfer Line
5
10
15
20
30
40
60
80
100
Condensation Rate, w, (lb)/(sqft)(hr)

Figure 4.18

Film Coefficient for Steam Condensing on a Vertical Tube — 1st Method

Evaluation of the film coefficient for the condensation of steam on a vertical tube: 1st method. (Refer to discussion under "Special Conditions" for explanation of different methods.)

Equation: $h = 0.925\rho k (g/N_{\mu} w')^{1/3}$

Text Reference: Section 4.13, equation 4.30.

Extensions: The graphical solution is for tubes longer than 20 feet. For tube lengths between 10 and 20 feet, the film coefficients obtained from the graph can be increased by 20%.

Special Conditions: The method of coefficient evaluation used in constructing this graph is for cases where the ratio of the condensate flow rate, (lb)/(hr)(tube), to the product of viscosity and diameter, is less than 1020; for cases in which this ratio exceeds 1020 use the graphical solution given in Fig. 4.20.*

Example: Steam is condensing on a 12 foot vertical tube at a rate of 10 lb/(hr)(sq ft). The outside surface temperature of the tube is 300 F. Calculate the film coefficient.

Solution: Enter the bottom scale of the graph (Fig. 4.19) at a condensation rate of 10 and rise to the radial line for tube height of 12 feet. From this point move horizontally right to intersect the transfer line and then rise to the radial line for a surface temperature of 300 F. From here move right to intersect the transfer line and then rise to the top scale where read the value of the film coefficient as slightly less than 1400 Btu/(hr)(sq ft)(°F).

Note: In using this graph it will frequently be necessary to solve the particular problem by trial-and-error since the flow rate per square foot of surface will not usually be known except by calculation from the film coefficient. Thus, in many cases, a flow rate will be assumed, the film coefficient evaluated and the assumption checked. When disagreement is marked, the procedure can be repeated until the required degree of accuracy is attained.

* For steam $w'/(\mu D)$ equals 1020 when wD equals approximately 540, 240, and 140 at 100 F, 200 F, and 300 F, respectively. Note that w' is in lbs/(hr)(tube) whereas w is in units of lb/(hr)(sq ft).

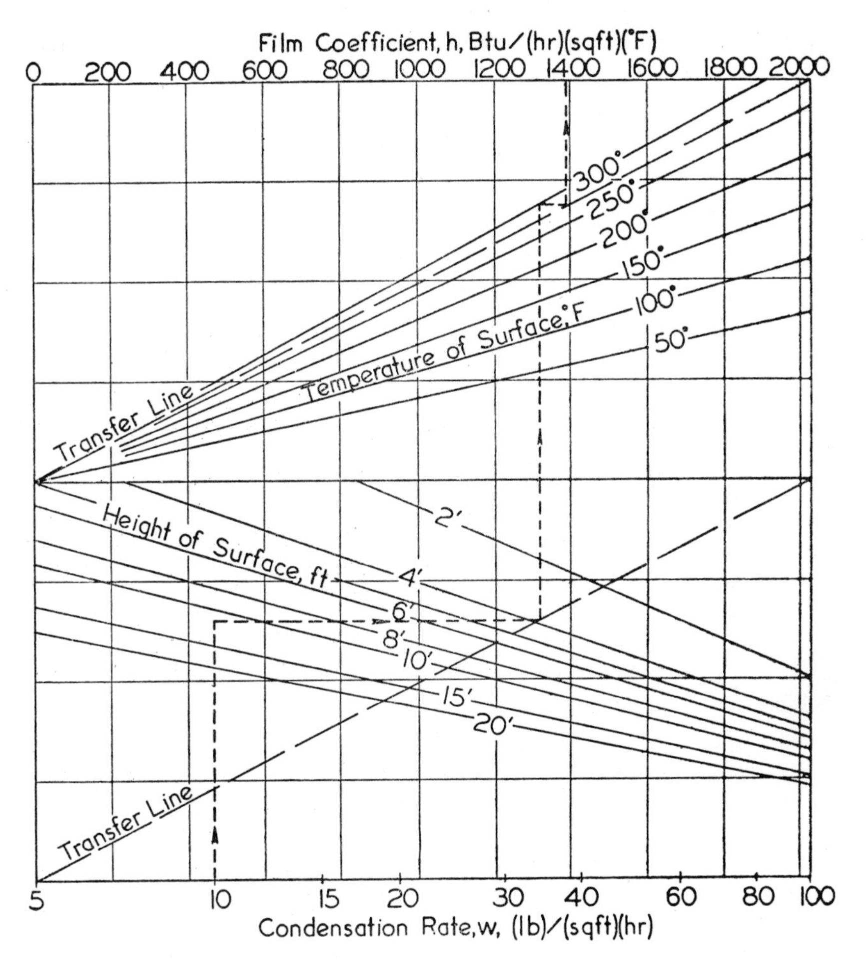
Film Coefficient, h, Btu/(hr)(sqft)(°F)
0 200 400 600 800 1000 1200 1400 1600 1800 2000
300°
250°
200°
150°
100°
50°
Temperature of Surface, °F
Transfer Line
Height of Surface, ft
2′
4′
6′
8′
10′
15′
20′
Transfer Line
5 10 15 20 30 40 60 80 100
Condensation Rate, w, (lb)/(sqft)(hr)

Figure 4.19

Film Coefficient for Steam Condensing on a Vertical Tube — 2nd Method

Evaluation of the film coefficient for the condensation of steam on a vertical tube: 2nd method. (Refer to discussion under "Special Conditions" for explanation of different methods.)

Equation: $h = 0.0084 \left(\frac{w'}{\mu D}\right)^{0.4} \left(\frac{k^3 \rho^2 g}{\mu^2}\right)^{1/3}$

Text References: Section 4.13, equation 4.31.

Extensions: The graph is for tubes longer than 20 feet; for tube lengths between 10 feet and 20 feet the actual film coefficient can be taken as 20% larger than the value obtained from the graph.

Special Conditions: The method of coefficient evaluation used in constructing this graph is for cases where the ratio of condensate flow rate, (lb)/(hr) (tube), to the product of viscosity and diameter, is greater than 1020; for cases in which this ratio is less than 1020 use the graphical solution given in Fig. 4.19.*

Example: Steam is condensing on a vertical 12 foot tube at a rate of 20 lb/(hr) (sq ft). The outside surface temperature of the tube is 250 F. Calculate the film coefficient.

Solution: Enter the bottom scale of the graph (Fig. 4.20) at a condensation rate of 20 and rise to the radial line for tube height of 12 feet. From this point move horizontally right to intersect the transfer line and then rise to the radial line for a surface temperature of 250 F. From here move left to intersect the transfer line and then rise to the top scale where read the value of the film coefficient as approximately 1150 Btu/(hr) (sq ft) (°F).

Note: In using this graph it will frequently be necessary to solve the particular problem by trial-and-error, since the flow rate per square foot of surface will not usually be known except by calculation from the film coefficient. Thus, in many cases, a flow rate will be assumed, the film coefficient evaluated, and the assumption checked. When disagreement is marked, the procedure can be repeated until the required degree of accuracy is attained.

* For steam $w'/(\mu D)$ equals 1020 when wD equals approximately 540, 240, and 140 at 100 F, 200 F, and 300 F, respectively. Note that w' is in lbs/(hr) (tube) whereas w is in units of lb/(hr) (sq ft).

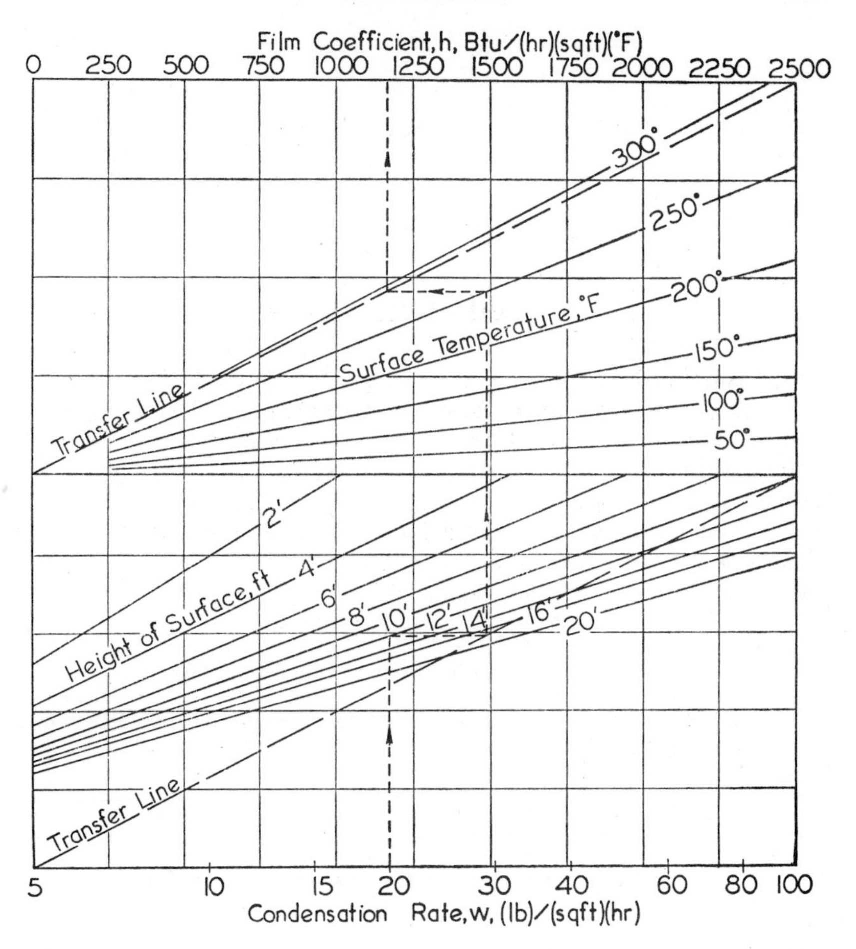
Film Coefficient, h, Btu/(hr)(sqft)(°F)
0 250 500 750 1000 1250 1500 1750 2000 2250 2500
300°
250°
200°
150°
100°
50°
Surface Temperature, °F
Transfer Line
2'
4'
6'
8'
10'
12'
14'
16'
20'
Height of Surface, ft
Transfer Line
5 10 15 20 30 40 60 80 100
Condensation Rate, w, (lb)/(sqft)(hr)

Figure 4.20

CHAPTER V

Combined Heat Transfer

5.1. General Equations. The three preceding chapters, together with chapter VI, provide methods of evaluating the film coefficients and conductances for each of the three basic mechanisms of heat transmission. However, as discussed in section 1.4, most practical problems involve thermal systems in which transfer occurs by series and/or parallel combination of two or more mechanisms. For such systems the overall heat transfer rate is given by equation 1.4,

$$q = U' (t_2 - t_1) = UA (t_2 - t_1) \qquad (5.1)$$

(For graphical solution refer to Fig. 5.1, p. 123)

where U', the overall coefficient of heat transfer, is given by an equation of the form,

$$U' = \frac{1}{\dfrac{1}{C_1' + C_2' + C_3'} + \dfrac{1}{C_4' + C_5' + C_6'} + \dfrac{1}{C_7' + C_8' + C_9'}} \qquad (5.2)$$

Each term in the denominator of equation 5.2 represents an element of the thermal path for which three conductances act in parallel whereas the denominator as a whole shows that the total path consists of three elements in series.

For transfer by conduction the conductance term as given by equation 2.5 is,

$$C_c' = kA/L \qquad (5.3)$$

For transfer by convection the conductance term as given by equation 4.2 is,

$$C_v' = hA \qquad (5.4)$$

For transfer by radiation the conductance term is given by the equation,

$$C_r' = h_r A \qquad (5.5)$$

in which the equivalent radiation coefficient, h_r, is calculable from equation 3.23.

The conductance terms are reciprocals of resistances hence, from equation 5.2,

$$U' = 1/R' \qquad (5.6)$$
$$= A/R$$

where the right hand term of equation 5.6, involving R in place of R', is applicable only when the area normal to the path of heat flow remains constant throughout the thermal system.

5.2. Controlling Resistances. The importance of accurate evaluation of any particular conductance for a parallel or series heat transfer system varies greatly among systems and depends in every case on that section of the thermal path for which the thermal resistance is greatest. If conductive heat transfer were being evaluated from surface-to-surface of a metal plate, the importance of exact determination of the thermal conductivity of the metal would be paramount since, all other conditions being the same, the rate of heat transfer would vary directly with the thermal conductivity. Thus, for a single path system of this kind, copper with a thermal conductivity of approximately 240, as compared to iron which has a value of approximately 24, would provide a heat transfer rate ten times greater than would the iron.

In practical applications, however, the thermal difference between copper and iron — or between any other metals or transfer surfaces — is usually of less importance than the difference in conductivities would indicate since the major or controlling thermal resistance is usually in a convective film rather than in the wall of the transfer surface. Consider, for example, a heat exchanger with hot air on one side and cold air on the other. Heat must flow through the air film on the hot side, through the metal wall, and through the cold-side air film; the convection film coefficient will depend on the air velocities (as well as on the diameter of the tubes, direction of flow, etc.), but will usually be of the order of 100. The conductance of the solid barrier, taking a thickness of 0.01 foot, would be $24/0.01 = 2400$ for iron and $240/0.01 = 24{,}000$ for copper. Thus the resistance of each film will be from 24 to 240 times greater than the wall resistance and it is evident that even a large difference in the thermal conductivity of the wall will affect the overall coefficient of the system by only a very small amount.

In many industrial problems the wall resistance of the transfer surface is so small compared to the film resistances as to permit neglecting wall resistance and evaluating the overall coefficient of heat transmission by means of the equation,

$$U' = \cfrac{1}{\cfrac{1}{h_i A_i} + \cfrac{1}{h_o A_o}} \tag{5.7}$$

where subscripts i and o refer to inside and outside, respectively. When evaluating U' for pipes or tubes it is frequently convenient to express the overall coefficient in terms of a lineal foot of tube rather than a square foot of surface; in this case equation 5.7 takes the form,

$$U' = \cfrac{1}{\cfrac{1}{h_i'} + \cfrac{1}{h_o'}} \tag{5.8}$$

where,

$$h_i' = h_i A_{i_L} \qquad h_o' = h_o A_{o_L} \tag{5.9}$$

(For graphical solutions refer to Figs. 5.2 through 5.6, pp. 125 through 133)

in which A_{i_L} and A_{o_L} are, respectively, the inside and outside areas of one lineal foot of tube. The values of A_{i_L} and A_{o_L} will vary, for a nominal tube diameter, with the type of tube or pipe that is used; the graphical solutions referred to under equation 5.9 give numerical values for standard pipe, extra heavy pipe, and for types K, L, and M of copper tube.

When dealing with heat transfer through either a plane wall or a thin tube the expression for the overall coefficient (neglecting resistance of the wall) can be written,

$$U' = A\left(\cfrac{1}{\cfrac{1}{h_i} + \cfrac{1}{h_o}}\right) \tag{5.10}$$

or,

$$U' = L\left(\cfrac{1}{\cfrac{1}{h_i'} + \cfrac{1}{h_o'}}\right)$$

(For graphical solution refer to Figs. 5.7 & 5.8, pp. 135-137)

where A is the wall area, L is the tube length and the expression in the parenthesis can be evaluated either from tables or by graphical means.

In contrast with the above situation a heavily insulated wall, as that of a cold storage warehouse, represents a thermal system for which the predominant part of the resistance is provided by the insulating material. In such a case the film resistance will be negligible in comparison to that of the insulating material and therefore can be neglected.

5.3. Increasing Heat Loss through Insulation. For some types of systems the object is to remove heat from its point or region of origin at the most rapid rate that is practicable. To assist heat loss, as well as for other reasons, copper wires are frequently insulated. At first glance such a system seems paradoxical since usually the deliberate addition of a thermal resistance serves to decrease rather than increase the rate of loss. With small diameter cylinders however, such as wires or refrigerant piping, the major thermal resistance is in the outside air film and since the circumference is small the exterior area limits heat transfer. By adding "insulating" material to the wire the circumference increases and hence a larger external area serves to greatly increase the conductance through the air film, thus,

$$C_{air\ film} = hA_o \tag{5.11}$$

where h, the film coefficient, does not vary greatly, but A_o increases proportionally with an increase in the diameter of the insulating material.

The addition of insulation therefore *reduces* the external resistance and by proper choice of an "insulating" material having a moderate to large thermal conductivity it is possible to achieve a reduction in external resistance which will exceed the increase in resistance due to conduction through the insulant. The overall effect of the "insulation" is to reduce the total resistance of the system, thereby *increasing* the rate of heat flow. The external diameter of the insulation for which heat flow is a maximum will depend on the thermal conductivity of the insulating material and, for uninsulated cylinders of *appreciable* diameter, the critical external insulated diameter, for most types of wrapping material, is likely to be *less* than the diameter of the *uninsulated* cylinder. It is for this reason that most pipes undergo reduction in heat transfer rate as soon as *any* insulation is added to the bare pipe. It can be shown that maximum loss occurs when the external diameter (ft) is equal to twice the thermal conductivity divided by the combined convection-radiation conductance for one square foot of outer surface.

5.4. Surface, Interface, and Mid-Wall Temperatures. Frequently in engineering problems it is necessary to know the temperature of a surface and the temperature gradient through the wall. Since for any series system the steady-state rate of heat flow through each section of the path must equal the rate through each other section it is possible to equate the rate for the system and the rate for any part of it, thus,

$$q = U'(t_h - t_c) = C'(t_h - t_x) \tag{5.12}$$

where C' is the conductance from the region at t_h to any subsequent point in the thermal path where the unknown temperature is t_x. Solving for the unknown temperature,

$$t_x = t_h - (U'/C')(t_h - t_c) \tag{5.13}$$

or

$$t_x = t_h - r'U'(t_h - t_c) \tag{5.14}$$

(For a limited graphical solution refer to Fig. 5.9, p. 139)

where r' is $1/C'$ or is equal to the resistance of that part of the thermal path (possibly made up of many separate parts) which lies between the region where temperature is t_h and the point at which the unknown temperature, t_x, exists. Equation 5.14 is, of course, valid for either a plane or a non-plane wall.

In the fields of heating, air conditioning, and refrigeration equation 5.14 is frequently used to calculate the inside and outside surface temperatures of a wall and, in some instances, to calculate the mid-point temperature of a homogeneous or of a heterogeneously symmetrical wall. The latter calculation is useful in estimating the probability of vapor transmission through the wall or of condensation of vapor within it. Figure 5.9 provides a graphical solution of equation 5.14 for surface and mid-point temperatures of a wall having "standard" values (refer to section 5.5) of the inside and outside combined (radiation plus convection) film coefficients. Mid-point temperatures are sometimes estimated for use in calculating transmission losses through such combined structural sections as a roof over a ceiling. A preferable procedure is to base transmission losses on the inside-outside air temperature difference used with a combined overall coefficient of heat transfer as given by the equation,

$$U = \frac{1}{\dfrac{1}{U_{ce}} + \dfrac{1}{nU_r}} \tag{5.15}$$

(For graphical solution refer to Fig. 5.10, p. 141)

where U_{ce} and U_r are the overall coefficients for the ceiling and for the roof (based on transfer to-or-from the attic air space), n is the ratio of roof area to ceiling area, and U is the combined overall coefficient based on transmission from room air to outside air.

5.5. Combined Coefficient for Convection and Radiation. For industrial problems involving parallel convective and radiant transfer to-or-from a surface the individual conductances or film coefficients must be calculated by the methods of chapters III and IV and then added to obtain the combined conductance or the equivalent film coefficient,

$$C = C_r + C_v \tag{5.16}$$

For the special case represented by transfer through the walls of a structure, empirical equations have been developed which permit direct calculation of the combined coefficient. For design of heating, air conditioning, and cold-storage systems so-called "standard" film coefficients have gained general acceptance and are the basis of the tabulated overall coefficients given in most texts and handbooks. Thus for the film on the inside wall of a room in which air movement is due only to natural convection, the standard film coefficient is taken as 1.65 Btu/(hr) (sq ft) (°F) and is based on 0.85 as a convective film coefficient and 0.80 as an equivalent radiant coefficient. For the outside film the "standard" coefficient is 6.0 Btu/(hr) (sq ft) (°F) and is based on 0.8 by radiation and 5.2 for convection based on a design wind velocity of 15 miles per hour. For wind velocities greater than 15 miles per hour or for rough exterior surfaces a more accurate evaluation of the combined film coefficient can be obtained from empirical equations based on the work of Houghten and McDermott,

$$h = 1.4 + 0.28V \quad \text{for very smooth surfaces (as glass)} \tag{5.17}$$

$$h = 1.6 + 0.3V \quad \text{for moderately smooth surfaces (as plaster)} \tag{5.18}$$

$$h = 2.0 + 0.4V \quad \text{for moderately rough surfaces (as finished concrete)} \tag{5.19}$$

$$h = 2.1 + 0.5V \quad \text{for very rough surfaces (as stucco)} \tag{5.20}$$

(For graphical solutions of these equations refer to Fig. 5.11, p. 143)

In problems which involve unusual radiation effects within a room, as in cold storage, quick freezing, or panel heating, it is convenient to evaluate the conductance of the wall from the inside surface to the outside air and then to combine this conductance with the calculated combined film coefficient for the inside surface by the equation,

$$U = \frac{1}{\frac{1}{C} + \frac{1}{h_i}} \tag{5.21}$$

The conductance, C, can be obtained from the known standard overall coefficient and from the standard inside film coefficient by solving the equation,

$$C = \frac{1}{\frac{1}{U} - \frac{1}{1.65}} \tag{5.22}$$

(For graphical solution refer to Figs. 5.12 & 5.13, pp. 145 & 147)

The conductance could be calculated directly from the known thermal characteristics of the wall elements, but in most cases it is more rapid to look up the standard overall coefficient and evaluate the conductance from equation 5.22.

5.6. The Heat Balance. In order for steady state to exist, the rate of heat reception at any surface or at any plane in a solid must be equal to the rate of heat loss. This concept permits setting up a heat balance and thereby determining the state at such a surface or plane. As a simple example, consider a refractory material such as a firebrick which is located inside a furnace in full view of the walls and ceiling and surrounded by high-temperature, but non-luminous, products of combustion. The firebrick will reach a steady-state condition at which its rate of convective heat gain from the surrounding gases plus its radiant gain from the luminous flame will be exactly equal to its rate of radiant heat loss to the lower temperature walls of the furnace space; the temperature of the brick at steady-state will necessarily be between the temperature of the gases and that of the furnace walls.

An opposite situation occurs when an object is cooled by being placed in a refrigerator or a cold storage room. If heat gain is occurring through the walls of the room, the inside surface of the walls will necessarily be at a temperature greater than that of the air surrounding the object. The object in the space will reach steady-state at a temperature between air and inside surface values. If the material in cold storage is highly temperature-sensitive, consideration must then be given to this radiant heating effect as it may be responsible for raising the steady-state temperature of the object enough to cause either damage or spoilage of the product. A reverse of this situation is represented by the freezing of crops or water on clear nights when the air temperature approaches but does not drop as low as 32 F; in such cases the radiation to the clear night sky (at an equivalent temperature of approximately —60 F) may be so great that the equilibrium temperature of the product or of the water may be below the freezing point.

In comfort conditioning of an inside environment, whether during the summer or winter, the heat balance principle can be applied to the occupants to determine that air temperature, for a defined radiant surround, at which optimum comfort will be realized. The so-called comfort equation states that the optimum inside-air temperature will differ from 70 F (for the average sedentary adult) by a number of degrees equal to the departure from 70 F, in the opposite direction, of the average surface temperature of the surround. Since the average surface temperature will vary with outside-air temperature and with the insulating effectiveness of the structure, it is evident that a functional relationship must exist among these values; the accepted form of the comfort equation is given by,

$$t_{optimum} = 70 + (70 - t_s) = 140 - t_s \tag{5.23}$$

(For graphical solution refer to Fig. 5.14, p. 149)

where t_s, the average surface temperature, can be calculated by the methods discussed in section 5.4.

5.7. Evaluation of the Mean Temperature Difference. In the field of engineering application, one of the more common types of heat transfer problem is that in which heat flows from a hot fluid to a cold fluid through an intervening solid surface. The usual type of heat exchanger, for example, permits flow of the hot and cold fluids on opposite sides of the transfer surface, the heat transfer occurring by convection from the warm fluid to the surface, by conduction through the metallic wall, and by convection from the cool side of the wall to the colder fluid. With common shell-and-tube exchangers the hot fluid enters at one end of the exchanger and undergoes a loss of temperature as it travels the length of the unit; similarly the cold fluid enters at one end (the same end as the hot fluid for *parallel* flow, the opposite end for *counterflow*) and gains in both internal energy and temperature as it passes through the unit.

Along any infinitesimal length of a heat exchanger the temperature difference between hot and cold fluid is constant and hence the rate of heat transfer at that small section can be readily evaluated. The overall heat transfer is then the summation of heat transferred at each of the infinitesimal lengths. In order to evaluate the overall transfer rate directly a mean value of the temperature difference must be developed for use in the basic heat transfer equation,

$$q = U' \, (t_h - t_c)_m \tag{5.24}$$

It can be shown that the correct value of the mean temperature difference for either a parallel flow or a counterflow system is the logarithmic mean of the temperature differences at entrance and at exit from the exchanger and as such may be evaluated from the equation,

$$(t_h - t_c)_m = \frac{(t_{h_1} - t_{c_1}) - (t_{h_2} - t_{c_2})}{\log_e[(t_{h_1} - t_{c_1})/(t_{h_2} - t_{c_2})]} \tag{5.25}$$

(For graphical solution refer to Fig. 2.2, p. 25)

When the objective of a heat transfer analysis is to design or select an exchanger to accomplish a given temperature rise or temperature reduction in a known quantity of fluid, equation 5.24 can be used directly. However, when the performance of an existing exchanger is to be evaluated, the equation does not so readily permit solution since both the transfer rate and the temperature difference at exit are then unknowns. The method of solution for cases of the latter kind is by trial-and-error, an exit value of the temperature difference being assumed, the corresponding mean temperature difference calculated, and the resultant overall heat transfer rate then evaluated; since the exit temperature difference and the overall transfer rate are related (in terms of temperature rise or drop of the two fluids in receiving or liberating the amount of energy) it is then possible to check the accuracy of the assumed exit value of the temperature difference; if assumed and calculated value do not check a revised assumption is made and the analysis repeated until satisfactory agreement between the assumed and calculated values is reached.

In terms of temperature difference, which determines rate of heat transmission, it is evident that fluids during phase change possess a marked advantage over fluids which are being heated or cooled in a homogeneous state. For simple heating or cooling there must be a change in temperature, hence a constantly decreasing temperature difference and a constantly decreasing rate of heat transfer with lessened effectiveness on the part of the exchanger surface which is downstream from the end at which the higher-temperature fluid enters. When phase change occurs, the fluid temperature remains constant and heat transfer continues (as far as the phase-changing fluid is concerned) at the initial rate. In addition, the convection film coefficient for evaporation or condensation is usually substantially larger than for simple heating or cooling hence its effect on the overall conductance is decidedly favorable.

Overall Rate of Heat Transmission

Evaluation of the overall rate of heat transmission when the overall coefficient of heat transmission is known.

Equation: $q = UA(t_2 - t_1)$

Text Reference: Section 5.1, equation 5.1.

Extensions: None.

Special Conditions: None.

Example: Heat transfer is occurring from a gas at a temperature of 375 F through a metal transfer surface to a liquid at a temperature of 50 F. The overall coefficient of heat transmission has been evaluated as 4 Btu/(hr) (sq ft) (°F) and the area of transfer surface is known to be 6 square feet. Evaluate the rate of transfer of heat.

Solution: Enter the temperature scale along the bottom of the graph (Fig. 5.1) at a hot body temperature of 375 F and rise to intersection with the line for a cold body temperature of 50 F. From this point move left to meet the transfer line and then rise to the center section of the graph where intersect the radial line which corresponds to an area of 6 square feet. From this point move horizontally left (in some cases this direction would be *right*) to intersect the transfer line and then rise to the top section of the graph where intersect the radial line corresponding to an overall coefficient of 4; from this point move horizontally left to the transfer line and then rise to the top scale of the graph where read the rate of heat transfer as 7800 Btu/(hr).

Check: $q = (4)(6)(375 - 50) = 7800.$

Note: For problems in which the area of transfer surface exceeds the scale values (shown as radials in the central section of the graph) by any multiple of 10 the actual rate of heat transfer will exceed the scale value by the same multiple of 10. Note also that the transfer line in the central section of the graph coincides with the radial line for an area of 8 square feet.

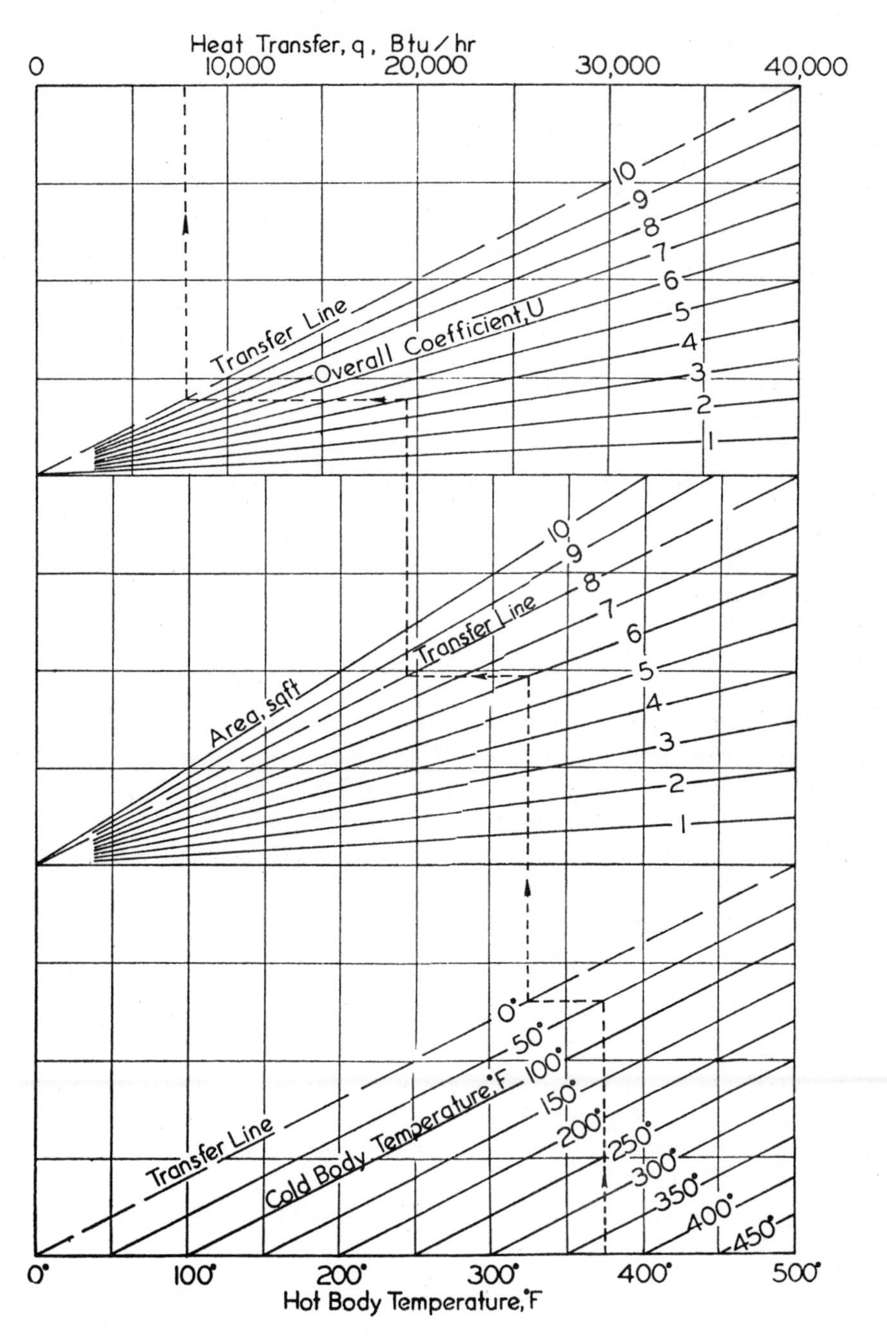
Heat Transfer, q, Btu / hr
0
10,000
20,000
30,000
40,000
Transfer Line
Overall Coefficient, U
10
9
8
7
6
5
4
3
2
1
Area, sqft
Transfer Line
Transfer Line
Cold Body Temperature, °F
0°
50°
100°
150°
200°
250°
300°
350°
400°
450°
0°
100°
200°
300°
400°
500°
Hot Body Temperature, °F

Figure 5.1

Film Coefficient per Lineal Foot of Standard Pipe*

Evaluation of the inside or outside film coefficient for standard pipe in terms of surface area associated with unit length of pipe.

Equations: $h_i' = h_i A_{i_L}$ $h_o' = h_o A_{o_L}$

Text Reference: Section 5.2, equation 5.9.

Extensions: Refer to Figs. 5.3 through 5.6 for types of pipe and tubing other than standard weight pipe.

When the overall coefficient of heat transfer is evaluated in terms of outside pipe surface this graph can be used to convert overall transfer rate or overall coefficient from a unit area basis to a unit length basis.

The reciprocal of the result given by Figs. 2.4 or 2.5 can be used in this graph or in Figs. 5.3 through 5.6 for conversion to a basis of unit length.

Special Conditions: Note that the diameters indicated on the graphical solution are *nominal* values; the graph has been constructed using the correct inside and outside diameters (hence surface areas) that are associated with a given value of the nominal diameter.

Example: Flow conditions within a given heat exchanger indicate that the inside film coefficient for 3-inch standard pipe is 1300 Btu per hour per °F per square foot of inside pipe surface. Determine the inside film coefficient corresponding to unit length of pipe.

Solution: Enter the bottom scale of the graph (Fig. 5.2) at an inside film coefficient of 1300 Btu/(hr) (sq ft) (°F) and rise to intersection with the radial corresponding to 3-inch pipe. From this point move horizontally to the left (for 4 inch nominal diameter pipe this direction would be to the *right*) to intersect the transfer line and then rise to the scale at the top of the graph where read the answer as 1050 Btu per hour per °F per lineal foot of pipe.

Note: If the outside film coefficient were to be determined the procedure would be the same except that the upper group of radials (for *outside*) would have been used instead of the lower group.

*The "Standard" pipe sizes shown on Fig. 5.2 are also designated as Schedule 40 sizes.

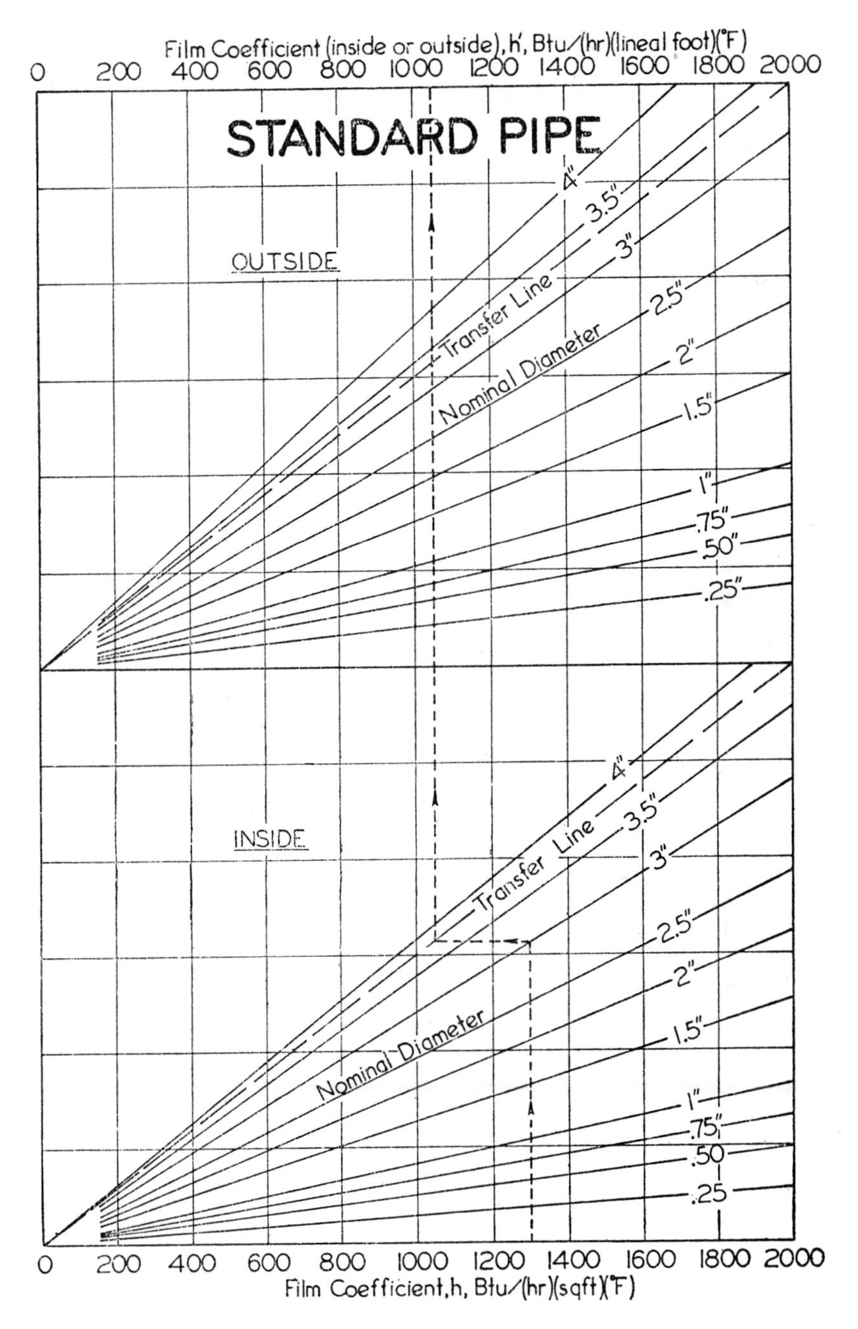
Film Coefficient (inside or outside), h', Btu/(hr)(lineal foot)(°F)
0 200 400 600 800 1000 1200 1400 1600 1800 2000
STANDARD PIPE
OUTSIDE
INSIDE
Transfer Line
Nominal Diameter
4"
3.5"
3"
2.5"
2"
1.5"
1"
.75"
.50"
.25"
.50
.25
0 200 400 600 800 1000 1200 1400 1600 1800 2000
Film Coefficient, h, Btu/(hr)(sqft)(°F)

Figure 5.2

Film Coefficient per Lineal Foot of Extra Heavy Pipe*

Evaluation of the inside or outside film coefficient for extra heavy pipe in terms of surface area associated with unit length.

Equations: $h_i' = h_i A_{i_L} \quad h_o' = h_o A_{o_L}$

Text References: Section 5.2, equation 5.9.

Extensions: Refer to Figs. 5.2 through 5.6 for other types of pipe and tube.

When the overall coefficient of heat transfer is evaluated in terms of outside pipe surface this graph can be used to convert to a basis of unit length. Similarly when the heat transfer rate is known in terms of outside area it can be converted, using the *outside* section of this graph, to a unit length basis.

The reciprocal of the result given by Figs. 2.4 or 2.5 can be used in this graph, or in Figs. 5.2 through 5.6, for conversion to a unit length basis.

Special Conditions: Note that stated diameters are *nominal* values.

Example: The overall heat transfer rate from liquid-to-liquid through the wall of a 1½-inch extra heavy pipe is known to be 1300 Btu per hour per square foot of *inside* surface. Determine the length of pipe needed, assuming that the transfer rate is constant along the length, to permit transfer of 50,000 Btu per hour.

Solution: Since the transfer rate is given in terms of inside surface area, the solution will be similar to that for an inside film coefficient: Enter the bottom scale of the graph (Fig. 5.3) at 1300 and rise to the radial line for 1½-inch pipe (using the lower section of the graph) then move horizontally left to the transfer line and rise to the top scale where read 520 Btu per hour per lineal foot of pipe as the transfer rate. The required length to give the stated flow of heat is then $50,000/520 = 96$ feet.

Note: Although it is rarely necessary to do so, the graph also provides a means of converting film coefficient, overall coefficient, or transfer rate from an inside surface area basis to an outside surface area basis and vice versa (refer to example given for Fig. 5.4).

*The "Extra Heavy" pipe sizes shown on Fig. 5.3 are also designated as Schedule 80 sizes.

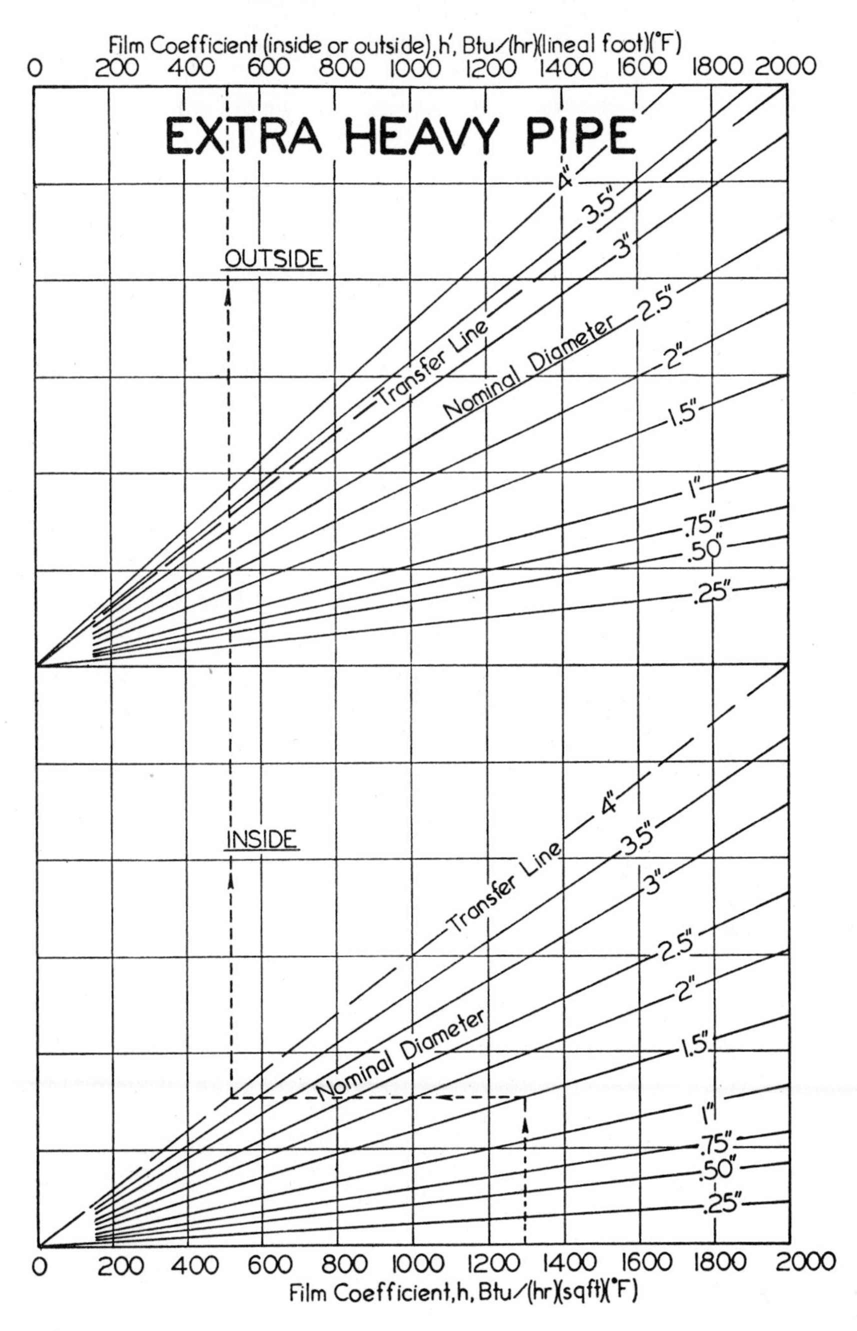
Film Coefficient (inside or outside), h', Btu/(hr)(lineal foot)(°F)
0 200 400 600 800 1000 1200 1400 1600 1800 2000
EXTRA HEAVY PIPE
OUTSIDE
4"
3.5"
3"
2.5"
2"
1.5"
1"
.75"
.50"
.25"
Transfer Line
Nominal Diameter
INSIDE
4"
3.5"
3"
2.5"
2"
1.5"
1"
.75"
.50"
.25"
Transfer Line
Nominal Diameter
0 200 400 600 800 1000 1200 1400 1600 1800 2000
Film Coefficient, h, Btu/(hr)(sqft)(°F)

Figure 5.3

Film Coefficient per Lineal Foot of Type K Copper Tube

Evaluation of the inside or outside film coefficient for Type K copper tube in terms of surface area associated with unit length.

Equations: $h_i' = h_i A_{i_L}$ $\quad h_o' = h_o A_{o_L}$

Text References: Refer to section 5.2, equation 5.9.

Extensions: Refer to Figs. 5.2 through 5.6 for other types of pipe and tube.

When the overall coefficient of heat transfer is evaluated in terms of outside pipe surface this graph can be used to convert to a basis of unit length. Similarly, when the heat transfer rate is known in terms of outside area it can be converted, using the *outside* section of this graph, that is, the upper half, to a unit length basis.

The reciprocal of the result given by Figs. 2.4 or 2.5 can be used in this graph, or in Figs. 5.2 through 5.6, for conversion to a unit length basis.

Special Conditions: Note that stated diameters are *nominal* values.

Example: The outside film coefficient for transfer through the wall of a 3 inch nominal diameter Type K copper tube is 1500 Btu per hour per °F per square foot of outside surface. (1) Determine the value of the outside film coefficient for unit length of tube. (2) Determine the value of the outside film coefficient when expressed in terms of unit of *inside* surface area.

Solution: (1) Enter the scale at the bottom of the graph (Fig. 5.4) at 1500 and rise to the upper section of the graph, for *outside,* where intersect the radial corresponding to 3 inch nominal diameter tube. From this point move horizontally to the left (for 4-inch tube this direction would be to the *right*) to the transfer line and then rise to the scale at the top of the graph where read 1220 as the outside film coefficient in Btu per hour per °F per lineal foot of tube. (2) To convert to a basis of inside surface area enter the top scale at 1220 and drop vertically (example line not shown on the graph) to the transfer line in the lower section. From this intersection move right to the radial line for 3-inch tube and then drop to the base scale where read h_i as 1600.

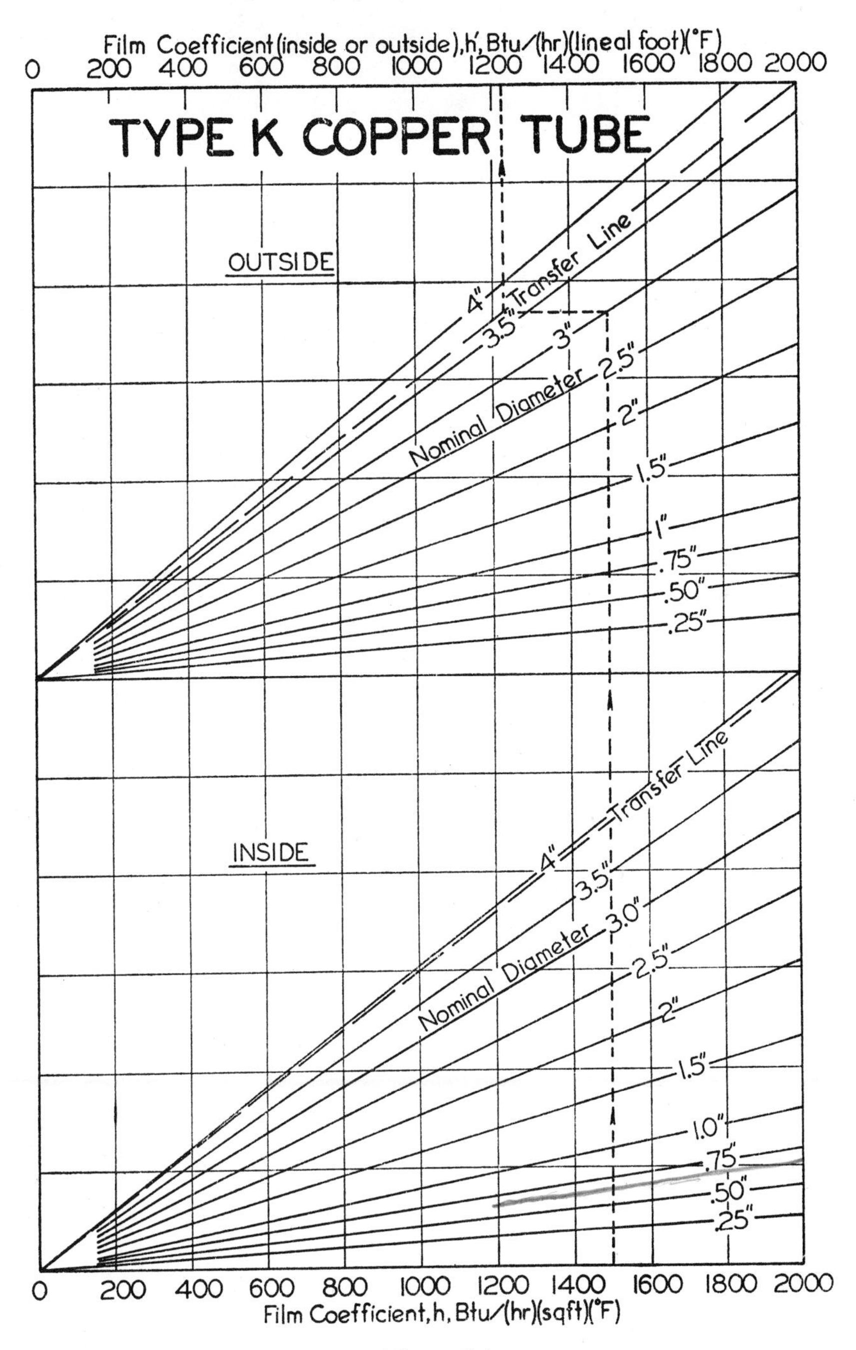
Film Coefficient (inside or outside), h', Btu/(hr)(lineal foot)(°F)
0 200 400 600 800 1000 1200 1400 1600 1800 2000
TYPE K COPPER TUBE
OUTSIDE
Transfer Line
4"
3.5"
3"
Nominal Diameter
2.5"
2"
1.5"
1"
.75"
.50"
.25"
INSIDE
Transfer Line
4"
3.5"
3.0"
Nominal Diameter
2.5"
2"
1.5"
1.0"
.75"
.50"
.25"
0 200 400 600 800 1000 1200 1400 1600 1800 2000
Film Coefficient, h, Btu/(hr)(sqft)(°F)

Figure 5.4

Film Coefficient per Lineal Foot of Type L Copper Tube

Evaluation of the inside or outside film coefficient for Type L copper tube in terms of surface area associated with unit length.

Equations: $h_i = h_i A_{i_L}$ $h_o = h_o A_{o_L}$

Text References: Section 5.2, equation 5.9.

Extensions: Refer to Figs. 5.2 through 5.6 for other types of pipe and tube.

When the overall coefficient of heat transfer is evaluated in terms of outside pipe surface this graph can be used to convert to a basis of unit length. Similarly, when the heat transfer rate is known in terms of outside area it can be converted, using the *outside* section of this graph, that is, the upper half, to a unit length basis.

The reciprocal of the result given by Figs. 2.4 or 2.5 can be used in this graph, or in Figs. 5.2 through 5.6, for conversion to a unit length basis.

Special Conditions: Note that stated diameters are *nominal* values.

Example: A liquid heating in a 1½-inch nominal diameter Type L copper tube has an inside film coefficient of 1700 Btu per hour per °F per square foot of transfer surface. Convert the inside film coefficient to a unit length basis.

Solution: Enter the bottom scale of the graph (Fig. 5.5) at 1700 and rise to the group of radials in the lower section of the graph where intersect the radial for 1½-inch tube. From this point move horizontally left (for 4-inch tube this direction would be *right*) to the transfer line and then rise to the scale at the top of the graph where read the converted value of the inside film coefficient as 680 Btu per hour per °F per lineal foot of tube.

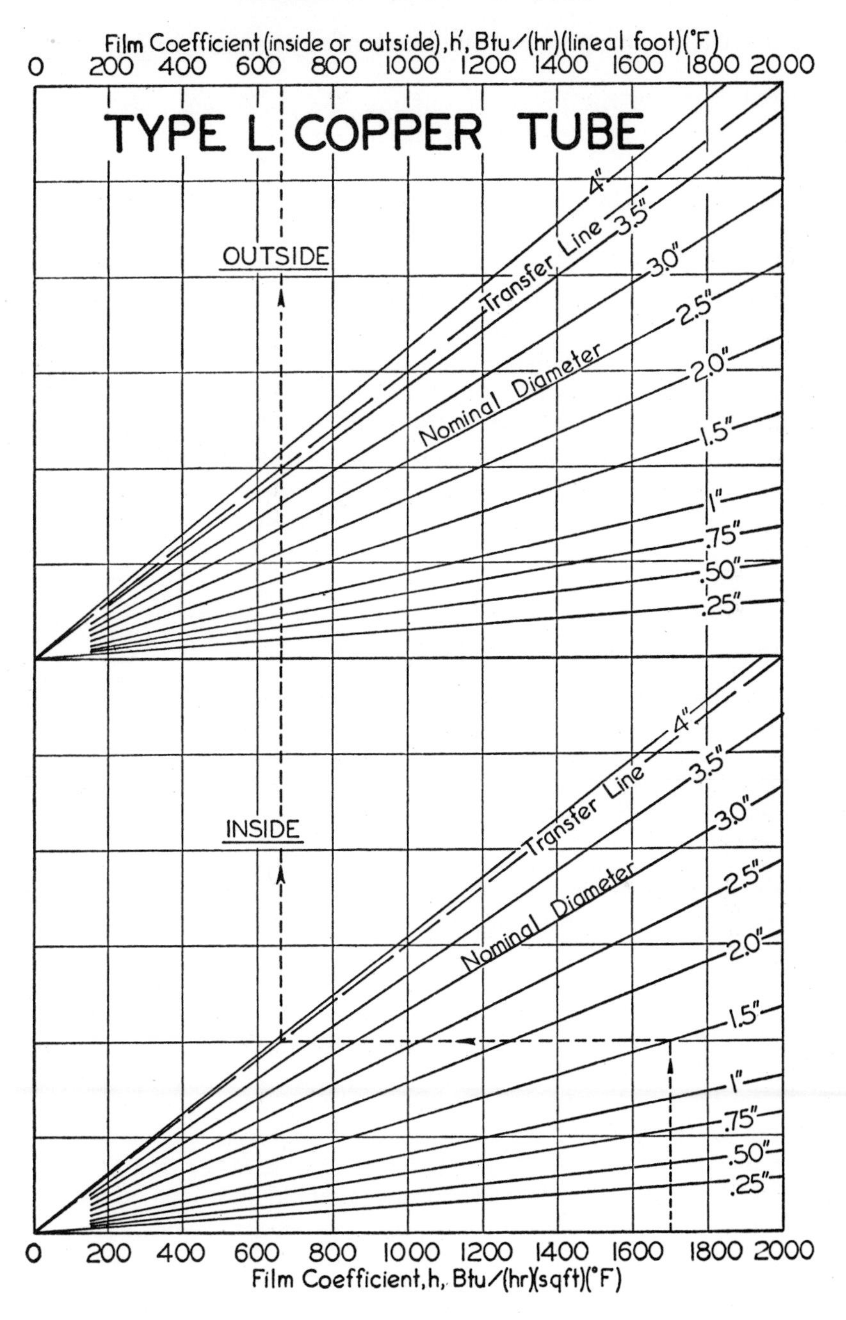

Film Coefficient (inside or outside), h', Btu/(hr)(lineal foot)(°F)
0 200 400 600 800 1000 1200 1400 1600 1800 2000
TYPE L COPPER TUBE
OUTSIDE
Transfer Line
Nominal Diameter
4"
3.5"
3.0"
2.5"
2.0"
1.5"
1"
.75"
.50"
.25"
INSIDE
Transfer Line
Nominal Diameter
4"
3.5"
3.0"
2.5"
2.0"
1.5"
1"
.75"
.50"
.25"
0 200 400 600 800 1000 1200 1400 1600 1800 2000
Film Coefficient, h, Btu/(hr)(sqft)(°F)

Figure 5.5

Film Coefficient per Lineal Foot of Type M Copper Tube

Evaluation of the inside or outside film coefficient for Type M copper tube in terms of the surface area associated with unit length.

Equations: $h_i = h_i A_{i_L} \quad h_o = h_o A_{o_L}$

Text References: Section 5.2, equation 5.9.

Extensions: Refer to Figs. 5.2 through 5.6 for other types of pipe and tube.

When the overall coefficient of heat transfer is evaluated in terms of outside pipe surface this graph can be used to convert to a basis of unit length. Similarly when the heat transfer rate is known in terms of outside area it can be converted, using the *outside* section of this graph, that is, the upper half, to a unit length basis.

The reciprocal of the result given by Figs. 2.4 or 2.5 can be used in this graph, or in Figs. 5.2 through 5.6, for conversion to a unit length basis.

Special Conditions: Note that stated diameters are *nominal* values.

Example: The overall coefficient of heat transfer, for a fluid at 200 F losing heat through the wall of a 3-inch nominal diameter Type M copper tube to a fluid at 100 F, has been evaluated as 800 Btu per hour per °F per square foot of inside surface. Determine the length of tube needed to transfer heat at a rate of 1,240,000 Btu per hour.

Solution: Enter the scale at the base of the graph (Fig. 5.6) at 800 and rise to the group of radials in the lower half of the chart (for *inside*) where intersect the one for 3-inch tube. From this point move horizontally left to the transfer line and then rise to the scale at the top of the chart where read 620 as the overall coefficient in Btu per hour per °F per lineal foot of tube. The heat transfer rate per lineal foot of tube is the product of the overall coefficient by the temperature difference or $620(200 - 100) = 62{,}000$ Btu per hour per lineal foot of tube. To transfer 1,240,000 Btu per hour the required tube length (assuming constancy of the coefficient and of the temperature difference) would be $1{,}240{,}000/62{,}000 = 20$ feet.

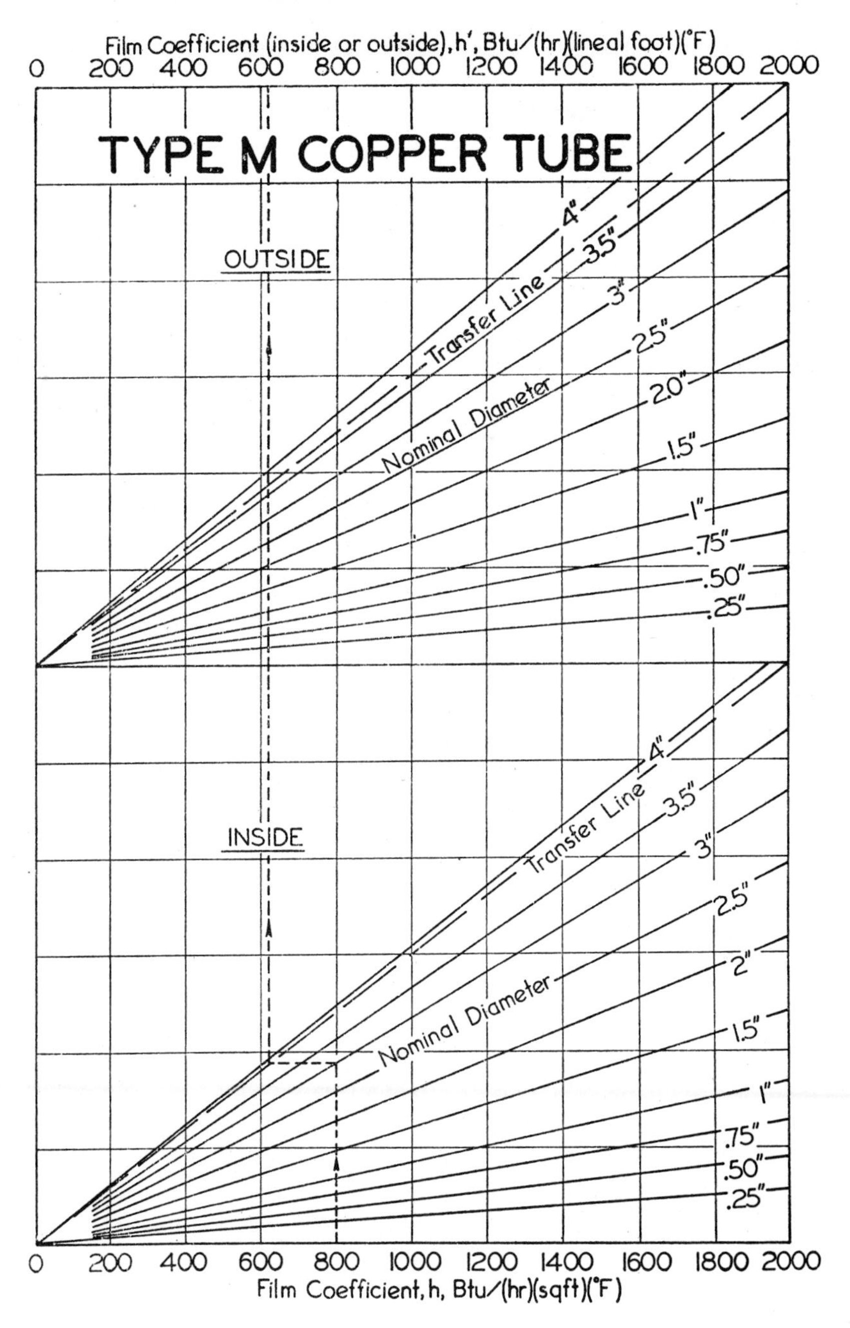

Film Coefficient (inside or outside), h', Btu/(hr)(lineal foot)(°F)
0
200
400
600
800
1000
1200
1400
1600
1800
2000
TYPE M COPPER TUBE
OUTSIDE
Transfer Line
Nominal Diameter
4"
3.5"
3"
2.5"
2.0"
1.5"
1"
.75"
.50"
.25"
INSIDE
Transfer Line
Nominal Diameter
4"
3.5"
3"
2.5"
2"
1.5"
1"
.75"
.50"
.25"
0
200
400
600
800
1000
1200
1400
1600
1800
2000
Film Coefficient, h, Btu/(hr)(sqft)(°F)

Figure 5.6

Overall Coefficient, U, Based on Film Coefficients Only — Range: 0 to 150

Evaluation of the overall coefficient of heat transfer, U, based on film coefficients only: Range from 0 to 150 Btu/(hr) (°F) (sq ft). (Refer to Fig. 5.8 for larger range).

Equation: $U = 1/(1/h_i + 1/h_o)$

Text Reference: Section 5.2, equation 5.10.

Extensions: The scales on the graph are marked in terms of film coefficients, but can be used for systems in which the total thermal resistance is made up of two parts, each conductance being known; in such cases the conductances would be used as though they were film coefficients.

As constructed, the graph is for plane surfaces (where the inside and outside areas are the same), however, with thin-walled tubes, the difference in surface area can be neglected and the graph used to evaluate the overall coefficient. For tubes in which the area difference must be taken into account, but for which the resistance of the tube wall is negligible, the inside and outside film coefficients can be evaluated in terms of one or the other (inside or outside) surface area and the overall coefficient then determined from the graph. In cases where the inside and outside film coefficients are known on a unit length basis (refer to Figs. 5.2 through 5.6) this graph can be used to directly determine the overall coefficient on a unit length basis.

Special Conditions: None.

Example: Heat transfer is occurring through a thin metal plate with inside and outside film coefficients of 300 and 200 respectively. Evaluate U.

Solution: Enter the base scale (Fig. 5.7) at 300 and rise to intersect the curve for an outside film coefficient of 200. From this point move horizontally right (in some cases this direction will be *left*) to the transfer line and then rise to the scale at the top of the graph where read the value of the overall coefficient of heat transfer as 120 Btu/(hr) (°F) (sq ft).

Check: $U = 1/[(1/300) + (1/200)] = 1/0.0083 = 120$

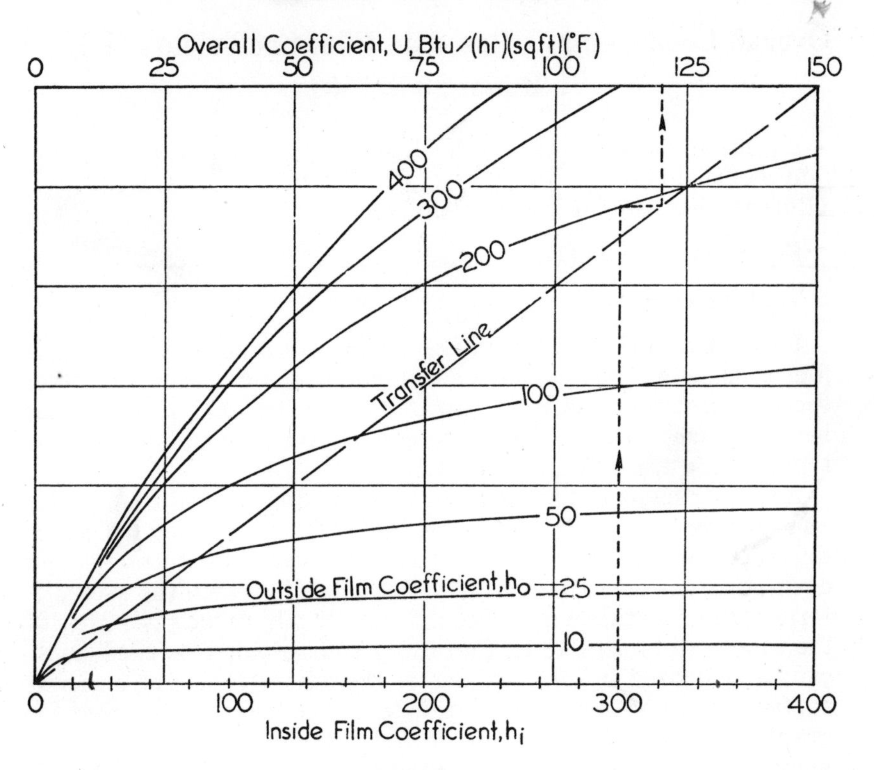
Overall Coefficient, U, Btu/(hr)(sqft)(°F)
0
25
50
75
100
125
150
400
300
200
Transfer Line
100
50
Outside Film Coefficient, h_o
25
10
0
100
200
300
400
Inside Film Coefficient, h_i

Figure 5.7

Overall Coefficient, U, Based on Film Coefficients Only — Range: 0 to 1500

Evaluation of the overall coefficient of heat transfer, U, based on film coefficients only: Range from 0 to 1500 Btu/(hr) (°F) (sq ft). (Refer to Fig. 5.7 for lower range.)

Equation: $U = 1/(1/h_i + 1/h_o)$

Text Reference: Section 5.2, equation 5.10.

Extensions: The scales on the graph are marked in terms of film coefficients, but can be used for systems in which the total thermal resistance is made up of two parts, each conductance being known; in such cases the conductances would be used as though they were film coefficients.

As constructed, the graph is for plane surfaces (where the inside and outside areas are the same), but with thin-walled tubes the difference in surface area can be neglected and the graph used in evaluating the overall coefficient. For tubes in which the area difference must be taken into account, but for which the resistance of the tube wall is negligible, the inside and outside film coefficients can be evaluated in terms of one or the other (inside or outside) surface area and the overall coefficient then determined from the graph. In cases where the inside and outside film coefficients are known on a unit length basis (refer to Figs. 5.2 through 5.6) this graph can be used to directly determine the overall coefficient on a unit length basis.

Special Conditions: None.

Example: For a brass exchanger tube, the inside and outside film coefficients, based on unit length of tube (refer to Figs. 5.2 through 5.6) are 1230 and 1400, respectively. For a 100 F fluid-to-fluid temperature difference, determine the required tube length to transfer 500,000 Btu/hr.

Solution: The dashed example line (Fig. 5.8) shows the method of determining the overall coefficient as 650 Btu/(hr) (°F) (lineal foot). The required tube length (assuming constancy of the overall coefficient) is then 500,000/(650) (100) = 7.7 feet.

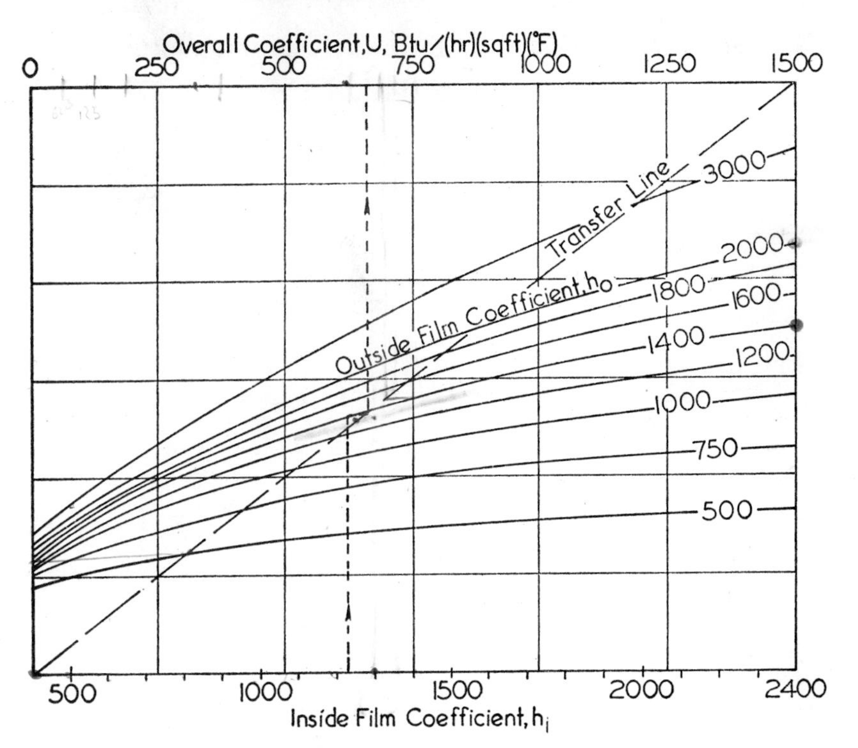
Overall Coefficient, U, Btu/(hr)(sqft)(°F)
0
250
500
750
1000
1250
1500
Transfer Line
Outside Film Coefficient, h_o
3000
2000
1800
1600
1400
1200
1000
750
500
500
1000
1500
2000
2400
Inside Film Coefficient, h_i

Figure 5.8

Surface Temperatures and Mid-Wall Temperature of a Homogeneous Building Wall

Evaluation of surface and of mid-wall temperatures of a homogeneous structural wall.

Equation: $t_x = t_h - r'U'(t_h - t_c)$

Text Reference: Section 5.4, equation 5.14.

Extensions: None.

Special Conditions: This graph is a *limited* solution of the stated equation; it is based on an inside air film coefficient of 1.65 Btu/(hr) (°F) (sq ft) and an outside air film coefficient (corresponding to 15 miles per hour) of 6.0. Both film coefficients are for combined transfer by radiation and convection. Solar effect is not taken account of nor is radiation to a clear night sky. The graph gives the temperature drop from inside air to inside surface (or to wall mid-point, or to outside surface) as a percentage of the temperature drop from inside air to outside air.

Example: A 12 inch plain brick wall of a warehouse (no inside finish) has an overall coefficient of heat transfer of 0.35 Btu/(hr) (sq ft) (°F). The air temperature within the warehouse is to be kept at 70 F when the outside air temperature is 10 F. In order to investigate the radiant cooling of temperature-sensitive materials stored within thermal "sight" of the walls it is necessary to determine the temperature of the inside surface.

Solution: Enter the scale at the bottom of the graph (Fig. 5.9) at an overall coefficient of 0.35 and rise to intersection with the line which is applicable to inside surface. From this intersection move horizontally left to the transfer line and then rise to the top scale where read 21% as the part of overall temperature drop which occurs between the inside air and the inside surface. The inside surface temperature is then $70 - 0.21(70 - 10) = 57$ F.

Check: Based on the standard inside film coefficient of 1.65 the result can be obtained by direct substitution into the stated equation,

$$t_x = 70 - (1/1.65)(0.35)(70 - 10) = 57 \text{ F}.$$

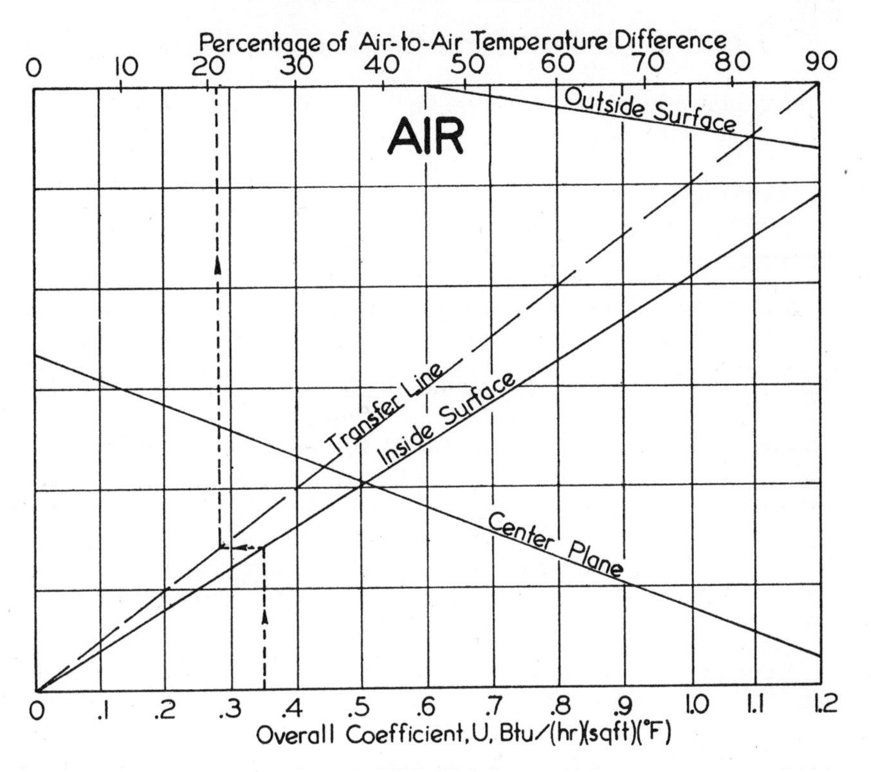
Percentage of Air-to-Air Temperature Difference
0
10
20
30
40
50
60
70
80
90
AIR
Outside Surface
Transfer Line
Inside Surface
Center Plane
0
.1
.2
.3
.4
.5
.6
.7
.8
.9
1.0
1.1
1.2
Overall Coefficient, U, Btu/(hr)(sqft)(°F)

Figure 5.9

Overall Coefficient for a Roof-Ceiling Combination

Evaluation of the overall coefficient of heat transfer for a roof-ceiling structural combination.

Equation: $U = \dfrac{1}{1/U_{ce} + 1/nU_r}$

Text Reference: Section 5.4, equation 5.15.

Extensions: The graph is applicable to any thermal system having two conductances in series provided the area (normal to the path of heat flow) in each conductance remains constant and provided the ratio of areas for the two conductances is known.

Special Conditions: The solution is for an unheated and unventilated attic and is based on the assumption that windows, dormers, and vertical wall spaces in the attic are small in area as compared with roof and are included as part of the roof area. If these areas are not small as compared with roof area their respective overall coefficients should be used in calculating attic losses and, in this case, the graph should not be used.

Example: An unheated attic has no vertical side walls and its ends are equivalent, thermally, to the roof. The overall coefficient of heat transfer for the roof is 0.2 and that for the ceiling is 0.08. The combined area of roof and vertical end walls of the attic is 700 square feet whereas the ceiling area is 500 square feet. Evaluate the combined overall coefficient of heat transfer for use in calculating the rate of heat loss from the heated section of the house through the attic.

Solution: The roof-ceiling area ratio is 700/500 = 1.4. Enter the scale at the bottom of the graph (Fig. 5.10) at a value of U_r of 0.2 and rise to intersect the radial for an area ratio of 1.4. From this point move horizontally left to the transfer line and then rise to intersect the line for U_{ce} of 0.08. From this intersection move horizontally right (in some problems this direction will be *left*) to the transfer line and then rise to the top scale where read the value of the combined coefficient as 0.062 Btu/(hr)(sq ft)(°F).

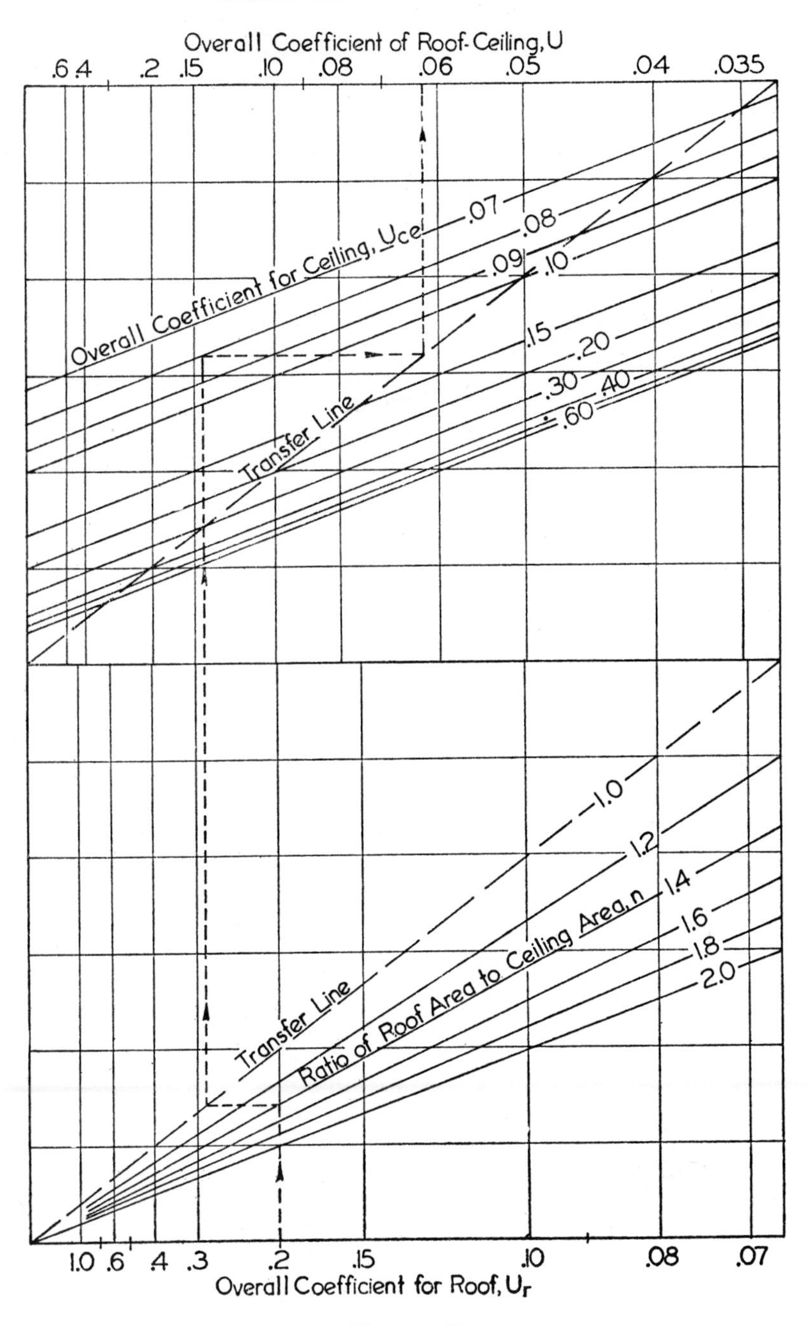

Overall Coefficient of Roof-Ceiling, U
.6
.4
.2
.15
.10
.08
.06
.05
.04
.035
Overall Coefficient for Ceiling, Uce
.07
.08
.09
.10
.15
.20
.30
.40
.60
Transfer Line
1.0
1.2
1.4
1.6
1.8
2.0
Ratio of Roof Area to Ceiling Area, n
Transfer Line
1.0
.6
.4
.3
.2
.15
.10
.08
.07
Overall Coefficient for Roof, Ur

Figure 5.10

Outside Film Coefficient for Building Walls

Evaluation of the outside film coefficient (as a function of wind velocity) for vertical walls.

Equation: $h = a + bV$

Text Reference: Section 5.5, equations 5.17 through 5.20.

Extensions: None.

Special Conditions: The solution given is for convection only or, using a different scale, for convection plus radiation but excluding solar effect and excluding radiant transfer to a clear night sky. Coefficients evaluated by this method are obviously not intended for use in determining instantaneous transfer rates, but rather for determining design values of the heat gain or heat loss of a structure under extreme load conditions. The identification of surface characteristic between the limits of "very smooth" and "very rough" is necessarily indefinite, but corresponds approximately to the following scale: very smooth for glass or marble; smooth for finished plaster; rough for finished concrete; very rough for stucco or unfinished concrete.

Example: A finished concrete wall is exposed to a design value of wind velocity equal to 42 miles per hour. Determine the equivalent outside film coefficient for combined heat transfer by convection and radiation.

Solution: Enter the scale at the bottom of the graph (Fig. 5.11) at a wind velocity of 42 miles per hour and rise to the line for a rough surface. From this intersection move horizontally to the left (for a very rough surface this direction would be to the *right*) to intersect the transfer line and then rise to the scale at the top of the graph where read the combined film coefficient as 18.8 Btu/(hr) (sq ft) (°F). If the film coefficient for convection only were required it could be read from the lower scale (at the top of the graph) as 18.0 Btu/(hr) (sq ft) (°F). Note that the radiation fraction of the combined coefficient is a constant at 0.8 Btu/(hr) (sq ft) (°F).

Check: By equation 5.19, $h = 2.0 + 0.4(42) = 18.8$

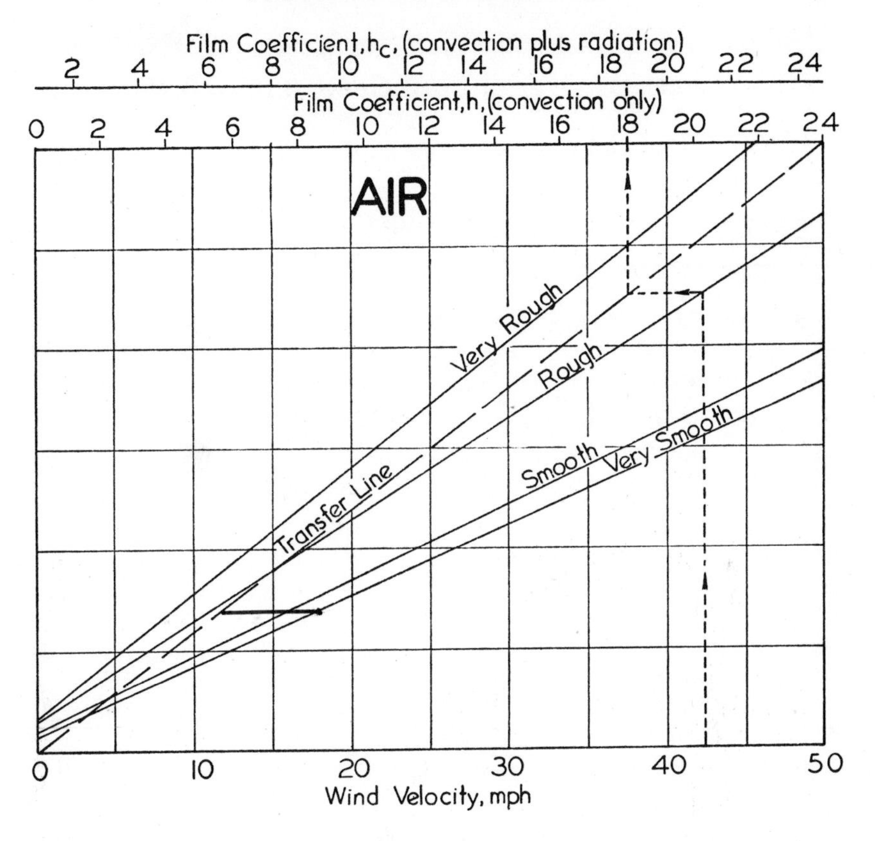

Film Coefficient, h_c, (convection plus radiation)
2 4 6 8 10 12 14 16 18 20 22 24
Film Coefficient, h, (convection only)
0 2 4 6 8 10 12 14 16 18 20 22 24
AIR
Very Rough
Rough
Transfer Line
Smooth
Very Smooth
0 10 20 30 40 50
Wind Velocity, mph

Figure 5.11

Conductance from Inside-Wall Surface to Outside Air — Range of Overall Coefficient: 0.10 to 0.34

Evaluation of conductance from inside surface to outside air: Range of U from 0.10 to 0.34 (for higher range refer to Fig. 5.13).

Equation: $C = 1/[(1/U) - (1/1.65)]$

Text Reference: Section 5.5, equation 5.22.

Extensions: When the conductance is known from inside air to any point in a wall the graph can be used to determine the conductance from the inside *surface* of the wall to the same point.

Special Conditions: The graph is based on the assumption that the equivalent inside film coefficient for convection plus radiation is constant at the "standard" value of 1.65 Btu/(hr) (sq ft) (°F).

Example: In designing a localized panel heating system it is desired to establish a heat balance on the inside surface of an exterior wall. This surface receives energy from room air by convection, receives energy from the room heating panel by radiation and loses energy by conduction to the outside. The conductive loss will be equal to the product of wall area, temperature difference from inside *surface* to outside air, and the conductance of the wall from inside surface to outside air; thus the conductance of the wall from inside surface to outside air must be evaluated. The overall coefficient of heat transfer for the wall is 0.207.

Solution: Enter the scale at the bottom of the graph (Fig. 5.12) at a U value of 0.207 and rise to the transfer line. From this intersection move horizontally left (for some problems this direction will be *right*) to the curve and then rise to the scale at the top of the graph where read the conductance as 0.235 Btu/(hr) (°F) (sq ft).

Check: By substitution in the stated equation,

$$C = 1/[(1/0.207) - (1/1.65)] = 1/4.23 = 0.236$$

Note: Unlike most of the graphical solutions this one requires rising directly to the transfer line and then moving over to the curve in contrast with the usual procedure of rising to the curve and moving to the transfer line.

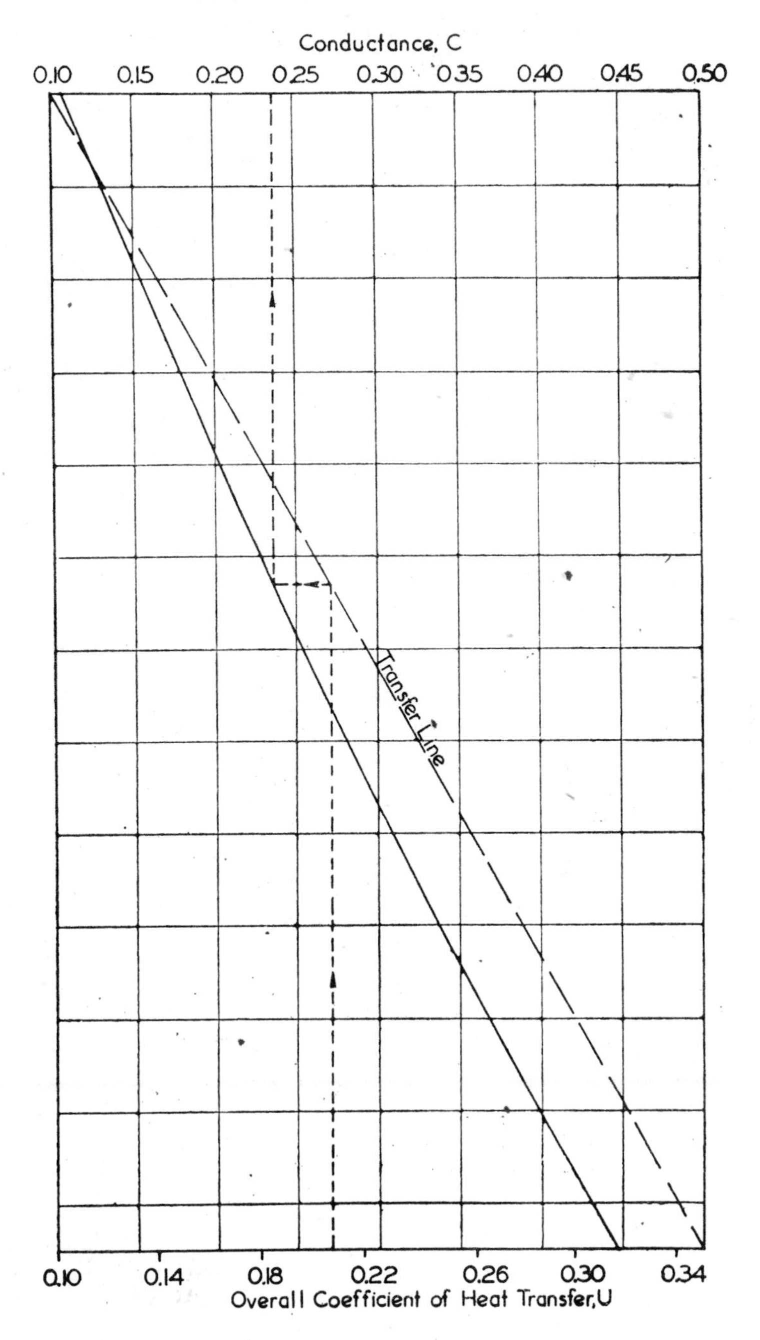
Conductance, C
0.10
0.15
0.20
0.25
0.30
0.35
0.40
0.45
0.50
Transfer Line
0.10
0.14
0.18
0.22
0.26
0.30
0.34
Overall Coefficient of Heat Transfer, U

Figure 5.12

Conductance from Inside-Wall Surface to Outside Air — Range of Overall Coefficient: 0.4 to 1.1

Evaluation of conductance from inside surface to outside air: Range of U from 0.4 to 1.1 (for lower range refer to Fig. 5.12).

Equation: $C = 1/[(1/U) - (1/1.65)]$

Text Reference: Section 5.5, equation 5.22.

Extensions: When the conductance is known from inside air to any point in a wall the graph can be used to determine the conductance from the inside *surface* of the wall to the same point.

Special Conditions: The graph is based on the assumption that the equivalent inside film coefficient for convection plus radiation is constant at the "standard" value of 1.65 Btu/(hr) (sq ft) (°F).

Example: Determine the conductance, inside surface to outside air, for a wall having an overall coefficient of heat transfer of 0.53 Btu/(hr) (sq ft) (°F).

Solution: Enter the scale at the bottom of the graph (Fig. 5.13) and rise to the transfer line. From this intersection move horizontally right (in some problems this direction will be *left*) to the curve and then rise to read the conductance on the scale at the top of the graph. Noting that the top scale reads from right to left the conductance for this wall is determined as 0.75 Btu/(hr) (sq ft) (°F).

Check: By substitution in the stated equation,

$$C = 1/[(1/0.53) - (1/1.65)] = 0.78$$

Note: Unlike most of the graphical solutions this one requires rising directly to the transfer line and then moving over to the curve in contrast with the usual procedure of rising to the curve and moving to the transfer line. Note also that the top scale of this particular graph is reversed and must therefore be read from right to left.

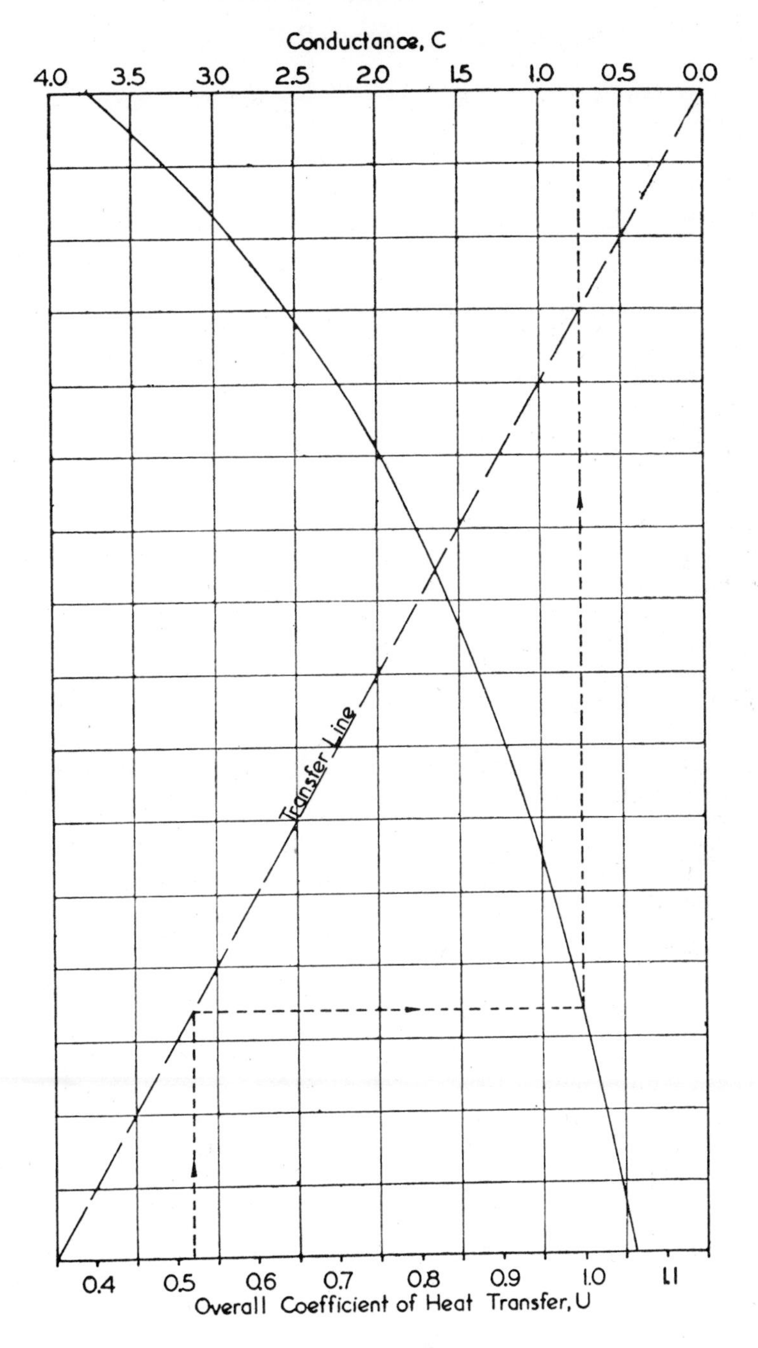
Conductance, C
4.0
3.5
3.0
2.5
2.0
1.5
1.0
0.5
0.0
Transfer Line
0.4
0.5
0.6
0.7
0.8
0.9
1.0
1.1
Overall Coefficient of Heat Transfer, U

Figure 5.13

Inside-Air Temperature Corrected for Radiation Effects

Evaluation of the optimum inside comfort air temperature as corrected for radiation from the inside surface of exterior walls.

Equation: $t_{optimum} = 140 - t_s$

Text Reference: Section 5.6, equation 5.23.

Extensions: None.

Special Conditions: Assumptions underlying the graph are that the inside film coefficient, on which U_e is based, is equal to the standard value of 1.65 Btu/(hr) (sq ft) (°F) and that the occupants of the space would experience optimum comfort with air *and* walls at 70 F. The latter assumption is applicable to average, healthy, sedentary adults. For occupied spaces in which the subjects are doing physical work the optimum temperature for air and walls will usually be something less than 70 F. The reading obtained from the graph can be corrected for such a condition by entering at an outside air temperature higher than the actual value by as many degrees as 70 F is higher than the selected air-wall optimum temperature, then subtracting this same number of degrees from the corrected air temperature which is obtained from the chart. Thus in an industrial working space, the selected optimum air-wall temperature might be 62 F; to use the graph for such a case one would add 8 F to the actual outside air temperature and then subtract 8 F from the corrected temperature read from the chart.

Example: The equivalent overall coefficient for a living room is 0.34. At 0 F outside air temperature what inside air temperature would be required to maintain comfort conditions?

Solution: Enter the graph at 0.34 on the bottom scale and rise to intersect the transfer line. From this point move horizontally to the right to the curve for 0 F and then rise to the top scale where read the answer as 78 F.

Note: Unlike most of the graphical solutions this one requires rising directly to the transfer line and then moving over to the curve in contrast with the usual procedure of rising to the curve and moving to the transfer line.

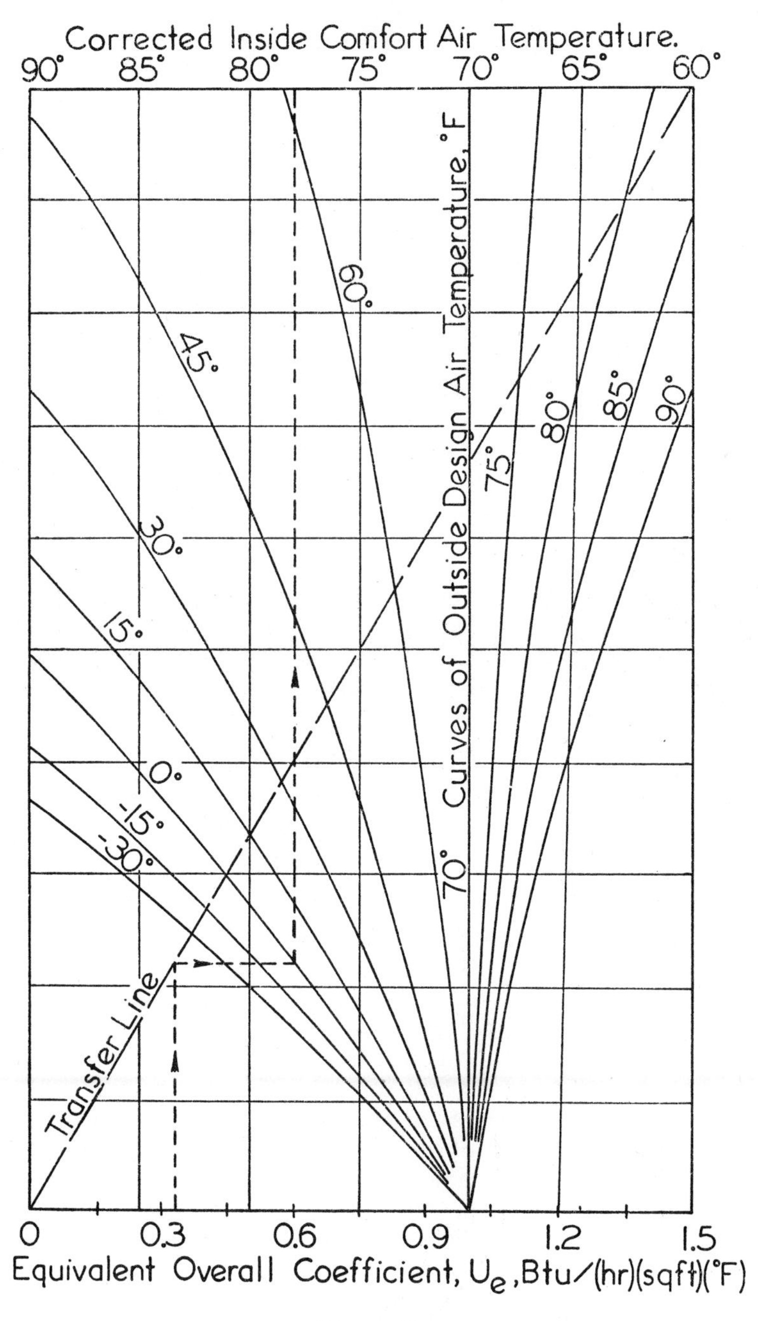
Corrected Inside Comfort Air Temperature.
90° 85° 80° 75° 70° 65° 60°
Curves of Outside Design Air Temperature, °F
60°
45°
30°
15°
0°
-15°
-30°
70°
75°
80°
85°
90°
Transfer Line
0 0.3 0.6 0.9 1.2 1.5
Equivalent Overall Coefficient, U_e, Btu/(hr)(sqft)(°F)

Figure 5.14

CHAPTER VI

Forced Convection

6.1. General Equations for Forced Convection. As discussed in chapter IV, the dimensionless parameters which control heat transfer under conditions of forced convection are the Nusselt number, *Nu*, the Reynolds number, *Re*, and the Prandtl number, *Pr*. In the flow region near the critical value of the Reynolds number, 2100, natural convection effects may be superimposed on the velocity pattern and the Grashof number, *Gr*, may then be an additional influencing factor. For Reynolds numbers beyond those corresponding to the transition region (that is, greater than 10,000) gravity effects become so small as compared with turbulence that the influence of the Grashof number is negligible. For any fluid heating or cooling under conditions of fully developed turbulent motion Nusselt proposed correlation of data by means of the dimensionless equation (4.11),

$$Nu = a(Re)^x(Pr)^y \qquad (6.1)$$

which, in terms of the fluid and system properties, becomes,

$$(hD/k) = a(DV\rho/\mu)^x(c_p\mu/k)^y \qquad (6.2)$$

The coefficient and the exponents in the above equation would be expected to be influenced by: (1) Flow conditions such as that of going from the transition region to the region of fully developed turbulence; (2) Thermal conditions such as whether the fluid is receiving or rejecting heat; (3) The geometry of the system such as whether the flow is within or outside of a tube. Fortunately, a large body of experimental data is available to show that over a wide range of conditions and for a wide variety of fluids, fixed values of the coefficient and of the exponents can be used.

For purposes of correlation and of comparative analysis, the dimensionless form of the forced convection equation is most advantageous. For direct calculation in particular cases, however, it is sometimes preferable to re-write equation 6.2 in the form,

$$h = \phi(D, V, \rho, c_p, \mu, k) \qquad (6.3)$$

which shows that the film coefficient, h, is evaluable for a given system in terms of the size of the surface, D, the velocity of the flow,

V, and four physical properties of the fluid which is receiving or losing energy: viscosity, μ; density, ρ; thermal conductivity, k; specific heat at constant pressure, c_p. Since all four fluid properties vary with temperature it is possible, for a fluid at fixed pressure, to re-write equation 6.3 in the form,

$$h = \phi(D, V, t) \tag{6.4}$$

which identifies the three major variables as: (1) A characteristic of the transfer surface alone, D; (2) A characteristic of the state of the fluid, t; (3) A characteristic of the system comprising object and fluid, V.

In determining the exponents for equation 6.1, consideration must be given to the direction of heat flow. For a fluid being heated, the temperature near the pipe wall will be higher than the mean value. For liquids the viscosity will therefore be less and the velocity a short distance from the wall will be greater than for a fluid at a uniform temperature. In this case the velocity profile through the pipe will be altered from the isothermal pattern and the mean velocity will more nearly approach the mid-stream velocity. For a fluid being cooled the opposite effect will occur since the viscosity will be greatest near the pipe wall; the velocity in that region will therefore be reduced and the ratio of maximum to mean fluid velocity will then be greater than for isothermal flow. From another point of view, the turbulence will be greater for a fluid heating than for one which is cooling, and since turbulence promotes mass transfer it follows that, if other conditions are the same, the film coefficient, h, would be expected to be greater for a fluid heating within a pipe than for one cooling. By the same reasoning, though the two cases are not directly parallel, the film coefficient for a fluid heating outside a pipe would be greater than for one which is cooling. However, at Reynolds numbers in excess of 10,000, turbulence is so great that the viscosity has but little influence on the velocity pattern and, for such cases, the same correlation would be expected to apply whether for heating or cooling.

6.2. Fluids within Pipes. For a liquid or a gas being heated within a tube, and for a gas being cooled within a tube, the recommended form of the Nusselt equation is,

$$Nu = 0.023\,(Re)^{0.8}(Pr)^{0.4} \tag{6.5}$$

(For graphical solution refer to Fig. 6.1, p. 157)

This equation is valid for all fluids when Re exceeds 10,000. It can be used down to an Re of 2100 for liquids having a viscosity not more than twice that of water and for gases for which the ρV product is greater than 1200 times the 2/3 power of the absolute pressure in atmospheres; physical properties of the fluid are evaluated at the bulk temperature.

For liquids cooling within a pipe the recommended equation is similar to 6.5, but with a different exponent on the Prandtl number,

$$Nu = 0.023(Re)^{0.8}(Pr)^{0.3} \quad (6.6)$$

(For graphical solution refer to Fig. 6.2, p. 159)

Since the Prandtl number for most gases is of the order of 0.78 and the viscosity of common gases does not vary greatly from 0.0435 lb/(hr)(ft), a simplified form of equation 6.5 can be established for obtaining approximate film coefficients for common gases which are being heated or cooled within tubes; thus, solving equation 6.5 for h and re-grouping,

$$h = 0.023[(\rho V)^{0.8}/D^{0.2}](c_p\mu/k)^{0.4}(k/c_p\mu)c_p\mu^{0.2}$$

$$= 0.023[c_p(\rho V)^{0.8}\mu^{0.2}/D^{0.2}](c_p\mu/k)^{-0.6}$$

Then substituting 0.78 for $c_p\mu/k$ and 0.0435 for μ gives,

$$h = 0.0144\, c_p(\rho V)^{0.8}/D^{0.2} \quad (6.7)$$

(For graphical solution refer to Fig. 6.3, p. 161)

6.3. Fluids Outside of Pipes. For turbulent flow of a fluid outside of and normal to a single pipe, most investigators agree that the film coefficient is approximately the same for either heating or cooling. Some disagreement exists, however, as to the most acceptable form of the equation. Boelter, Cherry, and Johnson[4] recommend the following form of the Nusselt equation for liquids or gases with Reynolds number greater than 31,

$$Nu = 0.437(Re)^{0.56}(Pr)^{0.33} \quad (6.8)$$

For an Re greater than 100 Stoever[3] recommends a somewhat different selection of constants,

$$Nu = 0.385(Re)^{0.56}(Pr)^{0.3} \quad (6.9)$$

(For graphical solution refer to Fig. 6.4, p. 163)

with physical properties evaluated at the film temperature.

For the Re range from 0.1 to 1000, McAdams[1] recommends, for gases, an equation of different form than Nusselt's,

$$Nu = 0.35 + 0.47(Re)^{0.52}(Pr)^{0.3} \quad (6.10)$$

with physical properties evaluated at the film temperature. Equation 6.10 is also applicable to liquids when Re is greater than 200. For gases in the range for which film temperatures are between 100 F and 300 F McAdams[1] suggests the following simplified and approximate equation,

$$h = 0.026 (\rho V)^{0.6} / D_o^{0.4} \tag{6.11}$$

(For graphical solution refer to Fig. 6.5, p. 165)

6.4. Applications to Particular Fluids. The major difficulty in practical application of the equations from sections 6.2 and 6.3 is the time required to search the literature for numerical values of the four physical properties (ρ, μ, c_p, k), each of which varies as a function of temperature. To assist the designer, a series of graphical solutions have been prepared for 43 liquids of the greatest industrial importance and for 28 commercially important gases or vapors. Each of these graphs gives a specific solution for an equation of the form of 6.4; the equations used in each case are:

(1) For a liquid or gas heating while flowing turbulently within a tube, and for a gas being cooled within a tube, the graphs are based on equation 6.5 re-written in the form,

$$h = 0.023 (V^{0.8}) (D^{-0.2}) (w^{0.8} k^{0.6} c_p^{0.4} \mu^{-0.4}) \tag{6.12}$$

(2) For liquids cooling while flowing turbulently within a tube, the graphs are based on equation 6.6 re-written in the form,

$$h = 0.023 (V^{0.8}) (D^{-0.2}) (w^{0.8} k^{0.7} c_p^{0.3} \mu^{-0.5}) \tag{6.13}$$

(3) For a liquid or a gas heating or cooling while flowing turbulently outside and normal to a tube the graphs are based on equation 6.9 re-written in the form,

$$h = 0.385 (V^{0.56}) (D^{-0.44}) (w^{0.56} k^{0.7} c_p^{0.3} \mu^{-0.26}) \tag{6.14}$$

The series of graphs for liquids (Figs. 6.7 through 6.49) give solutions of equations 6.12, 6.13, and 6.14 on a single graph for each particular fluid. The graphs for gases (Figs. 6.50 through 6.77) are similar to those for liquids except that the mass velocity $V\rho$ is used in place of the velocity V.

6.5. Extensions of Basic Film Coefficients. Many practical problems require the evaluation of film coefficients for conditions different than those for which the equations are directly applicable. In seeking solutions to such problems the alternatives are to develop entirely new correlations based on experimental determinations under test conditions such as exist in the actual problem, or to provide some approximate method of correcting the data obtainable from the basic equations. The following correction values are recommended:

(1) FLOW IN ANNULAR SPACES. This condition is of great practical importance since it includes the entire range of problems which relate to double-pipe exchangers as well as to those problems

in which flow occurs parallel to the tube bundle in a shell-and-tube heat exchanger. Although no generally accepted and thoroughly tested procedure is available, the method which seems to be most rational and which is frequently used in practice is to treat the annular space as equivalent to a pipe of such size that the ratio of pipe cross-section area to pipe surface area has the same value as the ratio for the annular exchanger. Thus,

$$A/P = \frac{(\pi/4)(D_o^2 - D_i^2)}{\pi D_i} = \frac{D_o^2 - D_i^2}{4D_i} = \frac{(\pi/4)D_e^2}{\pi D_e} = \frac{D_e}{4} \quad (6.15)$$

where A = cross-section area of annular space, sq ft, and P = perimeter of annular space, across which heat is flowing, ft. For the annular space of a double-pipe exchanger this equation gives,

$$D_e = (D_o^2 - D_i^2)/D_i \quad (6.16)$$

where D_o is the inside diameter of the outside (larger) pipe whereas D_i is the outside diameter of the inside (smaller) pipe. The equivalent diameter, D_e, is the value to be substituted in equations 6.5 and 6.6 for the inside diameter of the pipe in obtaining values of the film outside the inner pipe in cases of heat flow from fluid in the annular space to fluid flowing in the smaller pipe.

(2) FLOW OUTSIDE AND PARALLEL TO A TUBE BUNDLE. An equation similar to 6.15 gives the value of D_e for this case based on P equal to the sum of the outside circumference of all tubes in the tube bundle. Then,

$$D_e = 4[(\pi D_s^2)/(4\pi N D_t)] = D_s^2/(N D_t) \quad (6.17)$$

where D_s is the inside diameter of the shell, D_t the outside diameter of the tube, and N is the number of tubes.

(3) IRREGULAR CROSS-SECTIONS. For single tubes of non-circular cross-section, the basic equations can be used provided the value of the diameter — for use in the equations — is taken at an equivalent value equal to four times the actual cross-section area divided by the circumference. This approximation is reasonably close for flow within a conduit even when, as for rectangular ducts, discontinuities exist in the circumference. For flow outside and normal to the conduit the accuracy is less dependable but no other method of equal generality and accuracy has yet been established.

(4) FLOW INSIDE HELICAL COILS. Film resistance decreases as turbulence increases hence one would expect the convective film coefficient for flow within a coiled pipe to be greater than for flow at the same velocity through straight pipe having the same diameter. Some experimenters have found up to a 20% increase in the overall coefficient of heat transfer, but McAdams[1] suggests that, for practical problems of heat flow in coils, the effect of the helical

winding can be adequately expressed as a correction to the coefficient from the basic equation by noting that,

$$h_c = h_i(1 + 3.5D_i/D_c) \qquad (6.18)$$

(For graphical solution refer to Fig. 6.6, p. 167)

where h_c is the corrected film coefficient for liquid flowing in a helically coiled pipe where the coil diameter is D_c, h_i is the basic inside film coefficient, and D_i is the inside diameter of the pipe.

(5) Influence of Pipe Roughness. From the relationship between turbulence and convection one would expect the film coefficient to increase as a function of roughness. Experimental work has shown, however, that variations in internal pipe roughness great enough to have pronounced effect on pressure drop do not significantly alter the inside film coefficient. For most practical purposes it can therefore be considered that roughness is not an important factor and need not be considered in evaluating the film coefficient.

(6) Flow Outside and Normal to Tube Bundles. Stoever[3] recommends a 30% increase in the basic coefficient which is used for flow outside and normal to a single tube when the actual flow is normal to a bundle of staggered tubes. For this case the velocity to be used in the basic equation should be that corresponding to flow through the narrowest section between tubes. When flow is across a bundle of tubes that are in line, some reduction in the coefficient used for a staggered bundle would be expected. Stoever[3] suggests a 7½% reduction whereas the recommendation of McAdams[1] is equivalent to a 20% reduction. The latter value has the advantages of being conservative and of giving an h value which is the same as that of the uncorrected film coefficient for flow outside and normal to a single tube. The value of velocity to be used in the basic equation should be, as for staggered tube bundles, based on the narrowest space between tubes.

Most heat exchangers make use of baffles which direct the fluid alternately in either direction across the tube bundle. In such cases the film coefficient would usually be between the values for parallel and for normal flow, extreme turbulence possibly causing it to exceed both. An accurate evaluation of the coefficient for such a case would require detailed specifications of flow conditions within a given exchanger. However, as a first approximation, for a bundle of tubes which are staggered and baffled, the recommended coefficient is equal to the basic outside film coefficient for a single tube, and for a bundle of tubes which are in line and baffled, the recommended coefficient is equal to 80% of the basic outside film coefficient for a single tube.

Liquid or Gas Being Heated or Gas Being Cooled within a Tube

Evaluation of the film coefficient for a liquid or a gas being heated within a tube or for a gas being cooled within a tube.

Equation: $Nu = 0.023 (Re)^{0.8} (Pr)^{0.4}$

Text Reference: Section 6.2, equation 6.5.

Extensions: This graphical solution determines the value of the Nusselt number from known values of the Reynolds and Prandtl numbers. Note that graphical solutions are available for evaluating the Reynolds number (Fig. 4.2) and the Prandtl number (Fig. 4.4) from the physical properties of the fluid. Once the Nusselt number has been determined, graphical solutions are available (Figs. 4.7 and 4.8) for determining the value of the film coefficient.

Special Conditions: The equation on which this graph is based is valid for all fluids when *Re* exceeds 10,000 and can be used down to an *Re* of 2100 for liquids having a viscosity not more than twice that of water. It can be used down to *Re* of 2100 for gases provided the ρV product is greater than 1200 times the 2/3 power of the absolute pressure in atmospheres.

Example: A fluid is being heated within a pipe under conditions such that its Reynolds number and Prandtl number (evaluated from Figs. 4.2 and 4.4, respectively) are 60,000 and 30. The inside diameter of the tube is 1 inch and the thermal conductivity of the fluid is 0.1 Btu/(hr)(sq ft)(°F/ft). Determine the film coefficient.

Solution: Enter the scale at the bottom of the graph (Fig. 6.1) at a Prandtl number of 30 and rise to the line for Reynolds number of 60,000 then move horizontally right to intersect the transfer line and from this point rise to read the Nusselt number at the top scale as 580. The film coefficient is equal to $(k/D)(Nu) = [(0.1)/(1/12)](580) = 700$ Btu/(hr)(sq ft)(°F). (Note that the same value of the film coefficient could be obtained by using the Nusselt number in the graphical solution given in Fig. 4.8.)

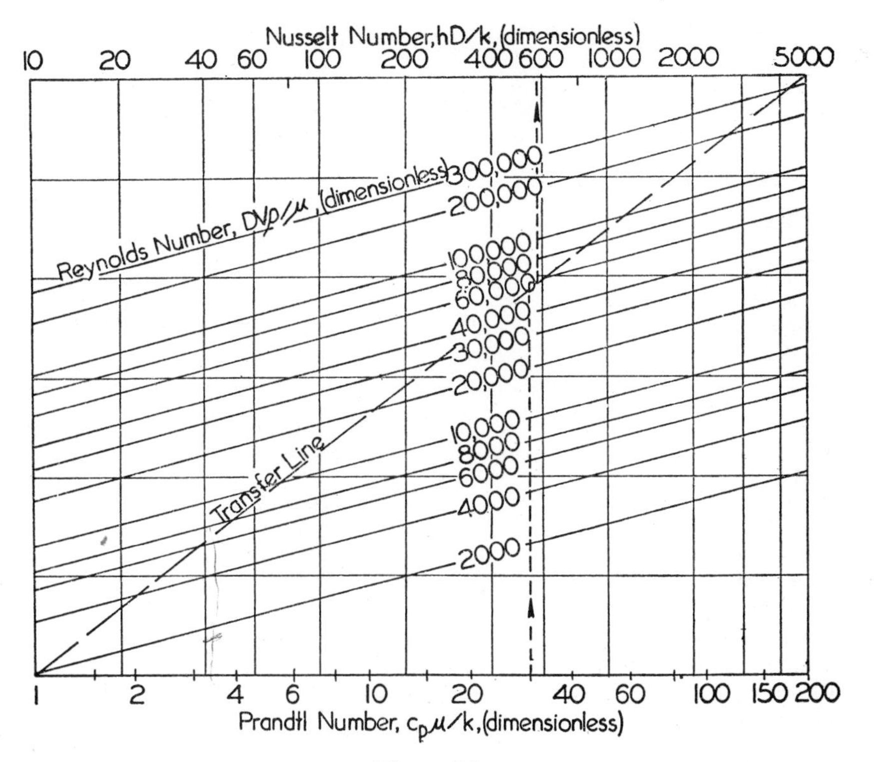
Nusselt Number, hD/k, (dimensionless)
10 20 40 60 100 200 400 600 1000 2000 5000
Reynolds Number, DVρ/μ, (dimensionless)
300,000
200,000
100,000
80,000
60,000
40,000
30,000
20,000
10,000
8000
6000
4000
2000
Transfer Line
1 2 4 6 10 20 40 60 100 150 200
Prandtl Number, $c_p\mu/k$, (dimensionless)

Figure 6.1

Liquid Cooling within a Tube

Evaluation of the film coefficient for a liquid being cooled within a tube.

Equation: $Nu = 0.023\,(Re)^{0.8}\,(Pr)^{0.3}$

Text Reference: Section 6.2, equation 6.6.

Extensions: This graphical solution determines the value of the Nusselt number from known values of the Reynolds and Prandtl numbers. Note that graphical solutions are available for evaluating the Reynolds number (Fig. 4.2) and the Prandtl number (Fig. 4.4) from the physical properties of the fluid. Once the Nusselt number has been determined, graphical solutions are available (Figs. 4.7 and 4.8) for determining the value of the film coefficient.

Special Conditions: The equation on which this graph is based is valid for all fluids when *Re* exceeds 10,000 and can be used down to an *Re* of 2100 for liquids having a viscosity not more than twice that of water.

Example: A liquid is cooling in a ¾ inch inside diameter tube under conditions such that its Reynolds number is 100,000, its Prandtl number is 150, and its thermal conductivity is 0.15 Btu/(hr) (sq ft) (°F/ft). Determine the film coefficient.

Solution: Enter the scale at the bottom of the graph (Fig. 6.2) at a *Pr* of 150 and rise to intersection with the line for a Reynolds number of 100,000. From this point move horizontally left (for some problems this direction will be to the *right*) to the transfer line and from that intersection rise to the scale at the top of the graph where read the value of the Nusselt number as 1100. The film coefficient can then be determined from the Nusselt number by graphical means (refer Figs. 4.7 and 4.8) or it can be calculated as $(k/D)\,(Nu) = [(0.15)/(0.75/12)]\,(1100) = 2640$ Btu/(hr) (sq ft) (°F).

Check: By substitution in the stated equation,

$$Nu = 0.023\,(100{,}000)^{0.8}\,(150)^{0.4} = 1034.$$

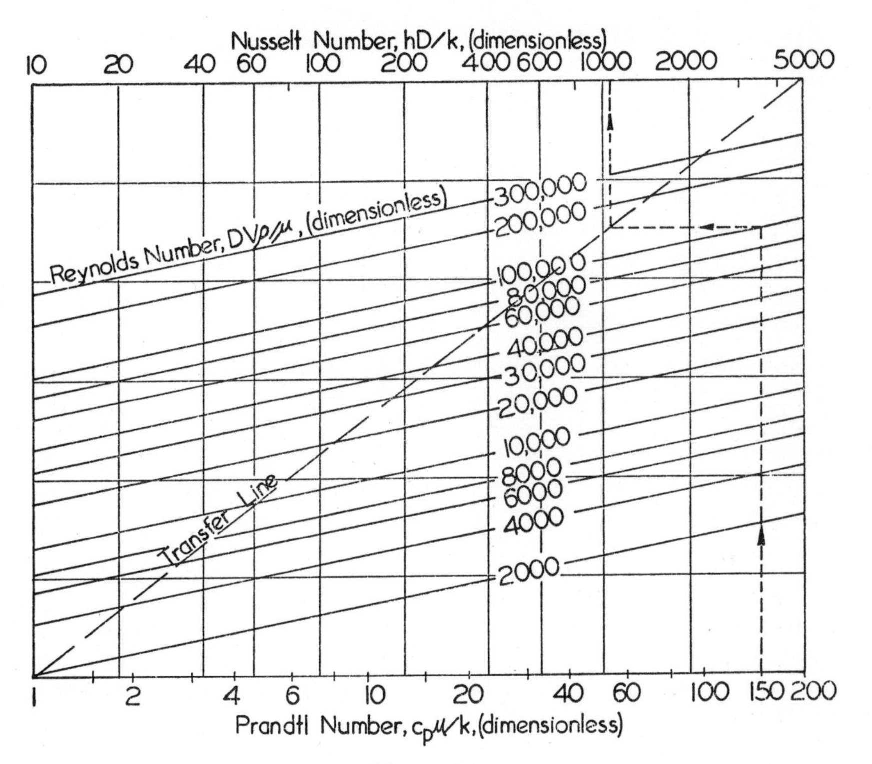
Nusselt Number, hD/k, (dimensionless)
10 20 40 60 100 200 400 600 1000 2000 5000
Reynolds Number, DVρ/μ, (dimensionless)
300,000
200,000
100,000
80,000
60,000
40,000
30,000
20,000
10,000
8000
6000
4000
2000
Transfer Line
1 2 4 6 10 20 40 60 100 150 200
Prandtl Number, cpμ/k, (dimensionless)

Figure 6.2

Gases Heating or Cooling Inside Tube — Approximate Solution

Evaluation of the film coefficient for gases heating or cooling within a tube. Approximate solution. (For exact solution refer to Fig. 6.1.)

Equation: $h = 0.0144\,(c_p)\,(\rho V)^{0.8}/D^{0.2}$

Text Reference: Section 6.2, equation 6.7.

Extensions: None.

Special Conditions: The equation on which this graph is based is derived from the general equation (solved in Fig. 6.1) by taking the Prandtl number as constant at 0.78 and assuming that the viscosity, for the common gases, can be considered constant at 0.0435 lb/(hr) (ft). When working with gases for which these two assumptions are invalid, the graph should not be used, and the solution as given in Fig. 6.1 should be used.

Example: A gas is being heated within a 2 inch inside diameter tube under conditions such that the mass velocity (product of density and velocity) is 22 lb/(sec) (sq ft). The specific heat of the gas at constant pressure is 0.6 Btu/(lb) (°F). Determine the film coefficient.

Solution: Enter the lower scale (Fig. 6.3) at a mass velocity of 22 and rise to intersect the radial line for 2 inch inside diameter. From this point move left to the transfer line, rise to intersect the radial line for specific heat of 0.6 and then move horizontally left to the transfer line. From the latter intersection rise to read the value of the film coefficient as 103 Btu/(hr) (sq ft) (°F).

Check: By substitution in the stated equation,

$$h = 0.0144\,(0.6)\,(22 \times 3600)^{0.8}/(2/12)^{0.2} = 102.7$$

noting that 3600 is the conversion factor for changing mass velocity from units of seconds to units of hours and 12 is the conversion factor for converting the diameter from inches to feet.

Note: The graph is constructed with properties of the system identified in units which are of greatest convenience for practical use, but which are not the consistent units of the stated equation. Conversion to proper units is taken care of by the construction of the graph.

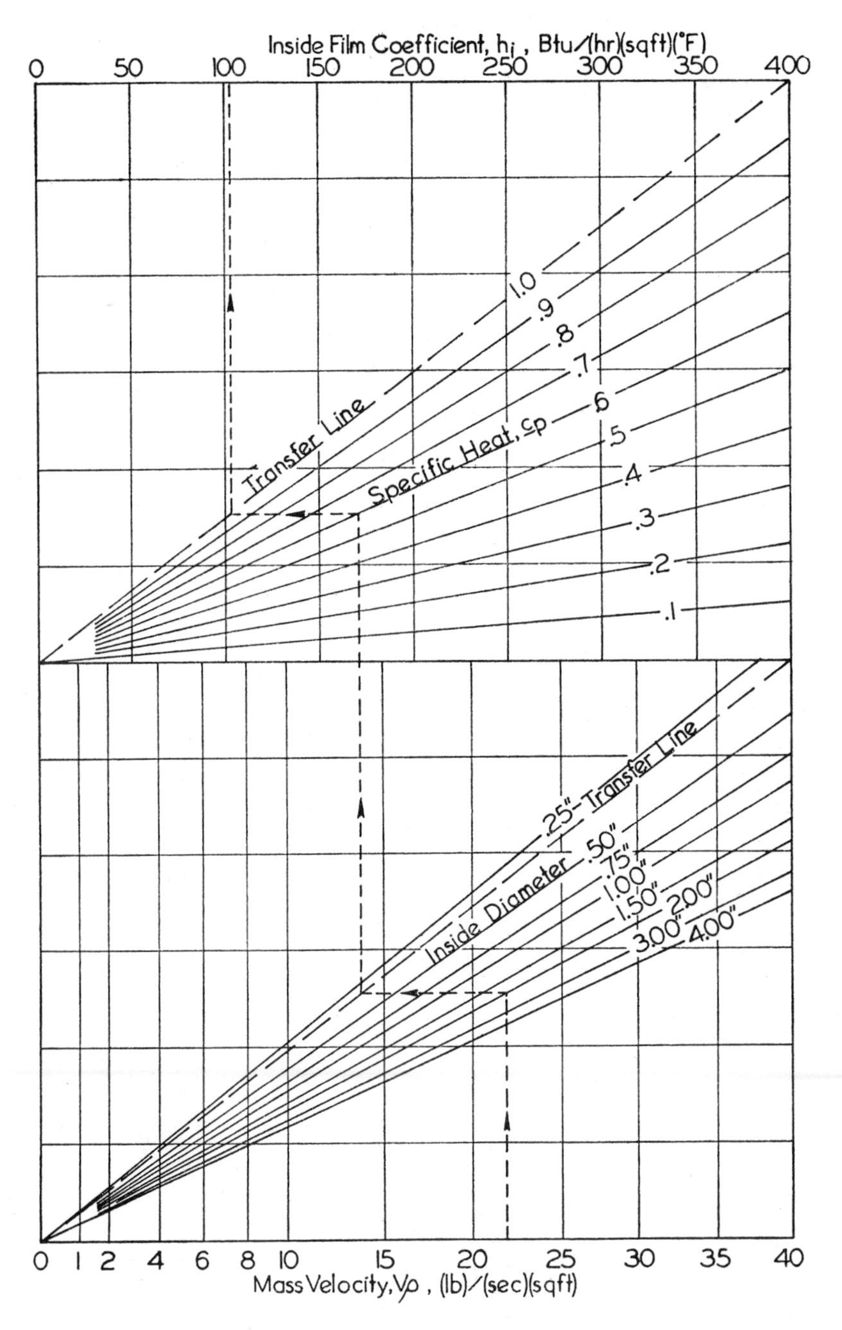
Inside Film Coefficient, h_i, Btu/(hr)(sqft)(°F)
0
50
100
150
200
250
300
350
400
1.0
.9
.8
.7
.6
.5
.4
.3
.2
.1
Transfer Line
Specific Heat, c_p
.25"
Transfer Line
Inside Diameter
.50"
.75"
1.00"
1.50"
2.00"
3.00"
4.00"
0
1
2
4
6
8
10
15
20
25
30
35
40
Mass Velocity, $V\rho$, (lb)/(sec)(sqft)

Figure 6.3

Liquids or Gases Heating or Cooling in Flow Outside and Normal to a Tube

Evaluation of the film coefficient for liquids or gases heating or cooling while in turbulent flow outside and normal to a single tube.

Equation: $Nu = 0.385\,(Re)^{0.56}\,(Pr)^{0.3}$
where the physical properties of the fluid are those at the corresponding film temperature.

Text Reference: Section 6.3, equation 6.9.

Extensions: For flow outside and normal to bundles of staggered or bundles of in-line tubes, refer to part 6 of section 6.5.

This graphical solution determines the value of the Nusselt number from known values of the Reynolds and Prandtl numbers. Note that graphical solutions are available for evaluating the Reynolds number (Fig. 4.2) and the Prandtl number (Fig. 4.4) from the physical properties of the fluid. Once the Nusselt number has been determined, graphical methods are available (Figs. 4.7 and 4.8) for evaluating the film coefficient.

Special Conditions: The graph is applicable to liquids or gases flowing at any Reynolds number greater than 100.

Example: A liquid is being heated while flowing outside and normal to a 1½ inch outside diameter tube. The Reynolds number (evaluated from Fig. 4.2) is 20,000 and the Prandtl number (evaluated from Fig. 4.4) is 40. The thermal conductivity is 0.1 Btu/(hr) (sq ft) (°F/ft) at the estimated temperature of the outside film. Determine the outside film coefficient.

Solution: Enter the bottom scale of the graph (Fig. 6.4) at a *Pr* of 40 and rise to intersection with the line for a Reynolds number of 20,000. From this point move horizontally right to intersect the transfer line and then rise to the top scale where read the value of the Nusselt number as 300. The film coefficient corresponding to the known Nusselt number can be obtained from Fig. 4.8 or calculated as $(k/D)\,(Nu) = [(0.1)/(1.5/12)]\,(300) = 240$ Btu/(hr) (sq ft) (°F).

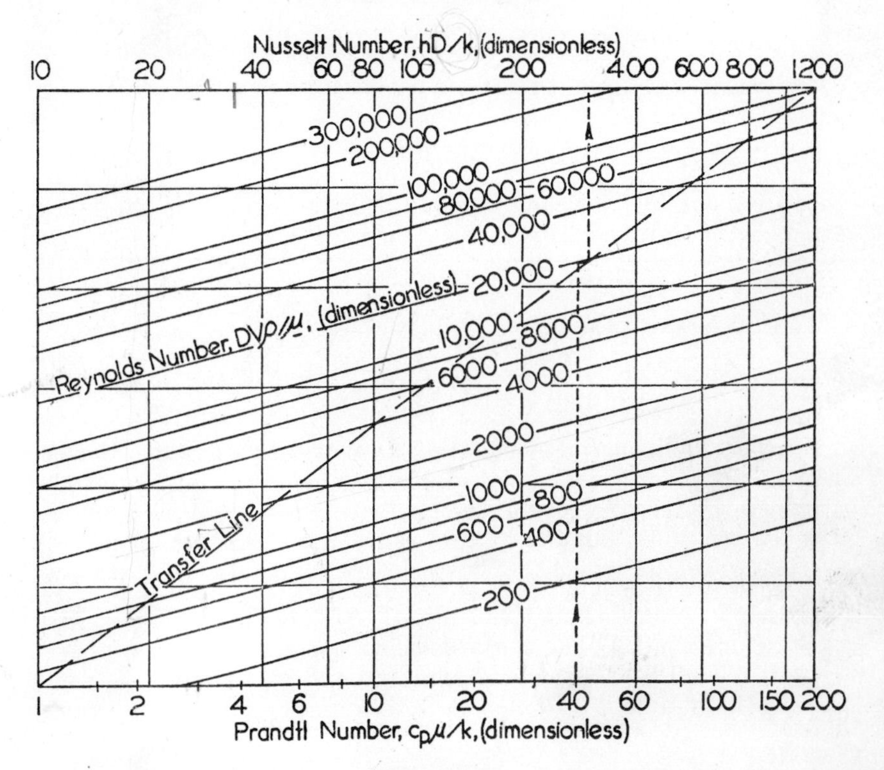
Nusselt Number, hD/k, (dimensionless)
10 20 40 60 80 100 200 400 600 800 1200
300,000
200,000
100,000
80,000
60,000
40,000
20,000
10,000
8000
6000
4000
2000
1000
800
600
400
200
Reynolds Number, DVρ/μ, (dimensionless)
Transfer Line
1 2 4 6 10 20 40 60 100 150 200
Prandtl Number, $c_p\mu/k$, (dimensionless)

Figure 6.4

Gases Flowing Outside and Normal to a Tube — Approximate Solution

Evaluation of the film coefficient for a gas flowing outside and normal to a single tube. Approximate method. (For gases at temperatures outside the range from 100 F to 300 F, use the more exact method given in Fig. 6.4.)

Equation: $h = 0.026\,(\rho V)^{0.6}/\,(D_o)^{0.4}$

Text Reference: Section 6.3, equation 6.11.

Extensions: For flow outside and normal to staggered tube bundles or in-line tube bundles, refer to part 6 of section 6.5.

Special Conditions: The equation on which this graph is based is applicable over the range of Reynolds numbers from 0.1 to 1000 provided the temperature of the gas is between 100 F and 300 F. For temperatures outside of this range use the exact graphical solution given in Fig. 6.4.

Example: A gas is being cooled while flowing normal to a bundle of staggered tubes. The mass velocity (product of density and velocity) is 30 lb/(sec) (sq ft) and the outside diameter of each tube in the bundle is 1½ inches. Determine the outside film coefficient.

Solution: Enter the bottom scale of the graph (Fig. 6.5) at a mass velocity of 30 and rise to intersect the radial line for 1½ inch outside diameter. From this point move horizontally left to the transfer line (for ½ inch diameter pipe this direction would be *right*) then rise to the scale at the top of the graph where read the value of the film coefficient as 635 Btu/(hr) (sq ft) (°F) for a *single* tube. For flow across a staggered tube bundle the recommended film coefficient for a single tube (part 6 of section 6.5) is 30% greater so the corrected value is then 1.3(635) = 826.

Note: The graph is constructed with properties of the system identified in units which are of greatest convenience for practical use, but which are not the consistent units of the stated equation. Conversion to proper units is taken care of by the construction of the graph.

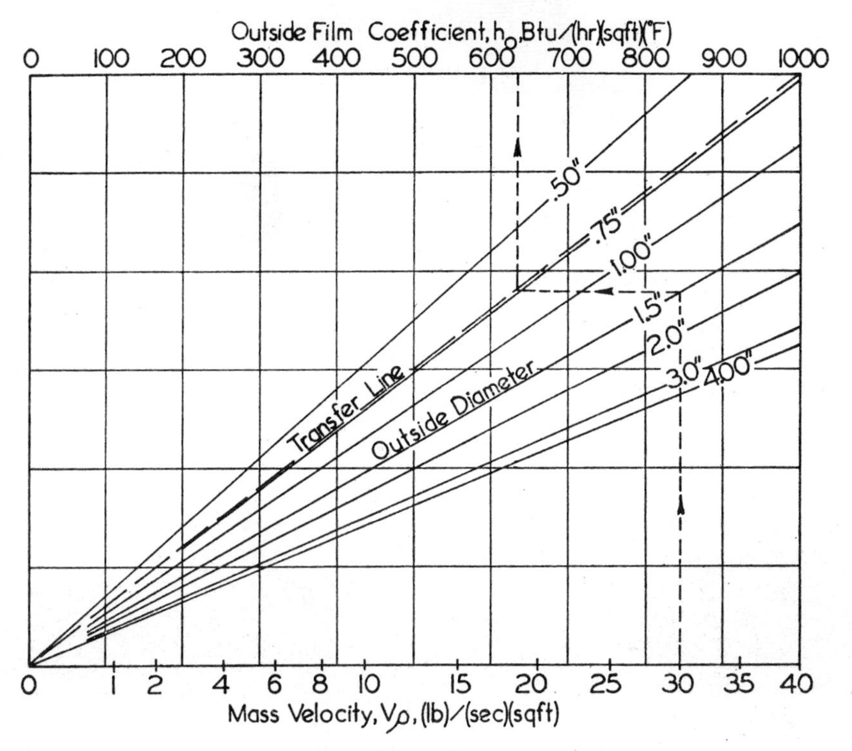
Outside Film Coefficient, h_o, Btu/(hr)(sqft)(°F)
0 100 200 300 400 500 600 700 800 900 1000
.50"
.75"
1.00"
1.5"
2.0"
3.0"
4.00"
Transfer Line
Outside Diameter
0 1 2 4 6 8 10 15 20 25 30 35 40
Mass Velocity, $V\rho$, (lb)/(sec)(sqft)

Figure 6.5

Correction to Basic Film Coefficient for Flow in Helical Coils

Evaluation of the corrected film coefficient for a liquid flowing in a helically coiled tube.

Equation: $h_c = h_i[1 + 3.5(D_i/D_c)]$
where h_i is the base film coefficient determined for flow through a straight tube, D_i is the tube inside diameter and D_c is the coil diameter.

Text Reference: Part 4 of section 6.5, equation 6.18.

Extensions: None.

Special Conditions: None.

Example: A liquid is flowing through a 2 inch inside diameter pipe coiled helically with a coil diameter of 20 inches. Flow conditions are such that the film coefficient through a straight pipe (as could be evaluated from Fig. 6.1) is 650 Btu/(hr)(sq ft)(°F). Determine the inside film coefficient for flow within the coil.

Solution: Enter the scale at the bottom of the graph (Fig. 6.6) at a value of the base coefficient of 650 and rise to intersect the radial line corresponding to the known diameter ratio of 2/20 = 0.1. From this intersection move horizontally left to the transfer line and then rise to the scale at the top of the graph where read the corrected value of the inside film coefficient as 880 Btu/(hr)(sq ft)(°F).

Check: By substitution in the stated equation,

$$h_c = 650(1 + 3.5 \times 2/20) = 878$$

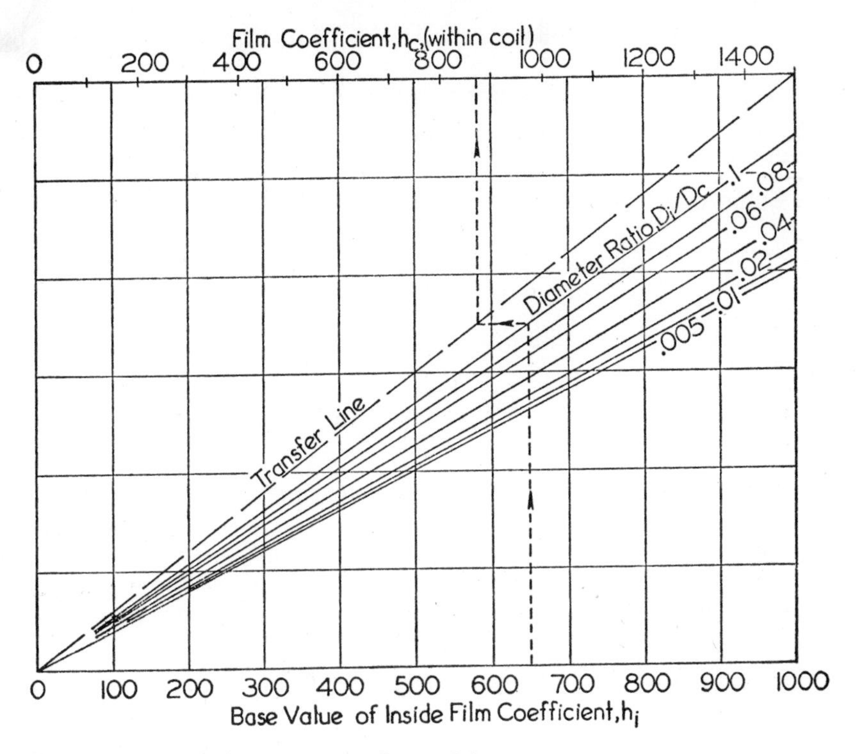
Film Coefficient, h_c, (within coil)
0
200
400
600
800
1000
1200
1400
Transfer Line
Diameter Ratio, D_i/D_c
.1
.08
.06
.04
.02
.01
.005
0
100
200
300
400
500
600
700
800
900
1000
Base Value of Inside Film Coefficient, h_i

Figure 6.6

Acetic Acid, 100% (Liquid)

Acetic Acid, 100% (liquid) heating or cooling in turbulent flow within a tube or in turbulent flow outside and normal to a single tube.

Equations: Liquid heating in a tube: $Nu = 0.023(Re)^{0.8}(Pr)^{0.4}$
Liquid cooling in a tube: $Nu = 0.023(Re)^{0.8}(Pr)^{0.3}$
Liquid heating or cooling outside and normal to a single tube: $Nu = 0.385(Re)^{0.56}(Pr)^{0.3}$

Text References: Chapter VI; equations 6.5, 6.6, 6.9, 6.12, 6.13, and 6.14.

Extensions: Refer to section 6.5 for extensions to annular spaces, tube bundles, and flow through helical coils.

Special Conditions: For a liquid heating or cooling within a tube, do not use the graph unless the value of velocity (fps) times diameter (inches) exceeds 1.2 for 100 F or 0.7 for 250 F.

For a liquid flowing outside and normal to a single tube, do not use the graph for velocity less than 1 fps unless the Reynolds number exceeds 100.

Example: Acetic Acid, 100% (liquid) is flowing within a 2 inch inside diameter tube at a velocity of 2 fps. The fluid is at a mean temperature of 150 F and is being heated. Determine the inside film coefficient.*

Solution: Enter the bottom scale of the graph (Fig. 6.7) at an inside velocity of 2 fps and rise to intersect the solid radial line for a 2 inch inside diameter tube. From this intersection move left to the transfer line and then rise to the top section of the graph where radial lines are given for liquid heating and cooling *inside* a tube. In this section intersect the solid radial for liquid heating at 150 F. From this intersection move left to the transfer line and then rise to the top scale of the graph where read the value of the inside film coefficient as 160 Btu/(hr)(sq ft)(°F).

***Note:** To determine other heat transfer coefficients for Acetic Acid, 100%, use Fig. 6.7 but refer to the examples on the following pages for the appropriate method: Outside film coefficient, page 174; outside film coefficient per lineal foot, page 170; inside film coefficient per lineal foot, use method similar to that for outside film coefficient per lineal foot; inside film coefficient for a helical coil, page 172; overall coefficient, page 176; overall coefficient per lineal foot, page 178.

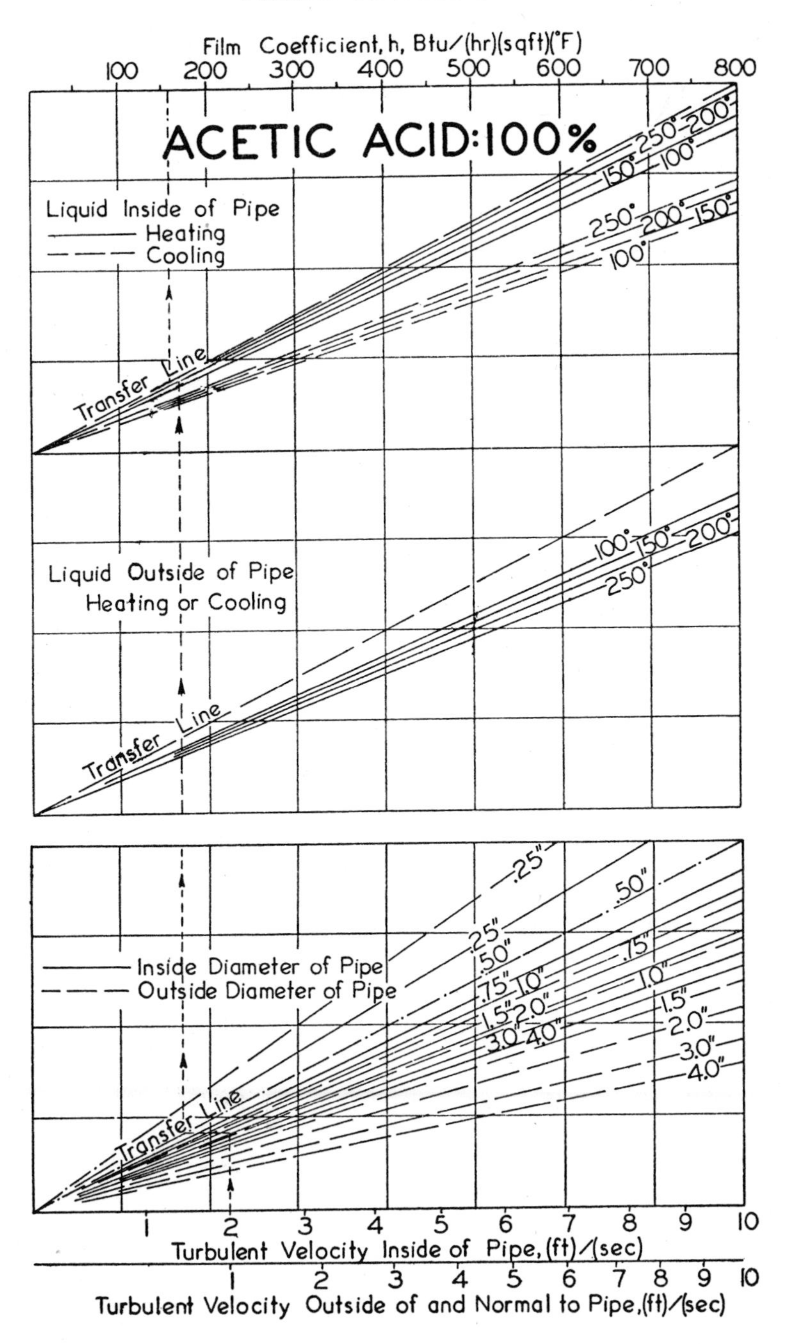
Film Coefficient, h, Btu/(hr)(sqft)(°F)
100 200 300 400 500 600 700 800
ACETIC ACID: 100%
Liquid Inside of Pipe
Heating
Cooling
250° 200°
150° 100°
250° 200° 150°
100°
Transfer Line
Liquid Outside of Pipe
Heating or Cooling
100° 150° 200°
250°
Transfer Line
Inside Diameter of Pipe
Outside Diameter of Pipe
.25"
.25"
.50"
.75" 1.0"
1.5" 2.0"
3.0" 4.0"
.50"
.75"
1.0"
1.5"
2.0"
3.0"
4.0"
Transfer Line
1 2 3 4 5 6 7 8 9 10
Turbulent Velocity Inside of Pipe, (ft)/(sec)
1 2 3 4 5 6 7 8 9 10
Turbulent Velocity Outside of and Normal to Pipe, (ft)/(sec)

Figure 6.7

Acetic Acid, 50% (Liquid)

Acetic Acid, 50% (liquid) heating or cooling in turbulent flow within a tube or in turbulent flow outside and normal to a single tube.

Equations: Liquid heating in a tube: $Nu = 0.023(Re)^{0.8}(Pr)^{0.4}$
Liquid cooling in a tube: $Nu = 0.023(Re)^{0.8}(Pr)^{0.3}$
Liquid heating or cooling outside and normal to a single tube: $Nu = 0.385(Re)^{0.56}(Pr)^{0.3}$

Text References: Chapter VI; equations 6.5, 6.6, 6.9, 6.12, 6.13, and 6.14.

Extensions: Refer to section 6.5 for extensions to annular spaces, tube bundles, and flow through helical coils.

Special Conditions: For a liquid heating or cooling within a tube, do not use the graph unless the value of velocity (fps) times diameter (inches) exceeds 3.5 for 50 F or 0.6 for 250 F.

For a liquid flowing outside and normal to a single tube, do not use the graph for velocity less than 1 fps unless the Reynolds number exceeds 100.

Example: Acetic Acid, 50% (liquid) is heating at a mean temperature of 100 F while flowing outside and normal to a 1″ O.D. Type M copper tube. The fluid velocity is 4 fps. Determine the outside film coefficient* in Btu per hour per °F per *lineal foot* of tube.

Solution: The dashed example line on the graph (Fig. 6.8) shows the method of evaluating the outside film coefficient, for the stated conditions, in terms of one square foot of outside surface of the tube. To convert this value, 570 Btu/(hr) (sq ft) (°F), to a lineal basis refer to Fig. 5.6 and, using a method similar to that shown by the dashed example line, enter the graph at h of 570 and come out at the top scale with a film coefficient of 180 Btu per hour per °F per lineal foot of tube.

***Note:** To determine other heat transfer coefficients for Acetic Acid, 50%, use Fig. 6.8 but refer to the examples on the following pages for the appropriate method: Outside film coefficient, page 174; inside film coefficient, page 168; inside film coefficient per lineal foot, use method similar to that for outside film coefficient per lineal foot; inside film coefficient for a helical coil, page 172; overall coefficient, page 176; overall coefficient per lineal foot, page 178.

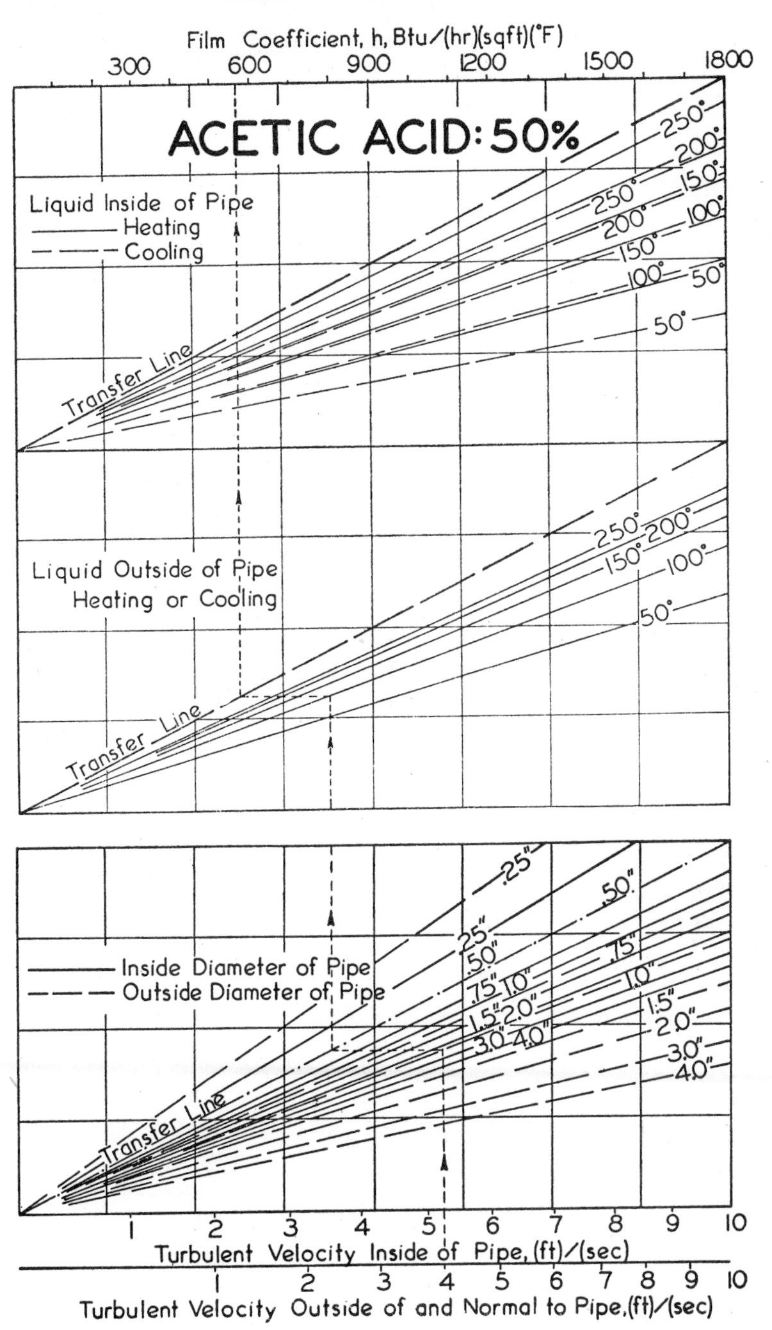
Film Coefficient, h, Btu/(hr)(sqft)(°F)
300
600
900
1200
1500
1800
ACETIC ACID: 50%
Liquid Inside of Pipe
Heating
Cooling
250°
200°
150°
100°
50°
Transfer Line
Liquid Outside of Pipe
Heating or Cooling
Inside Diameter of Pipe
Outside Diameter of Pipe
.25"
.50"
.75"
1.0"
1.5"
2.0"
3.0"
4.0"
Turbulent Velocity Inside of Pipe, (ft)/(sec)
Turbulent Velocity Outside of and Normal to Pipe, (ft)/(sec)

Figure 6.8

Acetone (Liquid)

Acetone (liquid) heating or cooling in turbulent flow within a tube or in turbulent flow outside and normal to a single tube.

Equations: Liquid heating in a tube: $Nu = 0.023(Re)^{0.8}(Pr)^{0.4}$
Liquid cooling in a tube: $Nu = 0.023(Re)^{0.8}(Pr)^{0.3}$
Liquid heating or cooling outside and normal to a single tube: $Nu = 0.385(Re)^{0.56}(Pr)^{0.3}$

Text References: Chapter VI; equations 6.5, 6.6, 6.9, 6.12, 6.13, and 6.14.

Extensions: Refer to section 6.5 for extensions to annular spaces, tube bundles, and flow through helical coils.

Special Conditions: For a liquid heating or cooling within a tube, do not use the graph if the velocity is less than 1 fps.

For a liquid flowing outside and normal to a single tube, do not use the graph for velocity less than 1 fps unless the Reynolds number exceeds 100.

Example: Acetone (liquid) is in turbulent flow, at 6 fps velocity, through a tube having an inside diameter of 0.25 inches. The fluid is cooling at a mean temperature of 50 F. The tube is wound in a helical coil having a diameter of 50 inches. Determine the inside film coefficient.*

Solution: The dashed example line on the graph (Fig. 6.9) shows the method of determining the base value of the inside film coefficient for the conditions of flow through a straight tube; this value is read at the top scale as 580. Now refer to Fig. 6.6, enter the bottom scale at 580, and rise to the radial line for a tube-to-coil ratio of $0.25/50 = 0.005$. From this intersection move left to the transfer line, then rise to read the corrected film coefficient for flow within the coil as 590 Btu/(hr) (sq ft) (°F).

***Note:** To determine other heat transfer coefficients for Acetone, use Fig. 6.9 but refer to the examples on the following pages for the appropriate method: Outside film coefficient, page 174; inside film coefficient, page 168; outside film coefficient per lineal foot, page 170; inside film coefficient per lineal foot, use method similar to that for outside film coefficient per lineal foot; overall coefficient, page 176; overall coefficient per lineal foot, page 178.

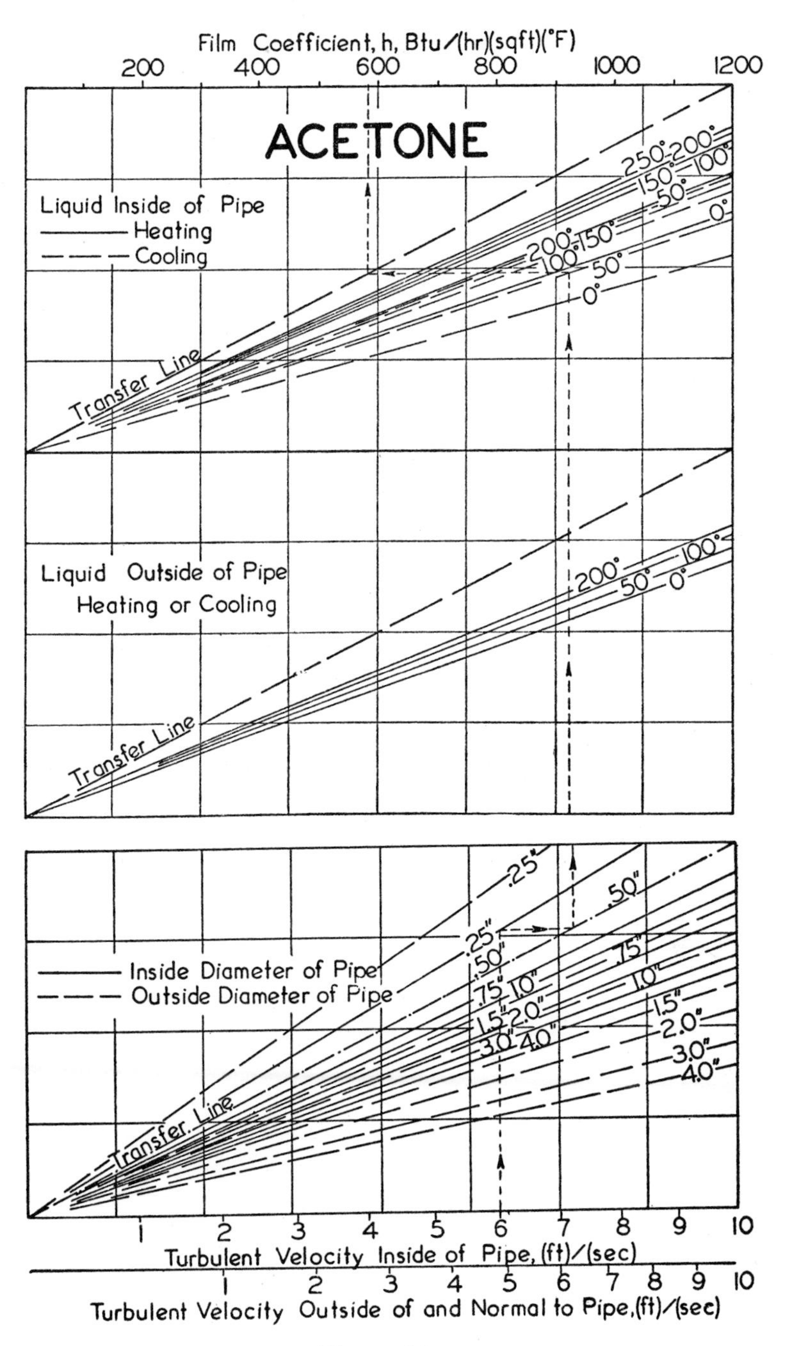

Film Coefficient, h, Btu/(hr)(sqft)(°F)
200
400
600
800
1000
1200
ACETONE
Liquid Inside of Pipe
Heating
Cooling
Transfer Line
250°
200°
150°
100°
50°
0°
Liquid Outside of Pipe
Heating or Cooling
Transfer Line
200°
100°
50°
0°
Inside Diameter of Pipe
Outside Diameter of Pipe
Transfer Line
.25"
.50"
.75"
1.0"
1.5"
2.0"
3.0"
4.0"
1 2 3 4 5 6 7 8 9 10
Turbulent Velocity Inside of Pipe, (ft)/(sec)
1 2 3 4 5 6 7 8 9 10
Turbulent Velocity Outside of and Normal to Pipe, (ft)/(sec)

Figure 6.9

Ammonia (Liquid)

Ammonia (liquid) heating or cooling in turbulent flow within a tube or in turbulent flow outside and normal to a single tube.

Equations: Liquid heating in a tube: $Nu = 0.023(Re)^{0.8}(Pr)^{0.4}$
Liquid cooling in a tube: $Nu = 0.023(Re)^{0.8}(Pr)^{0.3}$
Liquid heating or cooling outside and normal to a single tube: $Nu = 0.385(Re)^{0.56}(Pr)^{0.3}$

Text References: Chapter VI; equations 6.5, 6.6, 6.9, 6.12, 6.13, and 6.14.

Extensions: Refer to section 6.5 for extensions to annular spaces, tube bundles, and flow through helical coils.

Special Conditions: For a liquid heating or cooling within a tube, do not use the graph if the velocity is less than 1 fps.

For a liquid flowing outside and normal to a single tube, do not use the graph for velocity less than 1 fps unless the Reynolds number exceeds 100.

Example: Ammonia (liquid) is heating at a mean temperature of 0 F while flowing at 7 fps outside and normal to a bundle of staggered $3/4$ inch outside diameter tubes. Determine the outside film coefficient.* Estimate the outside coefficient for a similar, but baffled, tube bundle.

Solution: The base value of the outside film coefficient (for flow normal to a *single* tube) is determined as 1700 by following the dashed example line, Fig. 6.10. The corrected value for flow normal to a staggered bundle is 30% greater than the base value (refer to part 6 of section 6.5) hence is 1.3(1700) = 2210 Btu/(hr) (sq ft) (°F). For a baffled tube bundle (refer to part 6 of section 6.5) the film coefficient would be taken at the base value of 1700.

***Note:** To determine other heat transfer coefficients for Ammonia, use Fig. 6.10 but refer to the examples on the following pages for the appropriate method: Inside film coefficient, page 168; outside film coefficient per lineal foot, page 170; inside film coefficient per lineal foot, use method similar to that for outside film coefficient per lineal foot; inside film coefficient for a helical coil, page 172; overall coefficient, page 176; overall coefficient per lineal foot, page 178.

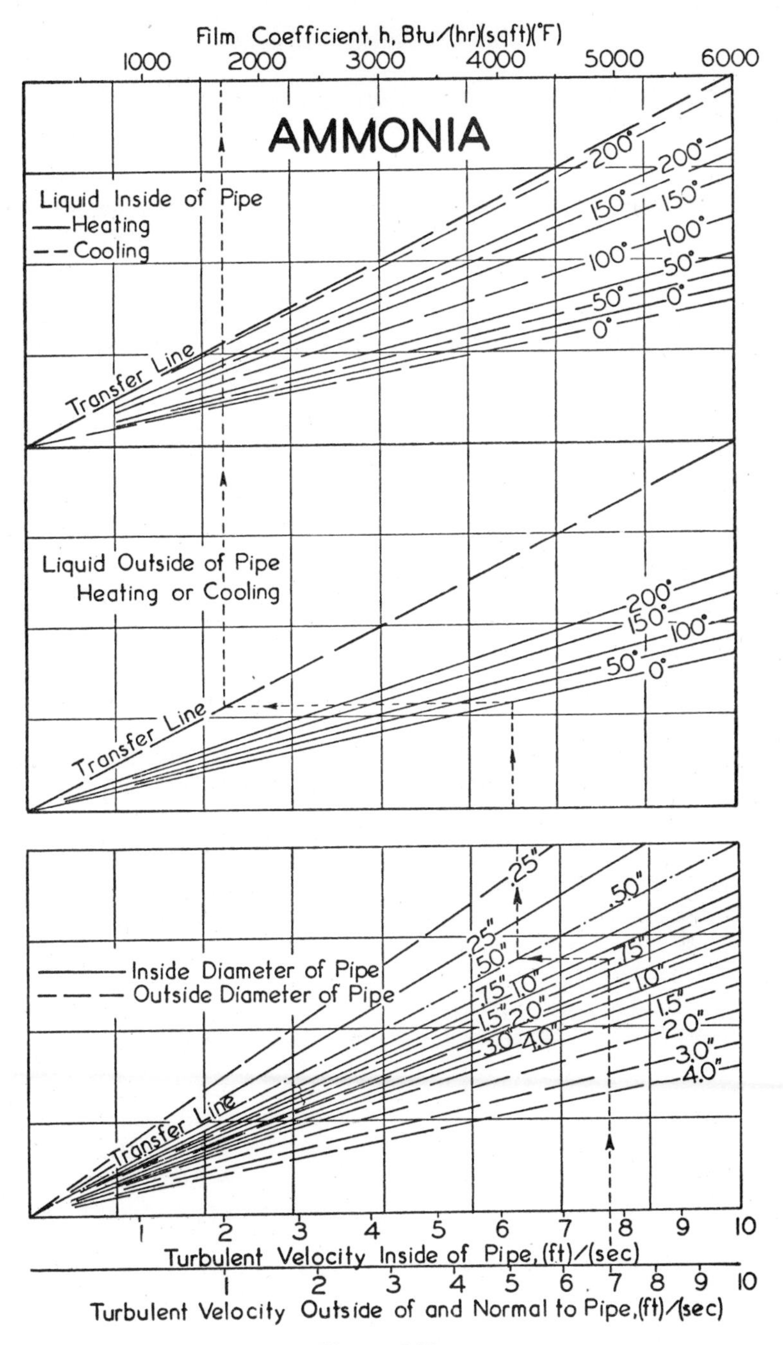
Film Coefficient, h, Btu/(hr)(sqft)(°F)
1000
2000
3000
4000
5000
6000
AMMONIA
Liquid Inside of Pipe
—Heating
-- Cooling
200°
150°
100°
50°
0°
Transfer Line
Liquid Outside of Pipe
Heating or Cooling
200°
150°
100°
50°
0°
Transfer Line
Inside Diameter of Pipe
Outside Diameter of Pipe
.25"
.50"
.75"
1.0"
1.5"
2.0"
3.0"
4.0"
Transfer Line
1 2 3 4 5 6 7 8 9 10
Turbulent Velocity Inside of Pipe, (ft)/(sec)
1 2 3 4 5 6 7 8 9 10
Turbulent Velocity Outside of and Normal to Pipe, (ft)/(sec)

Figure 6.10

Amyl Acetate (Liquid)

Amyl Acetate (liquid) heating or cooling in turbulent flow within a tube or in turbulent flow outside and normal to a single tube.

Equations: Liquid heating in a tube: $Nu = 0.023(Re)^{0.8}(Pr)^{0.4}$
Liquid cooling in a tube: $Nu = 0.023(Re)^{0.8}(Pr)^{0.3}$
Liquid heating or cooling outside and normal to a single tube: $Nu = 0.385(Re)^{0.56}(Pr)^{0.3}$

Text References: Chapter VI; equations 6.5, 6.6, 6.9, 6.12, 6.13, and 6.14.

Extensions: Refer to section 6.5 for extensions to annular spaces, tube bundles, and flow through helical coils.

Special Conditions: For a liquid heating or cooling within a tube, do not use the graph unless the value of velocity (fps) times diameter (inches) exceeds 1.6 for 50 F or 0.3 for 250 F.

For a liquid flowing outside and normal to a single tube, do not use the graph for velocity less than 1 fps unless the Reynolds number exceeds 100.

Example: Amyl Acetate (liquid) is flowing inside a tube of 2″ I.D. at a velocity of 2 fps. The fluid is heating at a mean temperature of 200 F. If the outside film coefficient is 300 determine the overall coefficient* of heat transfer assuming that the tube is so thin-walled that its thermal resistance is negligible and the difference between inside and outside surface areas can be neglected.

Solution: For the stated conditions, the base value of the inside film coefficient is determinable (dashed example line, Fig. 6.11) as 124 Btu/(hr) (sq ft) (°F). Now go to Fig. 5.7 and (by a method similar to that shown by the dashed line) for inside and outside film coefficients of 124 and 300, respectively, read the overall coefficient of heat transfer as 84 Btu/(hr) (sq ft) (°F).

***Note:** To determine other heat transfer coefficients for Amyl Acetate, use Fig. 6.11 but refer to the examples on the following pages for the appropriate method: Outside film coefficient, page 174; inside film coefficient, page 168; outside film coefficient per lineal foot, page 170; inside film coefficient per lineal foot, use method similar to that for outside film coefficient per lineal foot; inside film coefficient for a helical coil, page 172; overall coefficient per lineal foot, page 178.

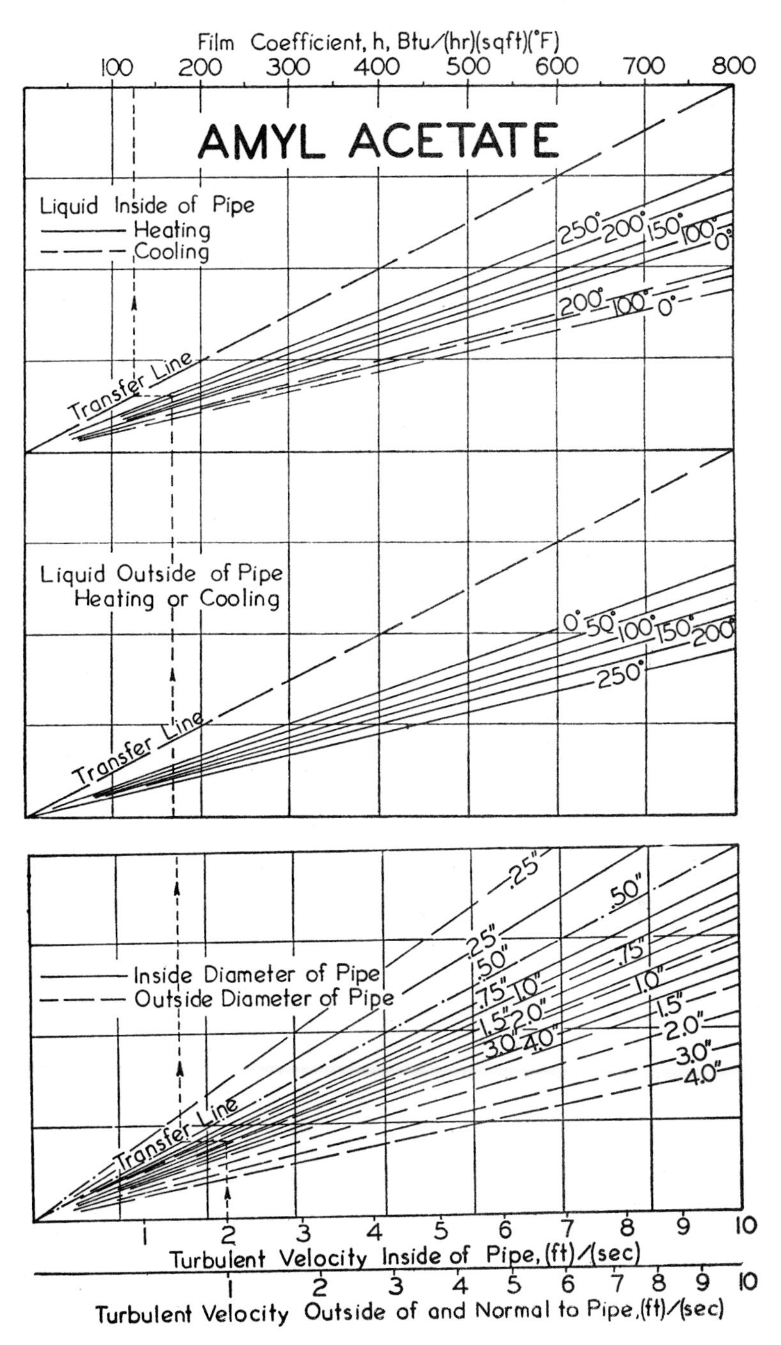
Film Coefficient, h, Btu/(hr)(sqft)(°F)
100 200 300 400 500 600 700 800
AMYL ACETATE
Liquid Inside of Pipe
Heating
Cooling
250° 200° 150° 100° 0°
200° 100° 0°
Transfer Line
Liquid Outside of Pipe
Heating or Cooling
0° 50° 100° 150° 200°
250°
Transfer Line
Inside Diameter of Pipe
Outside Diameter of Pipe
.25"
.50"
.75"
1.0"
1.5"
2.0"
3.0"
4.0"
Transfer Line
1 2 3 4 5 6 7 8 9 10
Turbulent Velocity Inside of Pipe, (ft)/(sec)
1 2 3 4 5 6 7 8 9 10
Turbulent Velocity Outside of and Normal to Pipe, (ft)/(sec)

Figure 6.11

Amyl Alcohol, Iso (Liquid)

Amyl Alcohol, Iso (liquid) heating or cooling in turbulent flow within a tube or in turbulent flow outside and normal to a single tube.

Equations: Liquid heating in a tube: $Nu = 0.023 (Re)^{0.8} (Pr)^{0.4}$
Liquid cooling in a tube: $Nu = 0.023 (Re)^{0.8} (Pr)^{0.3}$
Liquid heating or cooling outside and normal to a single tube: $Nu = 0.385 (Re)^{0.56} (Pr)^{0.3}$

Text References: Chapter VI; equations 6.5, 6.6, 6.9, 6.12, 6.13, and 6.14.

Extensions: Refer to section 6.5 for extensions to annular spaces, tube bundles, and flow through helical coils.

Special Conditions: For a liquid heating or cooling within a tube, do not use the graph unless the value of velocity (fps) times diameter (inches) exceeds 9.5 for 50 F or 0.8 for 250 F.

For a liquid flowing outside and normal to a single tube, do not use the graph for velocity less than 1 fps unless the Reynolds number exceeds 100.

Example: Amyl Alcohol, Iso (liquid) is flowing at 4 fps outside and normal to a phosphorized copper tube (Type L) having an outside diameter of 1″ and wall thickness of 0.065″. The fluid is heating at 200 F. The inside film coefficient is known to be 800 Btu/(hr) (°F) (sq ft of inside surface). Determine the overall coefficient* of heat transfer per *lineal* foot of tube.

Solution: The dashed example line on the graph (Fig. 6.12) determines the outside coefficient as 300. From Fig. 5.5, the inside and outside coefficients, 800 and 300, can be converted to values of 200 and 110, respectively, based on one lineal foot of tube. From Fig. 2.4 the thermal resistance of the tube is 0.00003 (based on outside area), giving a conductance of 33,000 which (Fig. 5.5) becomes 9,000 per lineal foot. The overall coefficient, equation 5.2, is then $U = 1/[1/200 + 1/9{,}000 + 1/110] = 70$ Btu/(hr) (°F) (lineal foot of tube).

*__Note:__ To determine other heat transfer coefficients for Amyl Alcohol, Iso, use Fig. 6.12 but refer to the examples on the following pages for the appropriate method: Outside film coefficient, page 174; inside film coefficient, page 168; outside film coefficient per lineal foot, page 170; inside film coefficient per lineal foot, use method similar to that for outside film coefficient per lineal foot; inside film coefficient for a helical coil, page 172; overall coefficient, page 176.

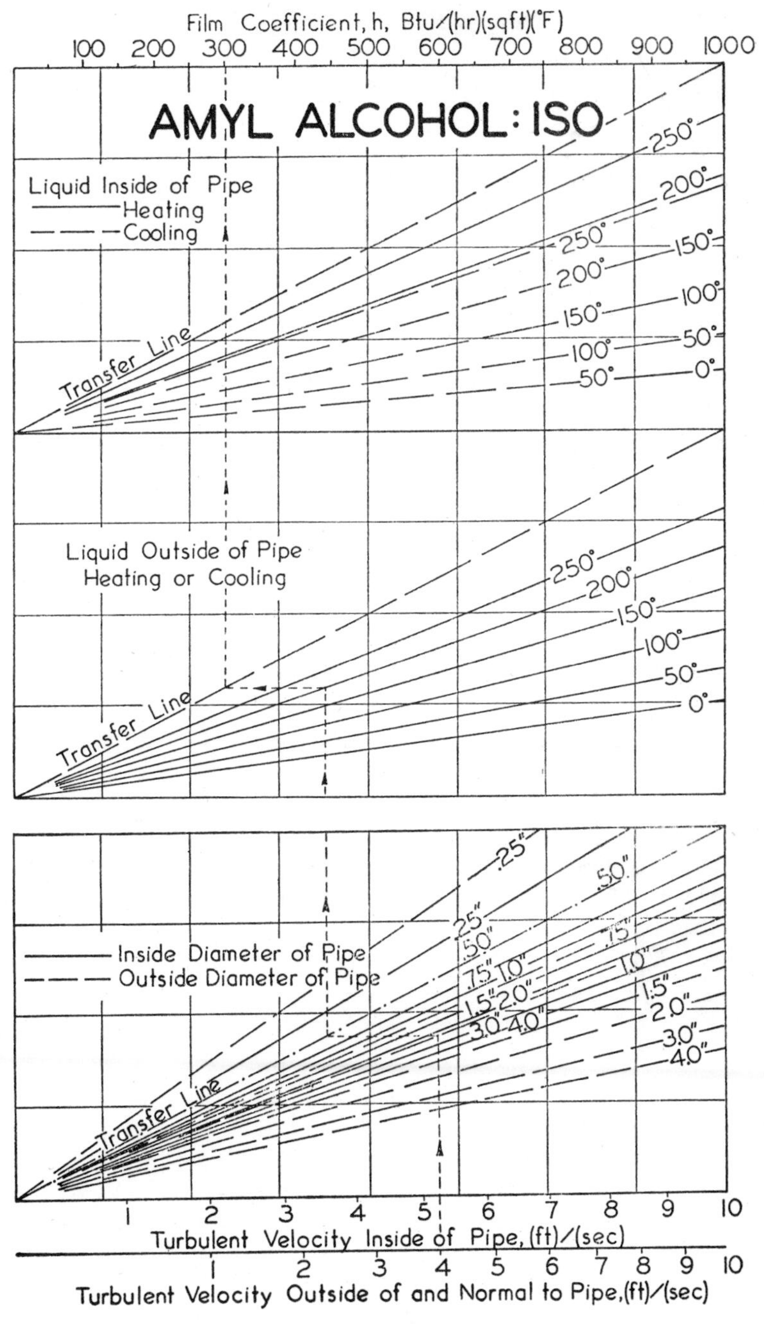
Film Coefficient, h, Btu/(hr)(sqft)(°F)
100 200 300 400 500 600 700 800 900 1000
AMYL ALCOHOL: ISO
Liquid Inside of Pipe
Heating
Cooling
250°
200°
150°
100°
50°
0°
250°
200°
150°
100°
50°
Transfer Line
Liquid Outside of Pipe
Heating or Cooling
250°
200°
150°
100°
50°
0°
Transfer Line
Inside Diameter of Pipe
Outside Diameter of Pipe
.25"
.50"
.25"
.50"
.75"
1.0"
1.5"
2.0"
3.0"
4.0"
.75"
1.0"
1.5"
2.0"
3.0"
4.0"
Transfer Line
1 2 3 4 5 6 7 8 9 10
Turbulent Velocity Inside of Pipe, (ft)/(sec)
1 2 3 4 5 6 7 8 9 10
Turbulent Velocity Outside of and Normal to Pipe, (ft)/(sec)

Figure 6.12

Aniline (Liquid)

Aniline (liquid) heating or cooling in turbulent flow within a tube or in turbulent flow outside and normal to a single tube.

Equations: Liquid heating in a tube: $Nu = 0.023(Re)^{0.8}(Pr)^{0.4}$
Liquid cooling in a tube: $Nu = 0.023(Re)^{0.8}(Pr)^{0.3}$
Liquid heating or cooling outside and normal to a single tube: $Nu = 0.385(Re)^{0.56}(Pr)^{0.3}$

Text References: Chapter VI; equations 6.5, 6.6, 6.9, 6.12, 6.13, and 6.14.

Extensions: Refer to section 6.5 for extensions to annular spaces, tube bundles, and flow through helical coils.

Special Conditions: For a liquid heating or cooling within a tube, do not use the graph unless the value of velocity (fps) times diameter (inches) exceeds 7.6 for 50 F or 0.7 for 250 F.

For a liquid flowing outside and normal to a single tube, do not use the graph for velocity less than 1 fps unless the Reynolds number exceeds 100.

Example: Aniline (liquid) is in turbulent flow, at 6 fps velocity, through a tube having an inside diameter of 0.25 inches. The fluid is heating at a mean temperature of 250 F. The tube is wound in a helical coil having a diameter of 50 inches. Determine the inside film coefficient.*

Solution: The dashed example line on the graph (Fig. 6.13) shows the method of determining the base value of the inside film coefficient for the conditions of flow through a straight tube; this value is read at the top scale as 690. Now refer to Fig. 6.6, enter the bottom scale at 690, and rise to the radial line for a tube-to-coil ratio of $0.25/50 = 0.005$. From this intersection move left to the transfer line, then rise to read the corrected film coefficient for flow within the coil as 695 Btu/(hr) (sq ft) (°F).

*__Note:__ To determine other heat transfer coefficients for Aniline, use Fig. 6.13 but refer to the examples on the following pages for the appropriate method: Outside film coefficient, page 174; inside film coefficient, page 168; outside film coefficient per lineal foot, page 170; inside film coefficient per lineal foot, use method similar to that for outside film coefficient per lineal foot; overall coefficient, page 176; overall coefficient per lineal foot, page 178.

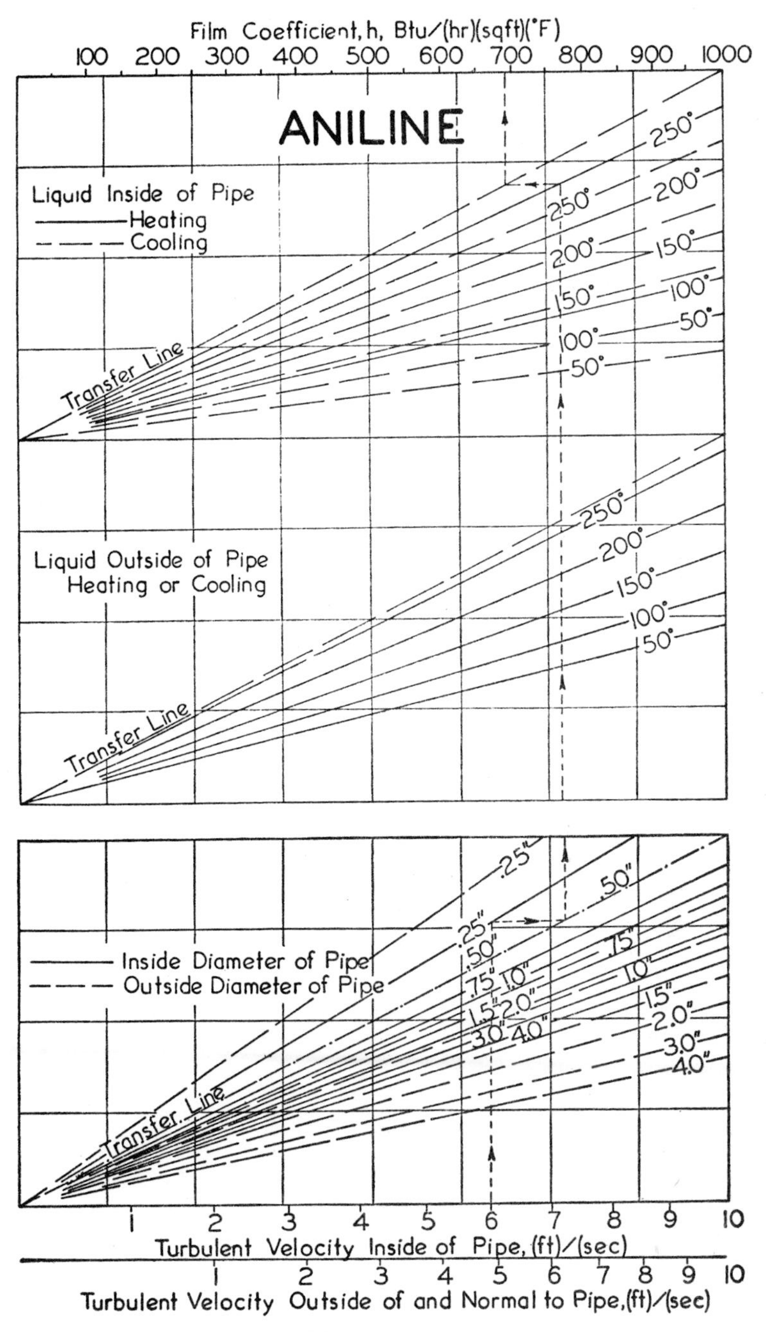
Film Coefficient, h, Btu/(hr)(sqft)(°F)
100 200 300 400 500 600 700 800 900 1000
ANILINE
Liquid Inside of Pipe
Heating
Cooling
250° 200° 150° 100° 50°
Transfer Line
Liquid Outside of Pipe
Heating or Cooling
Inside Diameter of Pipe
Outside Diameter of Pipe
.25" .50" .75" 1.0" 1.5" 2.0" 3.0" 4.0"
1 2 3 4 5 6 7 8 9 10
Turbulent Velocity Inside of Pipe, (ft)/(sec)
Turbulent Velocity Outside of and Normal to Pipe, (ft)/(sec)

Figure 6.13

Benzene (Liquid)

Benzene (liquid) heating or cooling in turbulent flow within a tube or in turbulent flow outside and normal to a single tube.

Equations: Liquid heating in a tube: $Nu = 0.023(Re)^{0.8}(Pr)^{0.4}$
Liquid cooling in a tube: $Nu = 0.023(Re)^{0.8}(Pr)^{0.3}$
Liquid heating or cooling outside and normal to a single tube: $Nu = 0.385(Re)^{0.56}(Pr)^{0.3}$

Text References: Chapter VI; equations 6.5, 6.6, 6.9, 6.12, 6.13, and 6.14.

Extensions: Refer to section 6.5 for extensions to annular spaces, tube bundles, and flow through helical coils.

Special Conditions: For a liquid heating or cooling within a tube, do not use the graph if the velocity is less than 1 fps.

For a liquid flowing outside and normal to a single tube, do not use the graph for velocity less than 1 fps unless the Reynolds number exceeds 100.

Example: Benzene (liquid) is cooling at a mean temperature of 100 F while flowing at 7 fps outside and normal to a bundle of staggered ¾ inch outside diameter tubes. Determine the outside film coefficient.* Estimate the outside coefficient for a similar, but baffled, tube bundle.

Solution: The base value of the outside film coefficient (for flow normal to a *single* tube) is determined as 460 by following the dashed example line, Fig. 6.14. The corrected value for flow normal to a staggered bundle is 30% greater than the base value (refer to part 6 of section 6.5) hence is 1.3(460) = 600 Btu/(hr) (sq ft) (°F). For a baffled tube bundle (refer to part 6 of section 6.5) the film coefficient would be taken at the base value of 460.

***Note:** To determine other heat transfer coefficients for Benzene, use Fig. 6.14 but refer to the examples on the following pages for the appropriate method: Inside film coefficient, page 168; outside film coefficient per lineal foot, page 170; inside film coefficient per lineal foot, use method similar to that for outside film coefficient per lineal foot; inside film coefficient for a helical coil, page 180; overall coefficient, page 176; overall coefficient per lineal foot, page 178.

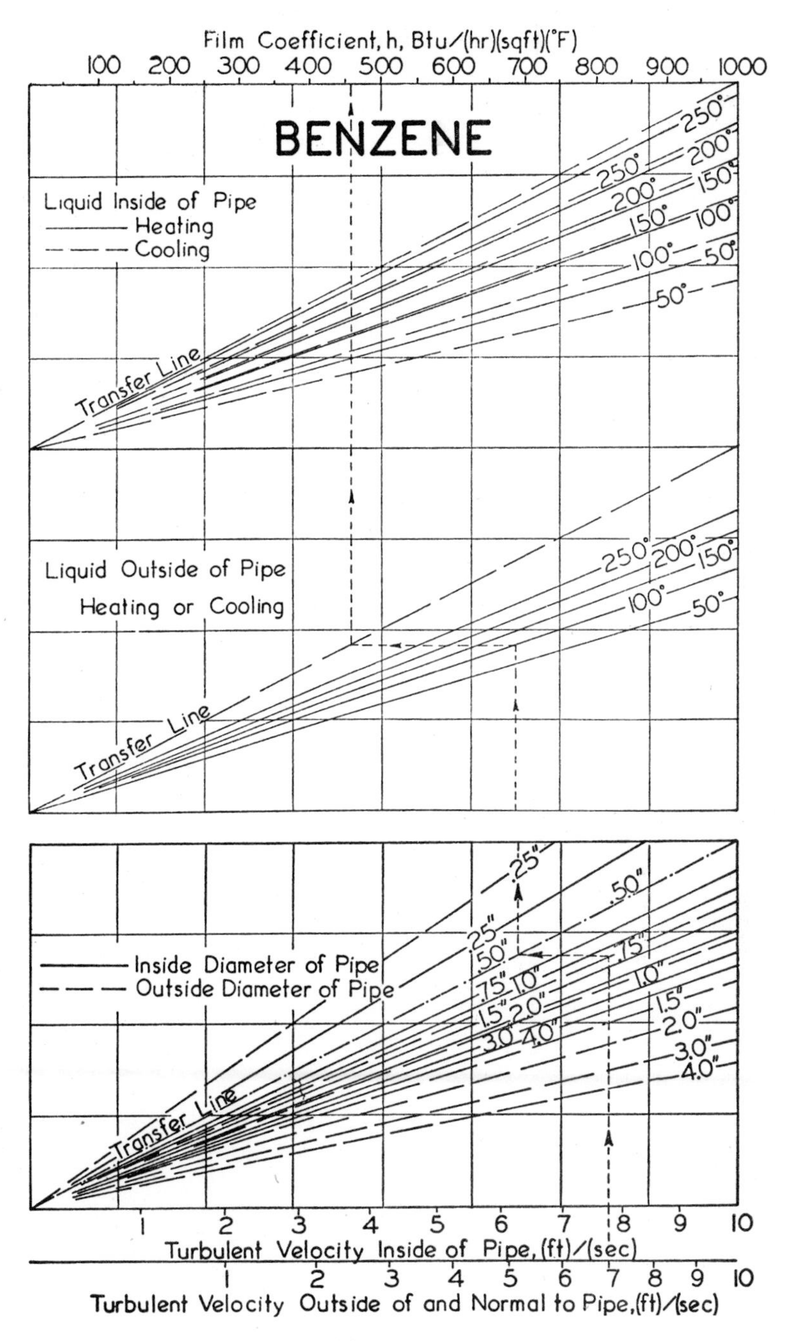
Film Coefficient, h, Btu/(hr)(sqft)(°F)
100 200 300 400 500 600 700 800 900 1000
BENZENE
Liquid Inside of Pipe
Heating
Cooling
250° 200° 150° 100° 50°
Transfer Line
Liquid Outside of Pipe
Heating or Cooling
250° 200° 150° 100° 50°
Transfer Line
Inside Diameter of Pipe
Outside Diameter of Pipe
.25" .50" .75" 1.0" 1.5" 2.0" 3.0" 4.0"
Transfer Line
1 2 3 4 5 6 7 8 9 10
Turbulent Velocity Inside of Pipe, (ft)/(sec)
1 2 3 4 5 6 7 8 9 10
Turbulent Velocity Outside of and Normal to Pipe, (ft)/(sec)

Figure 6.14

Brine, Calcium Chloride, 25% (Liquid)

Brine, Calcium Chloride, 25% (liquid) heating or cooling in turbulent flow within a tube or in turbulent flow outside and normal to a single tube.

Equations: Liquid heating in a tube: $Nu = 0.023(Re)^{0.8}(Pr)^{0.4}$
Liquid cooling in a tube: $Nu = 0.023(Re)^{0.8}(Pr)^{0.3}$
Liquid heating or cooling outside and normal to a single tube: $Nu = 0.385(Re)^{0.56}(Pr)^{0.3}$

Text References: Chapter VI; equations 6.5, 6.6, 6.9, 6.12, 6.13, and 6.14.

Extensions: Refer to section 6.5 for extensions to annular spaces, tube bundles, and flow through helical coils.

Special Conditions: For a liquid heating or cooling within a tube, do not use the graph unless the value of velocity (fps) times diameter (inches) exceeds 1.9 for 50 F or 0.2 for 250 F.

For a liquid flowing outside and normal to a single tube, do not use the graph for velocity less than 1 fps unless the Reynolds number exceeds 100.

Example: Brine, Calcium Chloride, 25% (liquid) is flowing within a 2 inch inside diameter tube at a velocity of 2 fps. The fluid is at a mean temperature of 0 F and is being cooled. Determine the inside film coefficient.*

Solution: Enter the bottom scale of the graph (Fig. 6.15) at an inside velocity of 2 fps and rise to intersect the solid radial line for a 2 inch inside diameter tube. From this intersection move left to the transfer line and then rise to the top section of the graph where radial lines are given for liquid heating and cooling *inside* a tube. In this section intersect the dashed radial for liquid cooling at 0 F. From this intersection move left to the transfer line and then rise to the top scale of the graph where read the value of the inside film coefficient as 170 Btu/(hr) (sq ft) (°F).

***Note:** To determine other heat transfer coefficients for Brine, Calcium Chloride, 25%, use Fig. 6.15 but refer to the examples on the following pages for the appropriate method: Outside film coefficient, page 182; outside film coefficient per lineal foot, page 170; inside film coefficient per lineal foot, use method similar to that for outside film coefficient per lineal foot; inside film coefficient for a helical coil, page 180; overall coefficient, page 176; overall coefficient per lineal foot, page 178.

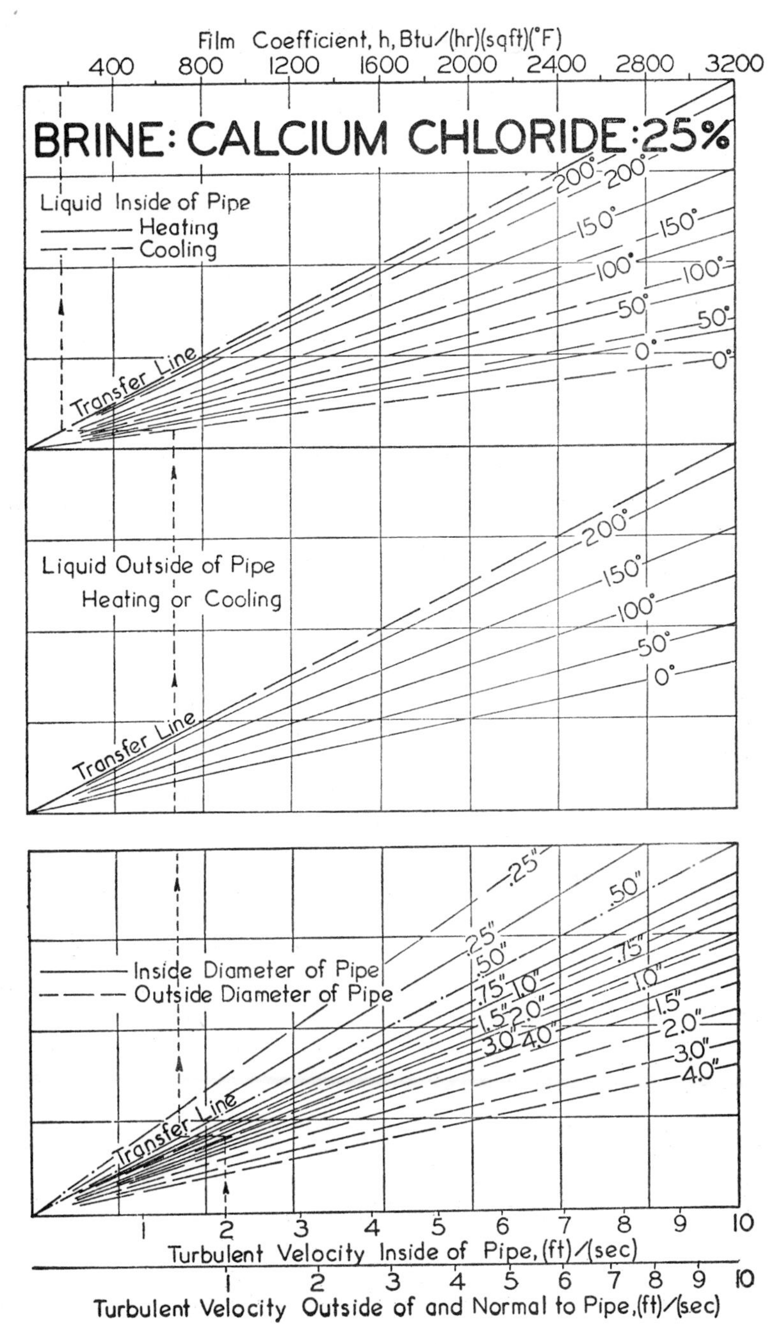

Film Coefficient, h, Btu/(hr)(sqft)(°F)
400
800
1200
1600
2000
2400
2800
3200
BRINE: CALCIUM CHLORIDE: 25%
Liquid Inside of Pipe
Heating
Cooling
200°
150°
100°
50°
0°
Transfer Line
Liquid Outside of Pipe
Heating or Cooling
Inside Diameter of Pipe
Outside Diameter of Pipe
.25"
.50"
.75"
1.0"
1.5"
2.0"
3.0"
4.0"
Turbulent Velocity Inside of Pipe, (ft)/(sec)
Turbulent Velocity Outside of and Normal to Pipe, (ft)/(sec)

Figure 6.15

Butyl Alcohol, N (Liquid)

Butyl Alcohol, N (liquid) heating or cooling, in turbulent flow within a tube or in turbulent flow outside and normal to a single tube.

Equations: Liquid heating in a tube: $Nu = 0.023(Re)^{0.8}(Pr)^{0.4}$
Liquid cooling in a tube: $Nu = 0.023(Re)^{0.8}(Pr)^{0.3}$
Liquid heating or cooling outside and normal to a single tube: $Nu = 0.385(Re)^{0.56}(Pr)^{0.3}$

Text References: Chapter VI; equations 6.5, 6.6, 6.9, 6.12, 6.13, and 6.14.

Extensions: Refer to section 6.5 for extensions to annular spaces, tube bundles, and flow through helical coils.

Special Conditions: For a liquid heating or cooling within a tube, do not use the graph unless the value of velocity (fps) times diameter (inches) exceeds 6.2 for 50 F or 0.6 for 250 F.

For a liquid flowing outside and normal to a single tube, do not use the graph for velocity less than 1 fps unless the Reynolds number exceeds 100.

Example: Butyl Alcohol, N (liquid) is cooling at a mean temperature of 200 F while flowing outside and normal to a 1″ O.D. Type M copper tube. The fluid velocity is 4 fps. Determine the outside film coefficient* in Btu per hour per °F per *lineal foot* of tube.

Solution: The dashed example line on the graph (Fig. 6.16) shows the method of evaluating the outside film coefficient, for the stated conditions, in terms of one square foot of outside surface of the tube. To convert this value, 360 Btu/(hr) (sq ft) (°F), to a lineal basis refer to Fig. 5.6 and, using a method similar to that shown by the dashed example line, enter the graph at h of 360 and come out at the top scale with a film coefficient of 100 Btu per hour per °F per lineal foot of tube.

***Note:** To determine other heat transfer coefficients for Butyl Alcohol, N, use Fig. 6.16 but refer to the examples on the following pages for the appropriate method: Outside film coefficient, page 182; inside film coefficient, page 184; inside film coefficient per lineal foot, use method similar to that for outside film coefficient per lineal foot; inside film coefficient for a helical coil, page 180; overall coefficient, page 176; overall coefficient per lineal foot, page 178.

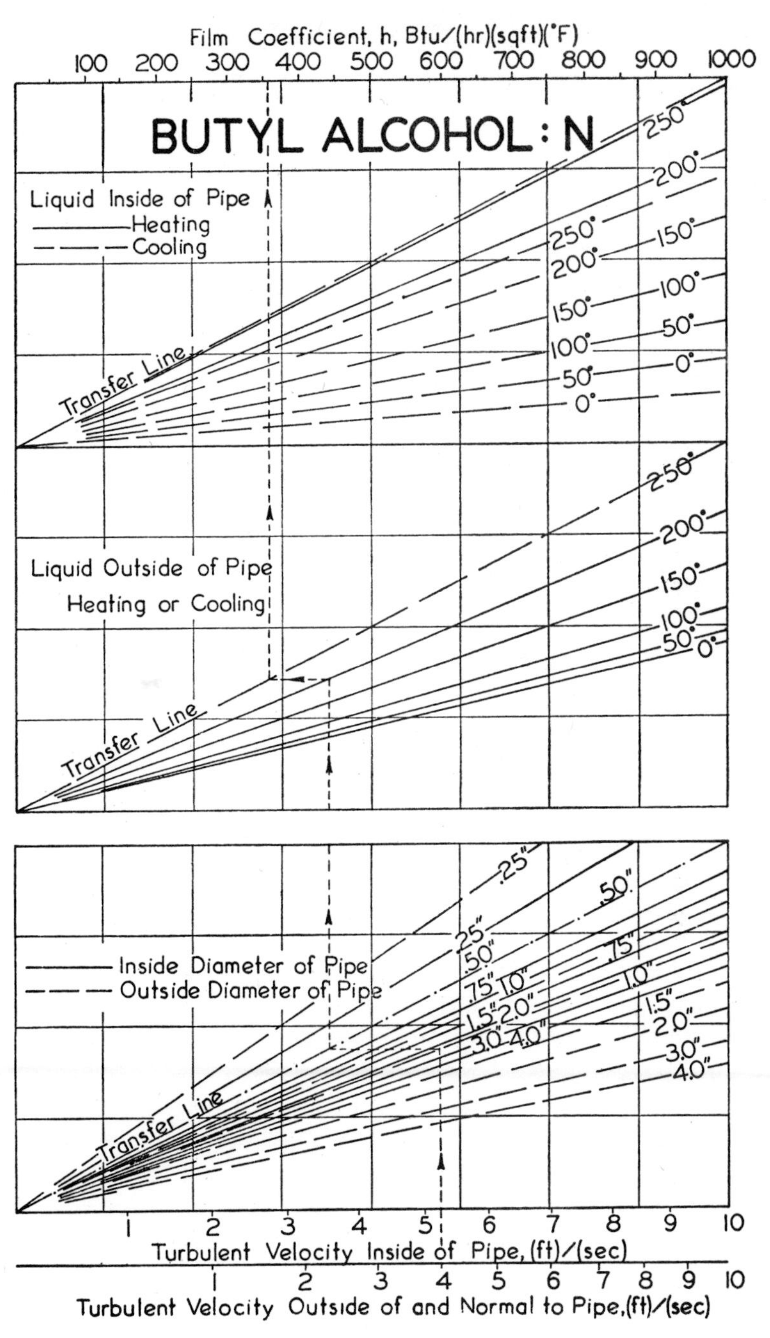

Film Coefficient, h, Btu/(hr)(sqft)(°F)
100 200 300 400 500 600 700 800 900 1000
BUTYL ALCOHOL: N
Liquid Inside of Pipe
Heating
Cooling
250°
200°
150°
100°
50°
0°
Transfer Line
Liquid Outside of Pipe
Heating or Cooling
Inside Diameter of Pipe
Outside Diameter of Pipe
.25"
.50"
.75"
1.0"
1.5"
2.0"
3.0"
4.0"
1 2 3 4 5 6 7 8 9 10
Turbulent Velocity Inside of Pipe, (ft)/(sec)
Turbulent Velocity Outside of and Normal to Pipe, (ft)/(sec)

Figure 6.16

Carbon Disulfide (Liquid)

Carbon Disulfide (liquid) heating or cooling in turbulent flow within a tube or in turbulent flow outside and normal to a single tube.

Equations: Liquid heating in a tube: $Nu = 0.023(Re)^{0.8}(Pr)^{0.4}$
Liquid cooling in a tube: $Nu = 0.023(Re)^{0.8}(Pr)^{0.3}$
Liquid heating or cooling outside and normal to a single tube: $Nu = 0.385(Re)^{0.56}(Pr)^{0.3}$

Text References: Chapter VI; equations 6.5, 6.6, 6.9, 6.12, 6.13, and 6.14.

Extensions: Refer to section 6.5 for extensions to annular spaces, tube bundles, and flow through helical coils.

Special Conditions: For a liquid heating or cooling within a tube, do not use the graph if the velocity is less than 1 fps.

For a liquid flowing outside and normal to a single tube, do not use the graph for velocity less than 1 fps unless the Reynolds number exceeds 100.

Example: Carbon Disulfide (liquid) is in turbulent flow, at 6 fps velocity, through a tube having an inside diameter of 0.25 inches. The fluid is cooling at a mean temperature of 200 F. The tube is wound in a helical coil having a diameter of 50 inches. Determine the inside film coefficient.*

Solution: The dashed example line on the graph (Fig. 6.17) shows the method of determining the base value of the inside film coefficient for the conditions of flow through a straight tube; this value is read at the top scale as 705. Now refer to Fig. 6.6, enter the bottom scale at 705, and rise to the radial line for a tube-to-coil ratio of $0.25/50 = 0.005$. From this intersection move left to the transfer line, then rise to read the corrected film coefficient for flow within the coil as 715 Btu / (hr) (sq ft) (°F).

***Note:** To determine other heat transfer coefficients for Carbon Disulfide, use Fig. 6.17 but refer to the examples on the following pages for the appropriate method: Outside film coefficient, page 182; inside film coefficient, page 184; outside film coefficient per lineal foot, page 186; inside film coefficient per lineal foot, use method similar to that for outside film coefficient per lineal foot; overall coefficient, page 176; overall coefficient per lineal foot, page 178.

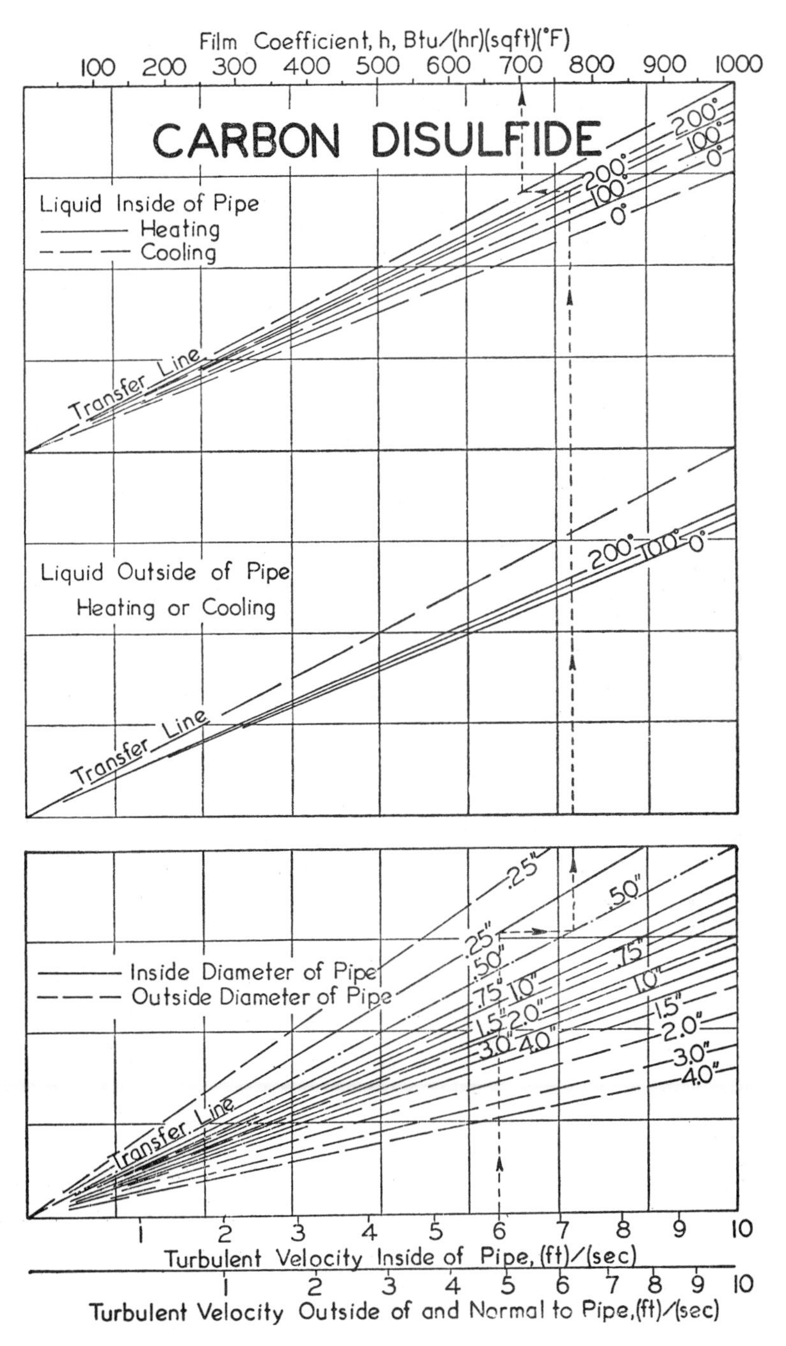

Film Coefficient, h, Btu/(hr)(sqft)(°F)
100 200 300 400 500 600 700 800 900 1000
CARBON DISULFIDE
Liquid Inside of Pipe
Heating
Cooling
200° 100° 0°
200° 100° 0°
Transfer Line
Liquid Outside of Pipe
Heating or Cooling
200° 100° 0°
Transfer Line
Inside Diameter of Pipe
Outside Diameter of Pipe
.25" .50" .75" 1.0" 1.5" 2.0" 3.0" 4.0"
.25" .50" .75" 1.0" 1.5" 2.0" 3.0" 4.0"
Transfer Line
1 2 3 4 5 6 7 8 9 10
Turbulent Velocity Inside of Pipe, (ft)/(sec)
1 2 3 4 5 6 7 8 9 10
Turbulent Velocity Outside of and Normal to Pipe, (ft)/(sec)

Figure 6.17

Carbon Tetrachloride (Liquid)

Carbon Tetrachloride (liquid) heating or cooling in turbulent flow within a tube or in turbulent flow outside and normal to a single tube.

Equations: Liquid heating in a tube: $Nu = 0.023 (Re)^{0.8} (Pr)^{0.4}$
Liquid cooling in a tube: $Nu = 0.023 (Re)^{0.8} (Pr)^{0.3}$
Liquid heating or cooling outside and normal to a single tube: $Nu = 0.385 (Re)^{0.56} (Pr)^{0.3}$

Text References: Chapter VI; equations 6.5, 6.6, 6.9, 6.12, 6.13, and 6.14.

Extensions: Refer to section 6.5 for extensions to annular spaces, tube bundles, and flow through helical coils.

Special Conditions: For a liquid heating or cooling within a tube, do not use the graph if the velocity is less than 1 fps.

For a liquid flowing outside and normal to a single tube, do not use the graph for velocity less than 1 fps unless the Reynolds number exceeds 100.

Example: Carbon Tetrachloride (liquid) is cooling at a mean temperature of 50 F while flowing at 7 fps outside and normal to a bundle of staggered 3/4 inch outside diameter tubes. Determine the outside film coefficient.* Estimate the outside coefficient for a similar, but baffled, tube bundle.

Solution: The base value of the outside film coefficient (for flow normal to a *single* tube) is determined as 350 by following the dashed example line, Fig. 6.18. The corrected value for flow normal to a staggered bundle is 30% greater than the base value (refer to part 6 of section 6.5) hence is 1.3(350) = 455 Btu/(hr) (sq ft) (°F). For a baffled tube bundle (refer to part 6 of section 6.5) the film coefficient would be taken at the base value of 350.

***Note:** To determine other heat transfer coefficients for Carbon Tetrachloride, use Fig. 6.18 but refer to the examples on the following pages for the appropriate method. Inside film coefficient, page 184; outside film coefficient per lineal foot, page 186; inside film coefficient per lineal foot, use method similar to that for outside film coefficient per lineal foot; inside film coefficient for a helical coil, page 188; overall coefficient, page 176; overall coefficient per lineal foot, page 178.

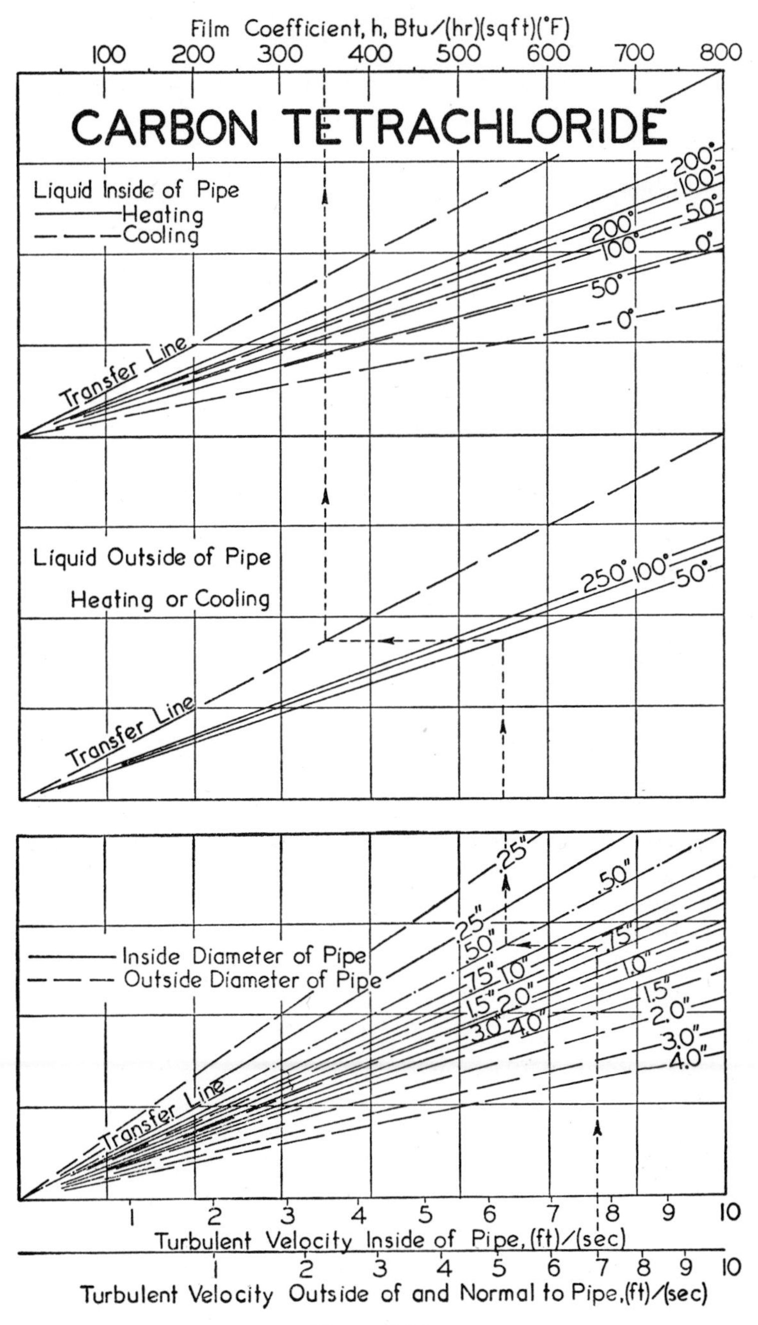
Film Coefficient, h, Btu/(hr)(sqft)(°F)
100 200 300 400 500 600 700 800
CARBON TETRACHLORIDE
Liquid Inside of Pipe
Heating
Cooling
200° 100° 50° 0°
200° 100° 50° 0°
Transfer Line
Liquid Outside of Pipe
Heating or Cooling
250° 100° 50°
Transfer Line
Inside Diameter of Pipe
Outside Diameter of Pipe
.25" .50" .75" 1.0" 1.5" 2.0" 3.0" 4.0"
.25" .50" .75" 1.0" 1.5" 2.0" 3.0" 4.0"
Transfer Line
1 2 3 4 5 6 7 8 9 10
Turbulent Velocity Inside of Pipe, (ft)/(sec)
1 2 3 4 5 6 7 8 9 10
Turbulent Velocity Outside of and Normal to Pipe, (ft)/(sec)

Figure 6.18

Chlorobenzene (Liquid)

Chlorobenzene (liquid) heating or cooling in turbulent flow within a tube or in turbulent flow outside and normal to a single tube.

Equations: Liquid heating in a tube: $Nu = 0.023(Re)^{0.8}(Pr)^{0.4}$
Liquid cooling in a tube: $Nu = 0.023(Re)^{0.8}(Pr)^{0.3}$
Liquid heating or cooling outside and normal to a single tube: $Nu = 0.385(Re)^{0.56}(Pr)^{0.3}$

Text References: Chapter VI; equations 6.5, 6.6, 6.9, 6.12, 6.13, and 6.14.

Extensions: Refer to section 6.5 for extensions to annular spaces, tube bundles, and flow through helical coils.

Special Conditions: For a liquid heating or cooling within a tube, do not use the graph if the velocity is less than 1 fps.

For a liquid flowing outside and normal to a single tube, do not use the graph for velocity less than 1 fps unless the Reynolds number exceeds 100.

Example: Chlorobenzene (liquid) is flowing inside a tube of 2″ I.D. at a velocity of 2 fps. The fluid is heating at a mean temperature of 50 F. If the outside film coefficient is 100 determine the overall coefficient* of heat transfer assuming that the tube is so thin-walled that its thermal resistance is negligible and the difference between inside and outside surface areas can be neglected.

Solution: For the stated conditions the base value of the inside film coefficient is determinable (dashed example line, Fig. 6.19) as 115 Btu/(hr) (sq ft) (°F). Now go to Fig. 5.7 and (by a method similar to that shown by the dashed line) for inside and outside film coefficients of 115 and 100, respectively, read the overall coefficient of heat transfer as 53 Btu/(hr) (sq ft) (°F).

***Note:** To determine other heat transfer coefficients for Chlorobenzene, use Fig. 6.19 but refer to the examples on the following pages for the appropriate method: Outside film coefficient, page 190; inside film coefficient, page 184; outside film coefficient per lineal foot, page 186; inside film coefficient per lineal foot, use method similar to that for outside film coefficient per lineal foot; inside film coefficient for a helical coil, page 188; overall coefficient per lineal foot, page 178.

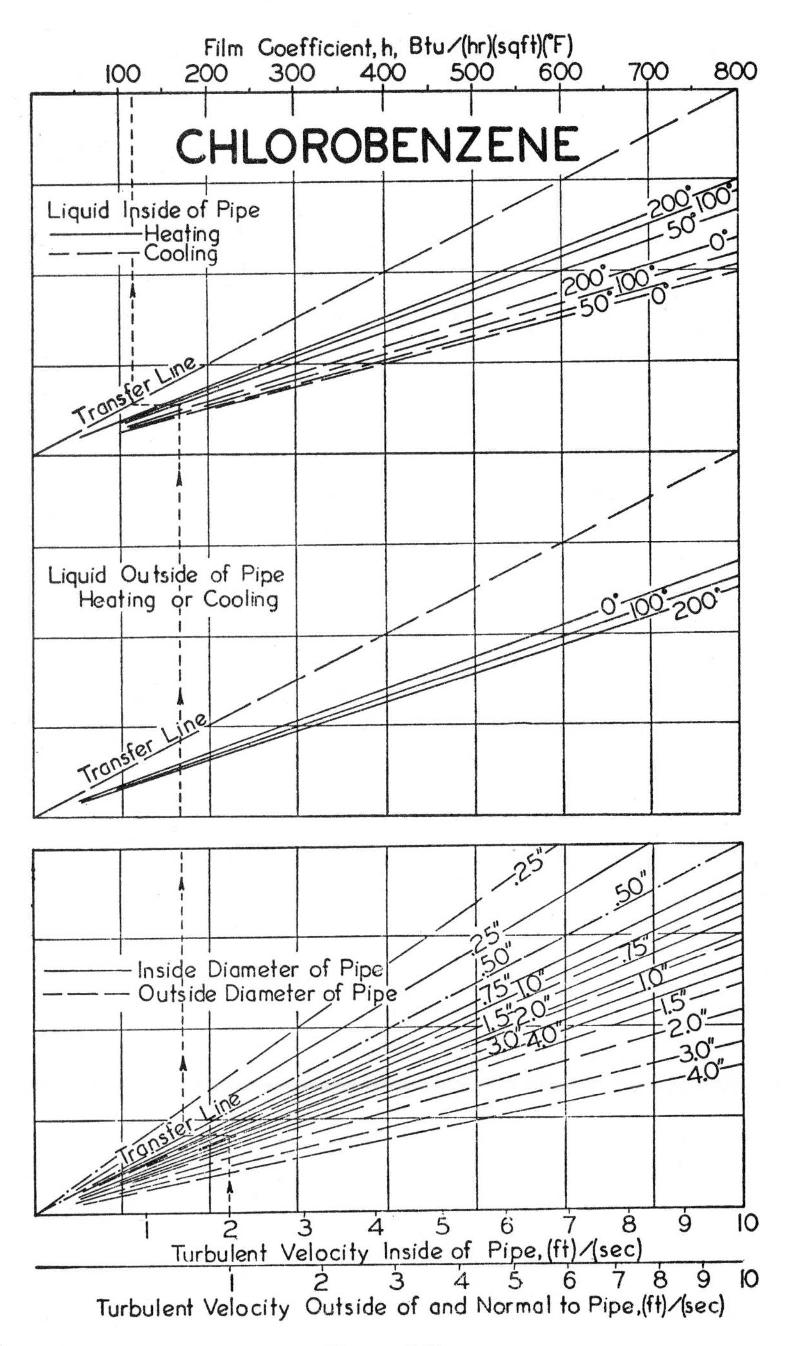
Film Coefficient, h, Btu/(hr)(sqft)(°F)
100 200 300 400 500 600 700 800
CHLOROBENZENE
Liquid Inside of Pipe
Heating
Cooling
200° 100° 50° 0°
200° 100° 50° 0°
Transfer Line
Liquid Outside of Pipe
Heating or Cooling
0° 100° 200°
Transfer Line
Inside Diameter of Pipe
Outside Diameter of Pipe
.25" .50" .75" 1.0" 1.5" 2.0" 3.0" 4.0"
.25" .50" .75" 1.0" 1.5" 2.0" 3.0" 4.0"
Transfer Line
1 2 3 4 5 6 7 8 9 10
Turbulent Velocity Inside of Pipe, (ft)/(sec)
1 2 3 4 5 6 7 8 9 10
Turbulent Velocity Outside of and Normal to Pipe, (ft)/(sec)

Figure 6.19

Chloroform (Liquid)

Chloroform (liquid) heating or cooling in turbulent flow within a tube or in turbulent flow outside and normal to a single tube.

Equations: Liquid heating in a tube: $Nu = 0.023(Re)^{0.8}(Pr)^{0.4}$
Liquid cooling in a tube: $Nu = 0.023(Re)^{0.8}(Pr)^{0.3}$
Liquid heating or cooling outside and normal to a single tube: $Nu = 0.385(Re)^{0.56}(Pr)^{0.3}$

Text References: Chapter VI; equations 6.5, 6.6, 6.9, 6.12, 6.13, and 6.14.

Extensions: Refer to section 6.5 for extensions to annular spaces, tube bundles, and flow through helical coils.

Special Conditions: For a liquid heating or cooling within a tube, do not use the graph if the velocity is less than 1 fps.

For a liquid flowing outside and normal to a single tube, do not use the graph for velocity less than 1 fps unless the Reynolds number exceeds 100.

Example: Chloroform (liquid) is flowing at 4 fps outside and normal to a phosphorized copper tube (Type L) having an outside diameter of 1″ and wall thickness of 0.065″. The fluid is heating at 0 F. The inside film coefficient is known to be 800 Btu/(hr) (°F) (sq ft of inside surface). Determine the overall coefficient* of heat transfer per lineal foot of tube.

Solution: The dashed example line on the graph (Fig. 6.20) determines the outside coefficient as 280. From Fig. 5.5, the inside and outside coefficients, 800 and 280, can be converted to values of 200 and 75, respectively, based on one lineal foot of tube. From Fig. 2.4 the thermal resistance of the tube is 0.00003 (based on outside area), giving a conductance of 33,000 which (Fig. 5.5) becomes 9,000 per lineal foot. The overall coefficient, equation 5.2, is then $U = 1/[1/200 + 1/9{,}000 + 1/75] = 54$ Btu/(hr) (°F) (lineal foot of tube).

***Note:** To determine other heat transfer coefficients for Chloroform, use Fig. 6.20 but refer to the examples on the following pages for the appropriate method: Outside film coefficient, page 190; inside film coefficient, page 184; outside film coefficient per lineal foot, page 186; inside film coefficient per lineal foot, use method similar to that for outside film coefficient per lineal foot; inside film coefficient for a helical coil, page 188; overall coefficient, page 192.

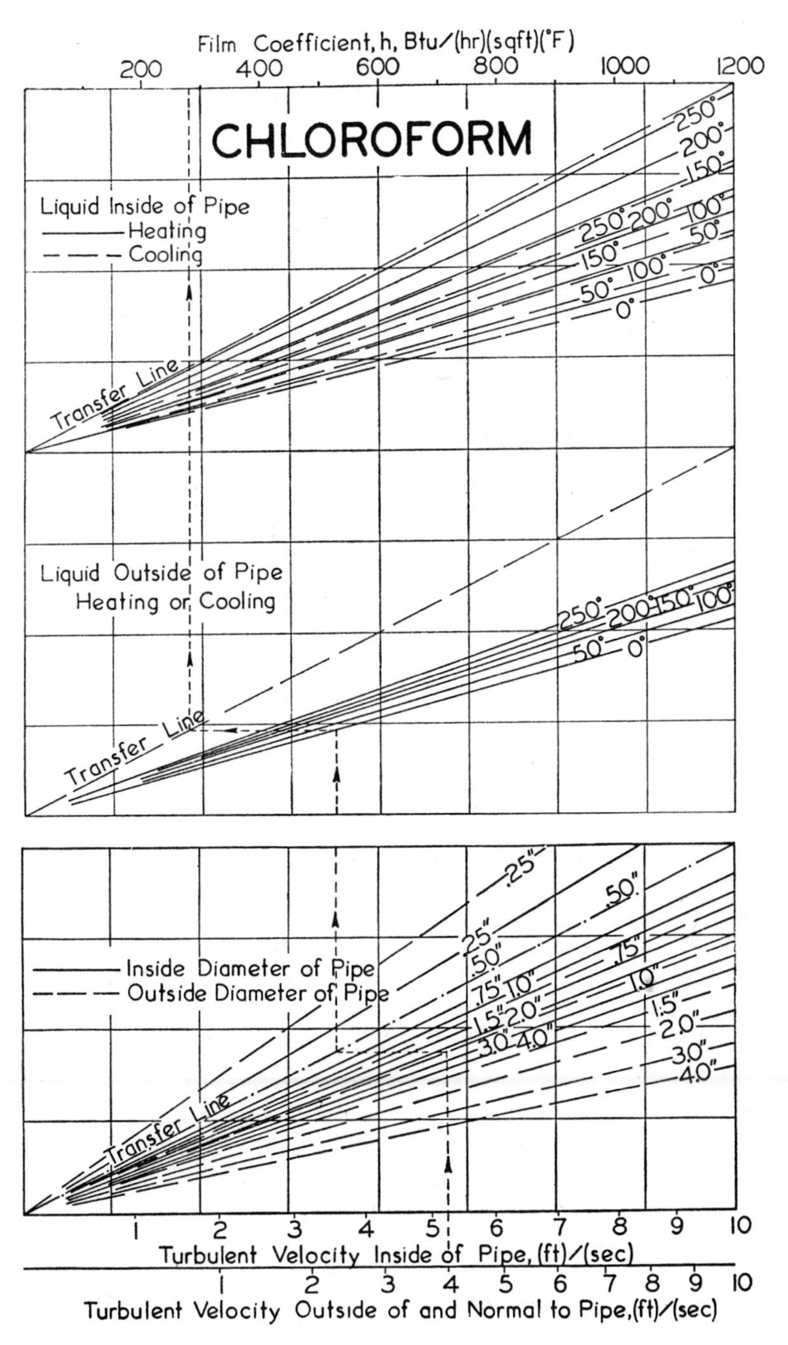
Film Coefficient, h, Btu/(hr)(sqft)(°F)
200 400 600 800 1000 1200
CHLOROFORM
Liquid Inside of Pipe
Heating
Cooling
250° 200° 150° 100° 50° 0°
250° 200° 150° 100° 50° 0°
Transfer Line
Liquid Outside of Pipe
Heating or Cooling
250° 200° 150° 100° 50° 0°
Transfer Line
Inside Diameter of Pipe
Outside Diameter of Pipe
.25" .50" .75" 1.0" 1.5" 2.0" 3.0" 4.0"
.25" .50" .75" 1.0" 1.5" 2.0" 3.0" 4.0"
Transfer Line
1 2 3 4 5 6 7 8 9 10
Turbulent Velocity Inside of Pipe, (ft)/(sec)
1 2 3 4 5 6 7 8 9 10
Turbulent Velocity Outside of and Normal to Pipe, (ft)/(sec)

Figure 6.20

Ethyl Acetate (Liquid)

Ethyl Acetate (liquid) heating or cooling in turbulent flow within a tube or in turbulent flow outside and normal to a single tube.

Equations: Liquid heating in a tube: $Nu = 0.023(Re)^{0.8}(Pr)^{0.4}$
Liquid cooling in a tube: $Nu = 0.023(Re)^{0.8}(Pr)^{0.3}$
Liquid heating or cooling outside and normal to a single tube: $Nu = 0.385(Re)^{0.56}(Pr)^{0.3}$

Text References: Chapter VI; equations 6.5, 6.6, 6.9, 6.12, 6.13, and 6.14.

Extensions: Refer to section 6.5 for extensions to annular spaces, tube bundles, and flow through helical coils.

Special Conditions: For a liquid heating or cooling within a tube, do not use the graph if the velocity is less than 1 fps.

For a liquid flowing outside and normal to a single tube, do not use the graph for velocity less than 1 fps unless the Reynolds number exceeds 100.

Example: Ethyl Acetate (liquid) is in turbulent flow, at 6 fps velocity, through a tube having an inside diameter of 0.25 inches. The fluid is cooling at a mean temperature of 77 F. The tube is wound in a helical coil having a diameter of 50 inches. Determine the inside film coefficient.*

Solution: The dashed example line on the graph (Fig. 6.21) shows the method of determining the base value of the inside film coefficient for the conditions of flow through a straight tube; this value is read at the top scale as 465. Now refer to Fig. 6.6, enter the bottom scale at 465, and rise to the radial line for a tube-to-coil ratio of $0.25/50 = 0.005$. From this intersection move left to the transfer line, then rise to read the corrected film coefficient for flow within the coil as 470 Btu/(hr) (sq ft) (°F).

***Note:** To determine other heat transfer coefficients for Ethyl Acetate, use Fig. 6.21 but refer to the examples on the following pages for the appropriate method: Outside film coefficient, page 190; inside film coefficient, page 184; outside film coefficient per lineal foot, page 186; inside film coefficient per lineal foot, use method similar to that for outside film coefficient per lineal foot; overall coefficient, page 192; overall coefficient per lineal foot, page 194.

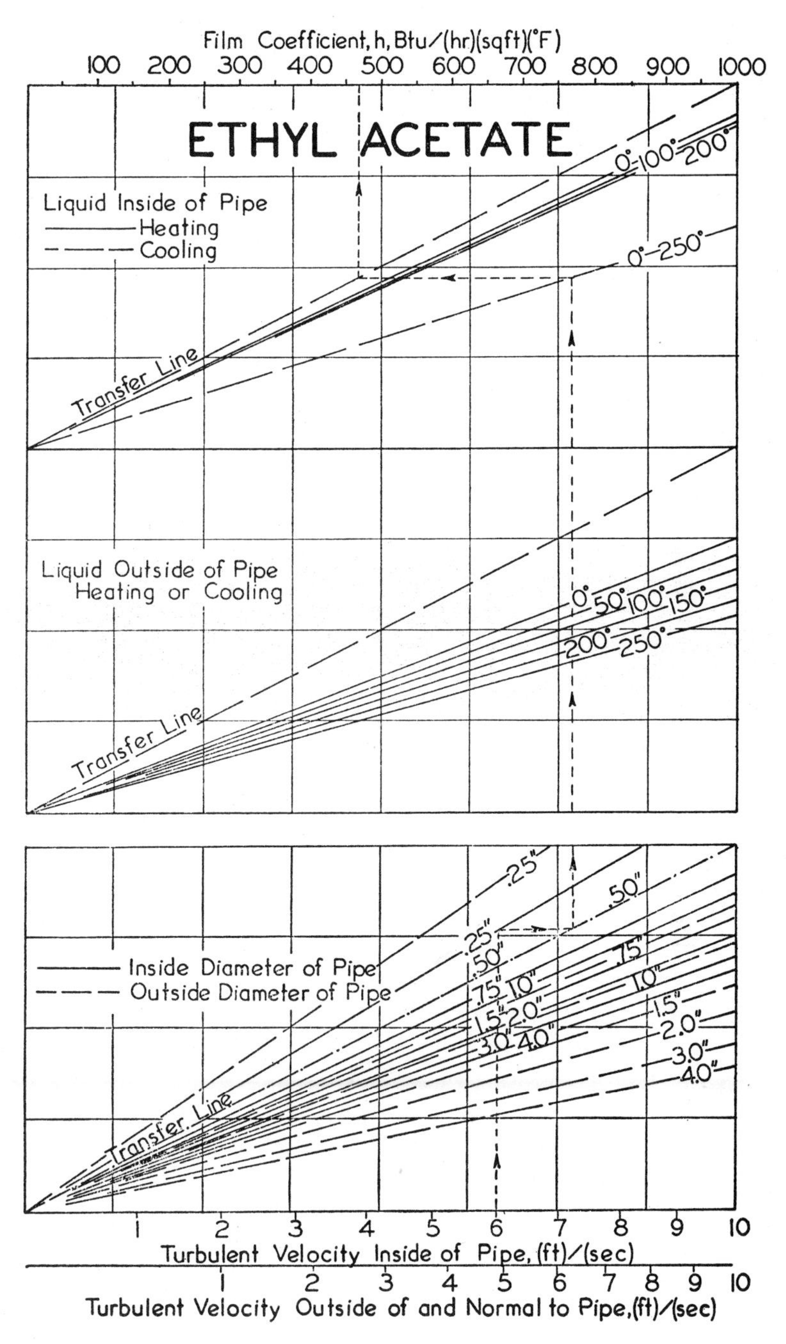
Film Coefficient, h, Btu/(hr)(sqft)(°F)
100 200 300 400 500 600 700 800 900 1000
ETHYL ACETATE
Liquid Inside of Pipe
Heating
Cooling
0°-100°-200°
0°-250°
Transfer Line
Liquid Outside of Pipe
Heating or Cooling
0° 50° 100° 150°
200° 250°
Transfer Line
Inside Diameter of Pipe
Outside Diameter of Pipe
.25" .50" .75" 1.0" 1.5" 2.0" 3.0" 4.0"
.25" .50" .75" 1.0" 1.5" 2.0" 3.0" 4.0"
Transfer Line
1 2 3 4 5 6 7 8 9 10
Turbulent Velocity Inside of Pipe, (ft)/(sec)
1 2 3 4 5 6 7 8 9 10
Turbulent Velocity Outside of and Normal to Pipe, (ft)/(sec)

Figure 6.21

Ethyl Alcohol, 100% (Liquid)

Ethyl Alcohol, 100% (liquid) heating or cooling in turbulent flow within a tube or in turbulent flow outside and normal to a single tube.

Equations: Liquid heating in a tube: $Nu = 0.023(Re)^{0.8}(Pr)^{0.4}$
Liquid cooling in a tube: $Nu = 0.023(Re)^{0.8}(Pr)^{0.3}$
Liquid heating or cooling outside and normal to a single tube: $Nu = 0.385(Re)^{0.56}(Pr)^{0.3}$

Text References: Chapter VI; equations 6.5, 6.6, 6.9, 6.12, 6.13, and 6.14.

Extensions: Refer to section 6.5 for extensions to annular spaces, tube bundles, and flow through helical coils.

Special Conditions: For a liquid heating or cooling within a tube, do not use the graph unless the value of velocity (fps) times diameter (inches) exceeds 2.4 for 50 F or 0.5 for 250 F.

For a liquid flowing outside and normal to a single tube, do not use the graph for velocity less than 1 fps unless the Reynolds number exceeds 100.

Example: Ethyl Alcohol, 100% (liquid) is heating at a mean temperature of 50 F while flowing at 7 fps outside and normal to a bundle of staggered 3/4 inch outside diameter tubes. Determine the outside film coefficient.* Estimate the outside coefficient for a similar, but baffled, tube bundle.

Solution: The base value of the outside film coefficient (for flow normal to a *single* tube) is determined as 435 by following the dashed example line (Fig. 6.22). The corrected value for flow normal to a staggered bundle is 30% greater than the base value (refer to part 6 of section 6.5) hence is 1.3(435) = 566 Btu/(hr) (sq ft) (°F). For a baffled tube bundle (refer to part 6 of section 6.5) the film coefficient would be taken at the base value of 435.

***Note:** To determine other heat transfer coefficients for Ethyl Alcohol, 100%, use Fig. 6.22 but refer to the examples on the following pages for the appropriate method: Inside film coefficient, page 184; outside film coefficient per lineal foot, page 186; inside film coefficient per lineal foot, use method similar to that for outside film coefficient per lineal foot; inside film coefficient for a helical coil, page 196; overall coefficient, page 192; overall coefficient per lineal foot, page 194.

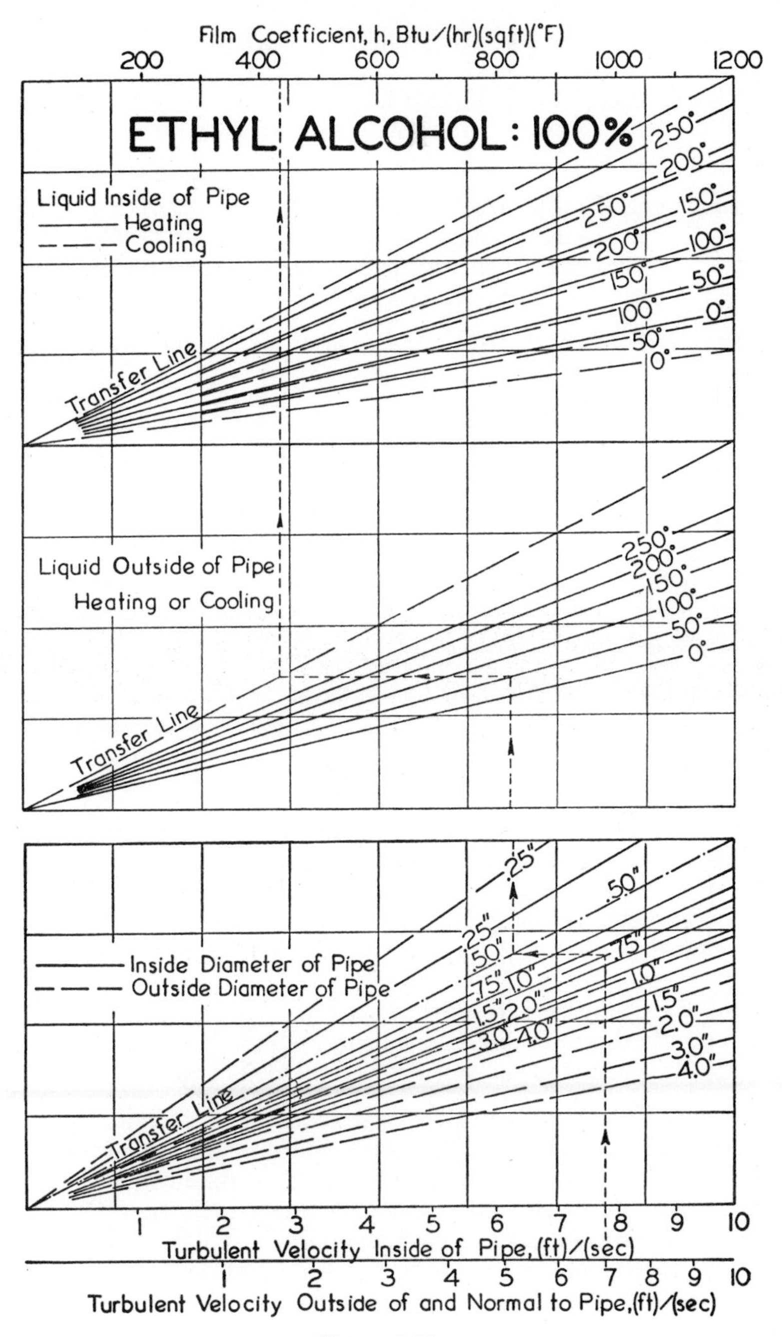

Film Coefficient, h, Btu/(hr)(sqft)(°F)
200
400
600
800
1000
1200
ETHYL ALCOHOL: 100%
Liquid Inside of Pipe
Heating
Cooling
250°
200°
150°
100°
50°
0°
Transfer Line
Liquid Outside of Pipe
Heating or Cooling
Inside Diameter of Pipe
Outside Diameter of Pipe
.25"
.50"
.75"
1.0"
1.5"
2.0"
3.0"
4.0"
Turbulent Velocity Inside of Pipe, (ft)/(sec)
Turbulent Velocity Outside of and Normal to Pipe, (ft)/(sec)

Figure 6.22

Ethyl Alcohol, 40% (Liquid)

Ethyl Alcohol, 40% (liquid) heating or cooling in turbulent flow within a tube or in turbulent flow outside and normal to a single tube.

Equations: Liquid heating in a tube: $Nu = 0.023(Re)^{0.8}(Pr)^{0.4}$
Liquid cooling in a tube: $Nu = 0.023(Re)^{0.8}(Pr)^{0.3}$
Liquid heating or cooling outside and normal to a single tube: $Nu = 0.385(Re)^{0.56}(Pr)^{0.3}$

Text References: Chapter VI; equations 6.5, 6.6, 6.9, 6.12, 6.13, and 6.14.

Extensions: Refer to section 6.5 for extensions to annular spaces, tube bundles, and flow through helical coils.

Special Conditions: For a liquid heating or cooling within a tube, do not use the graph unless the value of velocity (fps) times diameter (inches) exceeds 5.8 for 50 F or 0.7 for 250 F.

For a liquid flowing outside and normal to a single tube, do not use the graph for velocity less than 1 fps unless the Reynolds number exceeds 100.

Example: Ethyl Alcohol, 40% (liquid) is flowing within a 2 inch inside diameter tube at a velocity of 2 fps. The fluid is at a mean temperature of 250 F and is being cooled. Determine the inside film coefficient.*

Solution: Enter the bottom scale of the graph (Fig. 6.23) at inside velocity of 2 fps and rise to intersect the solid radial line for a 2 inch inside diameter tube. From this intersection move left to the transfer line and then rise to the top section of the graph where radial lines are given for liquid heating and cooling *inside* a tube. In this section intersect the dashed radial for liquid cooling at 250 F. From this intersection move left to the transfer line and then rise to the top scale of the graph where read the value of the inside film coefficient as 440 Btu/(hr) (sq ft) (°F).

***Note:** To determine other heat transfer coefficients for Ethyl Alcohol, 40%, use Fig. 6.23 but refer to the examples on the following pages for the appropriate method: Outside film coefficient, page 198; outside film coefficient per lineal foot, page 186; inside film coefficient per lineal foot, use method similar to that for outside film coefficient per lineal foot; inside film coefficient for a helical coil, page 196; overall coefficient, page 192; overall coefficient per lineal foot, page 194.

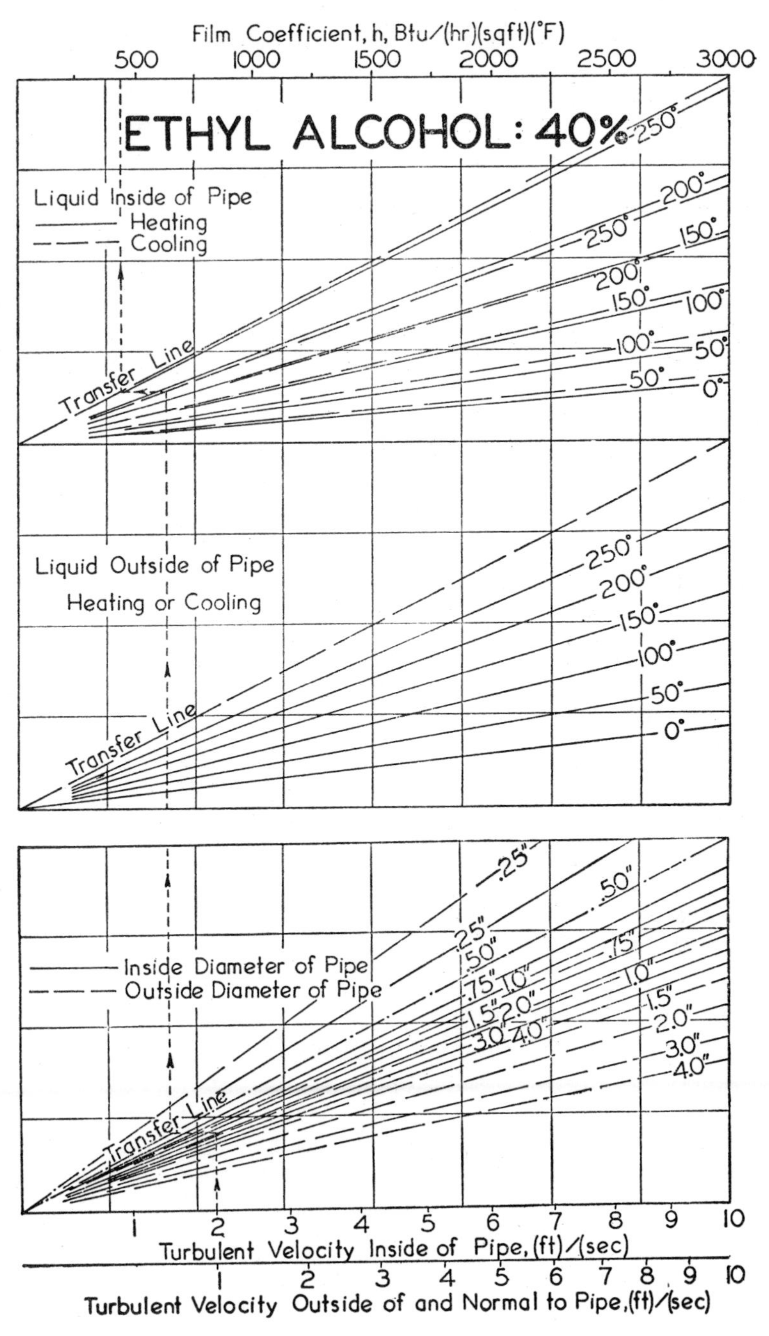

Film Coefficient, h, Btu/(hr)(sqft)(°F)
500 1000 1500 2000 2500 3000
ETHYL ALCOHOL: 40%
Liquid Inside of Pipe
Heating
Cooling
250°
200°
250°
150°
200°
150°
100°
100°
50°
50°
0°
Transfer Line
Liquid Outside of Pipe
Heating or Cooling
250°
200°
150°
100°
50°
0°
Transfer Line
Inside Diameter of Pipe
Outside Diameter of Pipe
.25"
.50"
.75"
1.0"
1.5"
2.0"
3.0"
4.0"
Transfer Line
1 2 3 4 5 6 7 8 9 10
Turbulent Velocity Inside of Pipe, (ft)/(sec)
1 2 3 4 5 6 7 8 9 10
Turbulent Velocity Outside of and Normal to Pipe, (ft)/(sec)

Figure 6.23

Ethyl Bromide (Liquid)

Ethyl Bromide (liquid) heating or cooling in turbulent flow within a tube or in turbulent flow outside and normal to a single tube.

Equations: Liquid heating in a tube: $Nu = 0.023(Re)^{0.8}(Pr)^{0.4}$
Liquid cooling in a tube: $Nu = 0.023(Re)^{0.8}(Pr)^{0.3}$
Liquid heating or cooling outside and normal to a single tube: $Nu = 0.385(Re)^{0.56}(Pr)^{0.3}$

Text References: Chapter VI; equations 6.5, 6.6, 6.9, 6.12, 6.13, and 6.14.

Extensions: Refer to section 6.5 for extensions to annular spaces, tube bundles, and flow through helical coils.

Special Conditions: For a liquid heating or cooling within a tube, do not use the graph if the velocity is less than 1 fps.

For a liquid flowing outside and normal to a single tube, do not use the graph for velocity less than 1 fps unless the Reynolds number exceeds 100.

Example: Ethyl Bromide (liquid) is heating at a mean temperature of 0 F while flowing outside and normal to a 1″ O.D. Type M copper tube. The fluid velocity is 4 fps. Determine the outside film coefficient* in Btu per hour per °F per *lineal foot* of tube.

Solution: The dashed example line on the graph (Fig. 6.24) shows the method of evaluating the outside film coefficient, for the stated conditions, in terms of one square foot of outside surface of the tube. To convert this value, 280 Btu/(hr) (sq ft) (°F), to a lineal basis refer to Fig. 5.6 and, using a method similar to that shown by the dashed example line, enter the graph at h of 280 and come out at the top scale with a film coefficient of 75 Btu per hour per °F per lineal foot of tube.

***Note:** To determine other heat transfer coefficients for Ethyl Bromide, use Fig. 6.24 but refer to the examples on the following pages for the appropriate method: Outside film coefficient, page 198; inside film coefficient, page 200; inside film coefficient per lineal foot, use method similar to that for outside film coefficient per lineal foot; inside film coefficient for a helical coil, page 196; overall coefficient, page 192; overall coefficient per lineal foot, page 194.

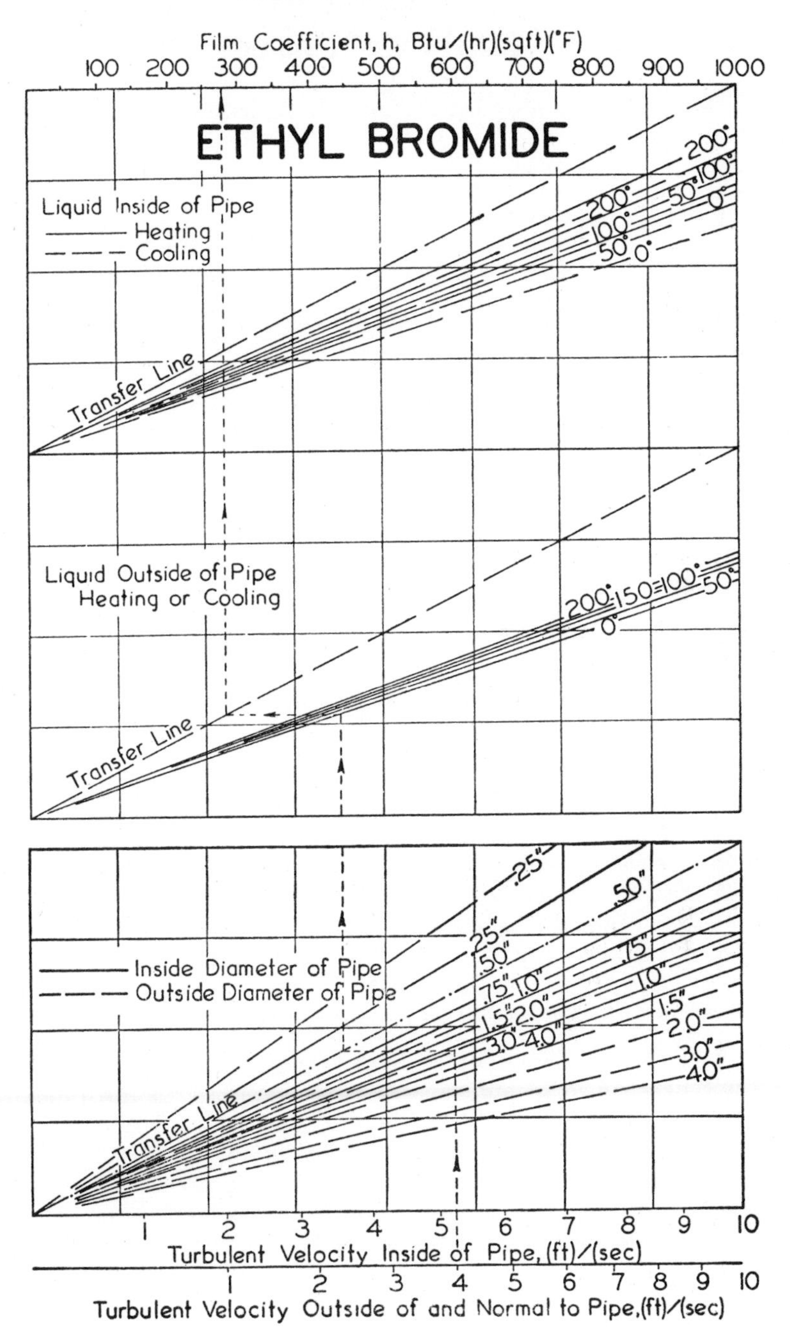

Film Coefficient, h, Btu/(hr)(sqft)(°F)
100 200 300 400 500 600 700 800 900 1000
ETHYL BROMIDE
Liquid Inside of Pipe
Heating
Cooling
200° 100° 50° 0°
200° 100° 50° 0°
Transfer Line
Liquid Outside of Pipe
Heating or Cooling
200° 150 100° 50° 0°
Transfer Line
Inside Diameter of Pipe
Outside Diameter of Pipe
.25" .50" .75" 1.0" 1.5" 2.0" 3.0" 4.0"
.25" .50" .75" 1.0" 1.5" 2.0" 3.0" 4.0"
Transfer Line
1 2 3 4 5 6 7 8 9 10
Turbulent Velocity Inside of Pipe, (ft)/(sec)
1 2 3 4 5 6 7 8 9 10
Turbulent Velocity Outside of and Normal to Pipe, (ft)/(sec)

Figure 6.24

Ethyl Ether (Liquid)

Ethyl Ether (liquid) heating or cooling in turbulent flow within a tube or in turbulent flow outside and normal to a single tube.

Equations: Liquid heating in a tube: $Nu = 0.023(Re)^{0.8}(Pr)^{0.4}$
Liquid cooling in a tube: $Nu = 0.023(Re)^{0.8}(Pr)^{0.3}$
Liquid heating or cooling outside and normal to a single tube: $Nu = 0.385(Re)^{0.56}(Pr)^{0.3}$

Text References: Chapter VI; equations 6.5, 6.6, 6.9, 6.12, 6.13, and 6.14.

Extensions: Refer to section 6.5 for extensions to annular spaces, tube bundles, and flow through helical coils.

Special Conditions: For a liquid heating or cooling within a tube, do not use the graph if the velocity is less than 1 fps.

For a liquid flowing outside and normal to a single tube, do not use the graph for velocity less than 1 fps unless the Reynolds number exceeds 100.

Example: Ethyl Ether (liquid) is in turbulent flow, at 6 fps velocity, through a tube having an inside diameter of 0.25 inches. The fluid is heating at a mean temperature of 250 F. The tube is wound in a helical coil having a diameter of 50 inches. Determine the inside film coefficient.

Solution: The dashed example line on the graph (Fig. 6.25) shows the method of determining the base value of the inside film coefficient for the conditions of flow through a straight tube; this value is read at the top scale as 825. Now refer to Fig. 6.6, enter the bottom scale at 825, and rise to the radial line for a tube-to-coil ratio of $0.25/50 = 0.005$. From this intersection move left to the transfer line, then rise to read the corrected film coefficient for flow within the coil as 840 Btu/(hr) (sq ft) (°F).

***Note:** To determine other heat transfer coefficients for Ethyl Ether, use Fig. 6.25 but refer to the examples on the following pages for the appropriate method: Outside film coefficient, page 198; inside film coefficient, page 200; outside film coefficient per lineal foot, page 202; inside film coefficient per lineal foot, use method similar to that for outside film coefficient per lineal foot; overall coefficient, page 192; overall coefficient per lineal foot, page 194.

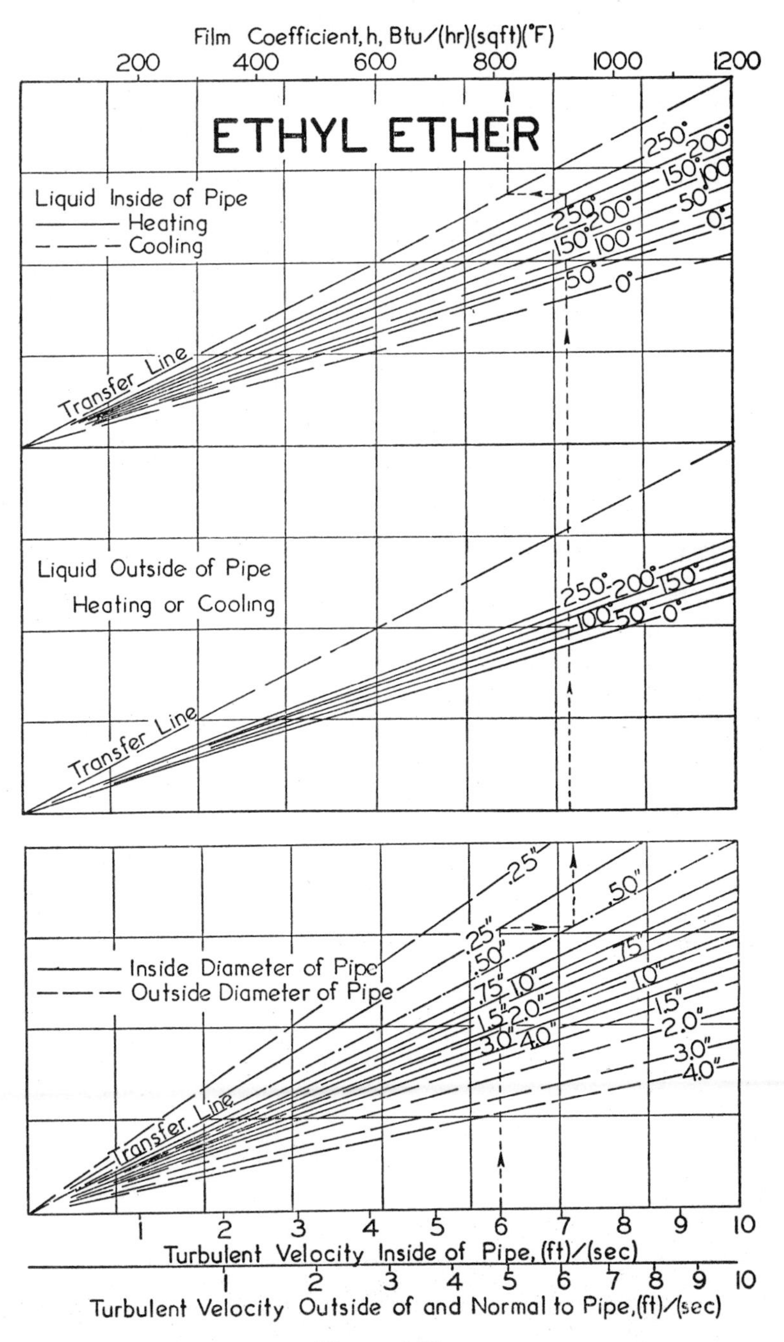
Film Coefficient, h, Btu/(hr)(sqft)(°F)
200
400
600
800
1000
1200
ETHYL ETHER
Liquid Inside of Pipe
Heating
Cooling
Transfer Line
Liquid Outside of Pipe
Heating or Cooling
Transfer Line
Inside Diameter of Pipe
Outside Diameter of Pipe
Transfer Line
Turbulent Velocity Inside of Pipe, (ft)/(sec)
Turbulent Velocity Outside of and Normal to Pipe, (ft)/(sec)

Figure 6.25

Ethyl Iodide (Liquid)

Ethyl Iodide (liquid) heating or cooling in turbulent flow within a tube or in turbulent flow outside and normal to a single tube.

Equations: Liquid heating in a tube: $Nu = 0.023(Re)^{0.8}(Pr)^{0.4}$
Liquid cooling in a tube: $Nu = 0.023(Re)^{0.8}(Pr)^{0.3}$
Liquid heating or cooling outside and normal to a single tube: $Nu = 0.385(Re)^{0.56}(Pr)^{0.3}$

Text References: Chapter VI; equations 6.5, 6.6, 6.9, 6.12, 6.13, and 6.14.

Extensions: Refer to section 6.5 for extensions to annular spaces, tube bundles, and flow through helical coils.

Special Conditions: For a liquid heating or cooling within a tube, do not use the graph if the velocity is less than 1 fps.

For a liquid flowing outside and normal to a single tube, do not use the graph for velocity less than 1 fps unless the Reynolds number exceeds 100.

Example: Ethyl Iodide (liquid) is cooling at a mean temperature of 200 F while flowing at 7 fps outside and normal to a bundle of staggered ¾ inch outside diameter tubes. Determine the outside film coefficient.* Estimate the outside coefficient for a similar, but baffled, tube bundle.

Solution: The base value of the outside film coefficient (for flow normal to a *single* tube) is determined as 565 by following the dashed example line, Fig. 6.26. The corrected value for flow normal to a staggered bundle is 30% greater than the base value (refer to part 6 of section 6.5) hence is 1.3(565) = 735 Btu/(hr)(sq ft)(°F). For a baffled tube bundle (refer to part 6 of section 6.5) the film coefficient would be taken at the base value of 565.

*__Note:__ To determine other heat transfer coefficients for Ethyl Iodide, use Fig. 6.26 but refer to the examples on the following pages for the appropriate method: Inside film coefficient, page 200; outside film coefficient per lineal foot, page 202; inside film coefficient per lineal foot, use method similar to that for outside film coefficient per lineal foot; inside film coefficient for a helical coil, page 204; overall coefficient, page 192; overall coefficient per lineal foot, page 194.

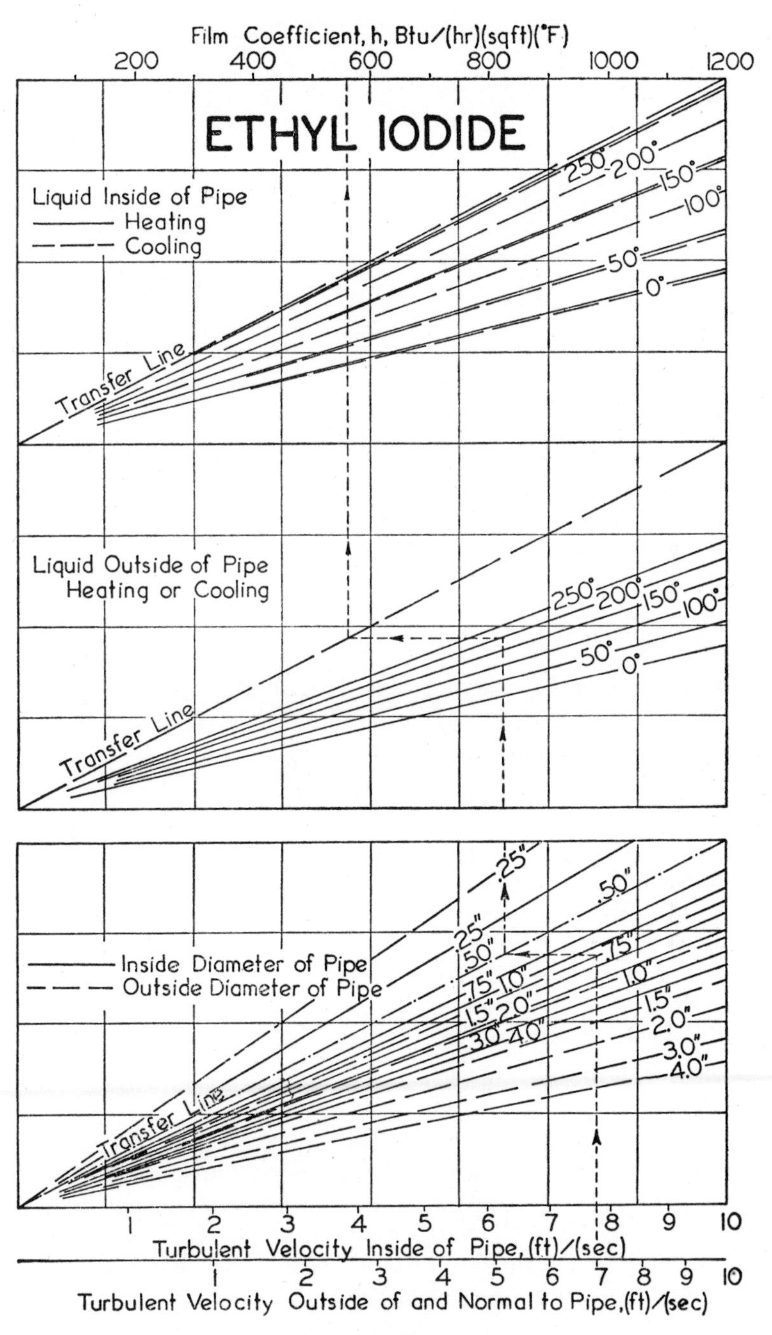
Film Coefficient, h, Btu/(hr)(sqft)(°F)
200
400
600
800
1000
1200
ETHYL IODIDE
Liquid Inside of Pipe
Heating
Cooling
250°
200°
150°
100°
50°
0°
Transfer Line
Liquid Outside of Pipe
Heating or Cooling
250°
200°
150°
100°
50°
0°
Transfer Line
Inside Diameter of Pipe
Outside Diameter of Pipe
.25"
.50"
.75"
1.0"
1.5"
2.0"
3.0"
4.0"
Transfer Line
1 2 3 4 5 6 7 8 9 10
Turbulent Velocity Inside of Pipe, (ft)/(sec)
1 2 3 4 5 6 7 8 9 10
Turbulent Velocity Outside of and Normal to Pipe, (ft)/(sec)

Figure 6.26

Ethylene Glycol, 50% (Liquid)

Ethylene Glycol, 50% (liquid) heating or cooling in turbulent flow within a tube or in turbulent flow outside and normal to a single tube.

Equations: Liquid heating in a tube: $Nu = 0.023(Re)^{0.8}(Pr)^{0.4}$
Liquid cooling in a tube: $Nu = 0.023(Re)^{0.8}(Pr)^{0.3}$
Liquid heating or cooling outside and normal to a single tube: $Nu = 0.385(Re)^{0.56}(Pr)^{0.3}$

Text References: Chapter VI; equations 6.5, 6.6, 6.9, 6.12, 6.13, and 6.14.

Extensions: Refer to section 6.5 for extensions to annular spaces, tube bundles, and flow through helical coils.

Special Conditions: For a liquid heating or cooling within a tube, do not use the graph unless the value of velocity (fps) times diameter (inches) exceeds 6.3 for 50 F or 0.7 for 250 F.

For a liquid flowing outside and normal to a single tube, do not use the graph for velocity less than 1 fps unless the Reynolds number exceeds 100.

Example: Ethylene Glycol, 50% (liquid) is flowing inside a tube of 2″ I.D. at a velocity of 2 fps. The fluid is heating at a mean temperature of 200 F. If the outside film coefficient is 50 determine the overall coefficient* of heat transfer assuming that the tube is so thin-walled that its thermal resistance is negligible and the difference between inside and outside surface areas can be neglected.

Solution: For the stated conditions the base value of the inside film coefficient is determinable (dashed example line, Fig. 6.27) as 310 Btu/(hr) (sq ft) (°F). Now go to Fig. 5.7 and (by a method similar to that shown by the dashed line) for inside and outside film coefficients of 310 and 50, respectively, read the overall coefficient of heat transfer as 43 Btu/(hr) (sq ft) (°F).

***Note:** To determine other heat transfer coefficients for Ethylene Glycol, 50% use Fig. 6.27 but refer to the examples on the following pages for the appropriate method: Outside film coefficient, page 206; inside film coefficient, page 200; outside film coefficient per lineal foot, page 202; inside film coefficient per lineal foot, use method similar to that for outside film coefficient per lineal foot; inside film coefficient for a helical coil, page 204; overall coefficient per lineal foot, page 194.

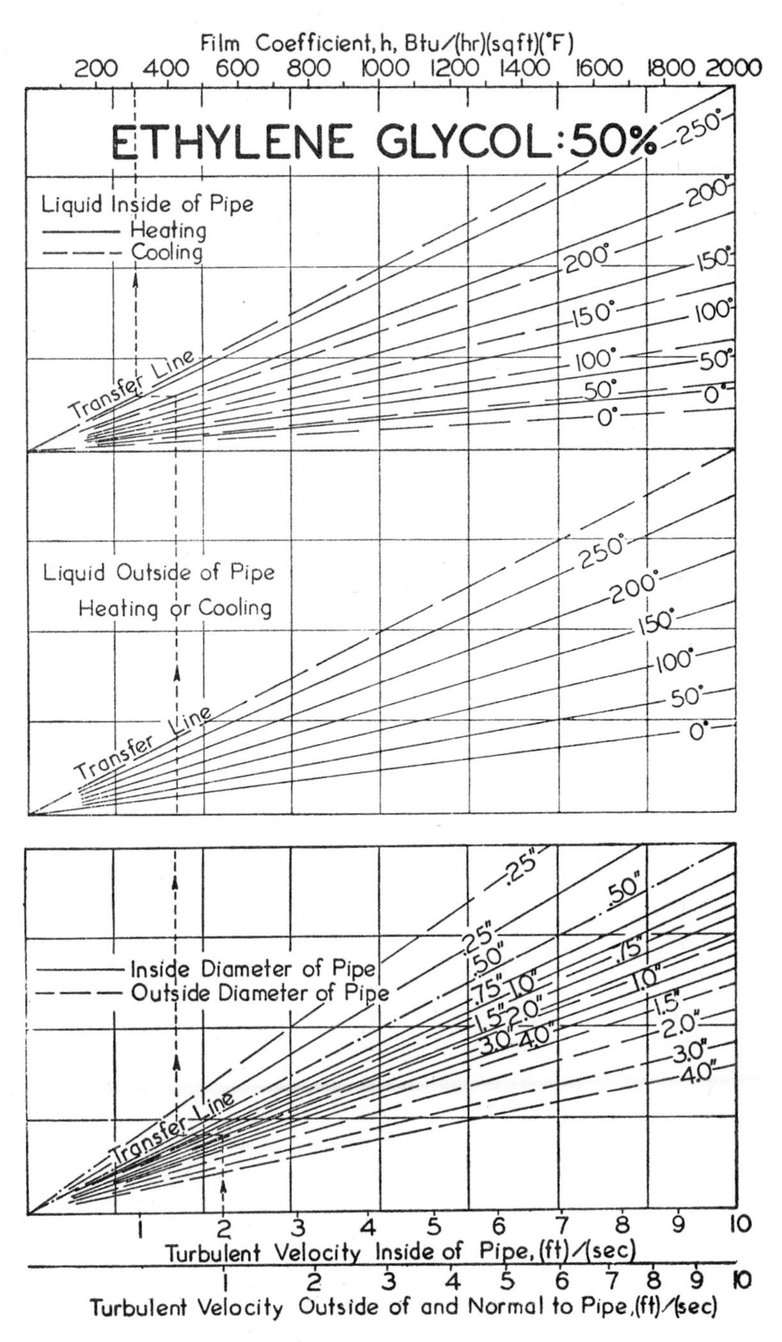
Film Coefficient, h, Btu/(hr)(sqft)(°F)
200 400 600 800 1000 1200 1400 1600 1800 2000
ETHYLENE GLYCOL: 50%
Liquid Inside of Pipe
Heating
Cooling
250°
200°
150°
100°
50°
0°
Transfer Line
Liquid Outside of Pipe
Heating or Cooling
Inside Diameter of Pipe
Outside Diameter of Pipe
.25"
.50"
.75"
1.0"
1.5"
2.0"
3.0"
4.0"
1 2 3 4 5 6 7 8 9 10
Turbulent Velocity Inside of Pipe, (ft)/(sec)
Turbulent Velocity Outside of and Normal to Pipe, (ft)/(sec)

Figure 6.27

Freon, 11 (Liquid)

Freon, 11 (liquid) heating or cooling in turbulent flow within a tube or in turbulent flow outside and normal to a single tube.

Equations: Liquid heating in a tube: $Nu = 0.023(Re)^{0.8}(Pr)^{0.4}$
Liquid cooling in a tube: $Nu = 0.023(Re)^{0.8}(Pr)^{0.3}$
Liquid heating or cooling outside and normal to a single tube: $Nu = 0.385(Re)^{0.56}(Pr)^{0.3}$

Text References: Chapter VI; equations 6.5, 6.6, 6.9, 6.12, 6.13, and 6.14.

Extensions: Refer to section 6.5 for extensions to annular spaces, tube bundles, and flow through helical coils.

Special Conditions: For a liquid heating or cooling within a tube, do not use the graph if the velocity is less than 1 fps.

For a liquid flowing outside and normal to a single tube, do not use the graph for velocity less than 1 fps unless the Reynolds number exceeds 100.

Example: Freon, 11 (liquid) is flowing at 4 fps outside and normal to a phosphorized copper tube (Type L) having outside diameter of 1″ and wall thickness of 0.065″. The fluid is cooling at 67 F. The inside film coefficient is known as 800 Btu/(hr) (°F) (sq ft of inside surface). Determine the overall coefficient* of heat transfer per *lineal* foot of tube.

Solution: The dashed example line on the graph (Fig. 6.28) determines the outside coefficient as 270. From Fig. 5.5 the inside and outside coefficients, 800 and 270, can be converted to values of 200 and 70, respectively, based on one lineal foot of tube. From Fig. 2.4 the thermal resistance of the tube is 0.00003 (based on outside area), giving a conductance of 33,000 which (Fig. 5.5) becomes 9,000 per lineal foot. The overall coefficient, equation 5.2, is then $U = 1/[1/200 + 1/9{,}000 + 1/70] = 52$ Btu/(hr) (°F) (lineal foot of tube).

*__Note:__ To determine other heat transfer coefficients for Freon, 11, use Fig. 6.28 but refer to the examples on the following pages for the appropriate method: Outside film coefficient, page 206; inside film coefficient, page 200; outside film coefficient per lineal foot, page 202, inside film coefficient per lineal foot, use method similar to that for outside film coefficient per lineal foot; inside film coefficient for a helical coil, page 204; overall coefficient, page 208.

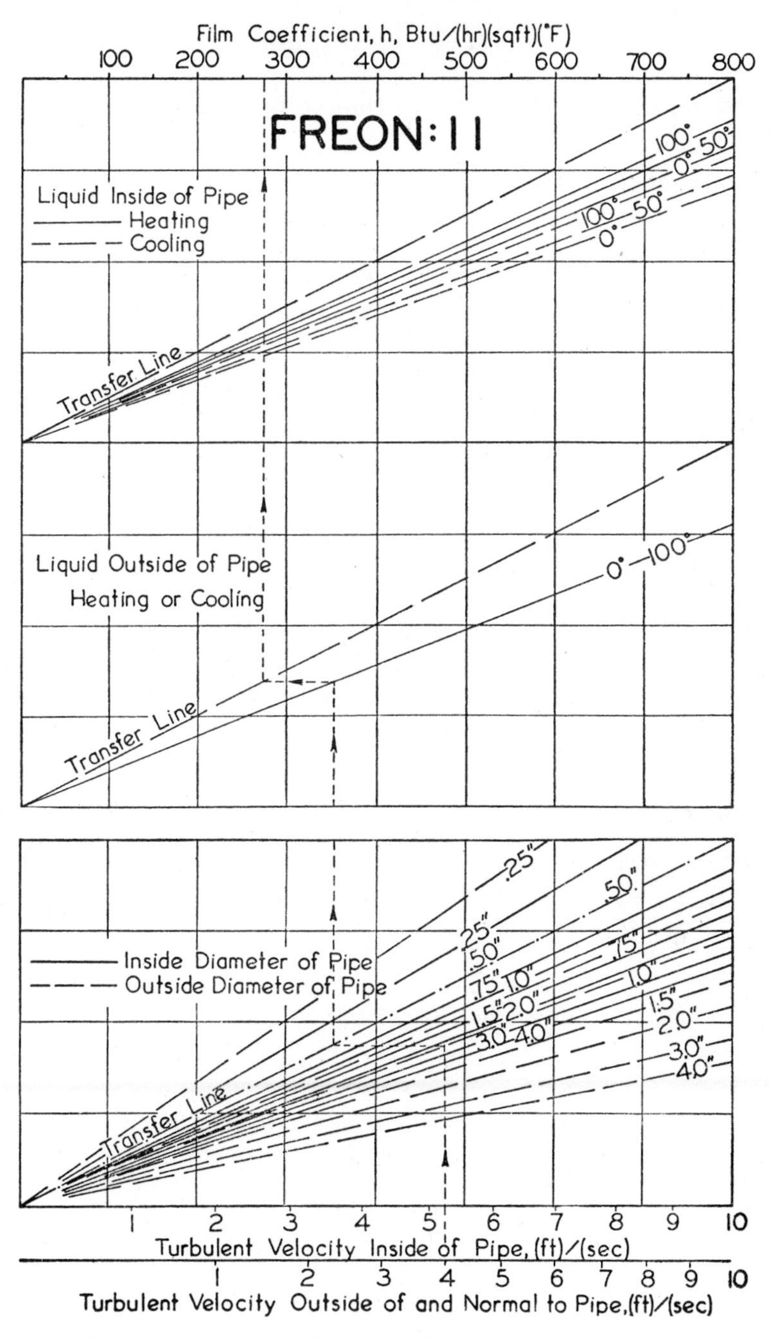
Film Coefficient, h, Btu/(hr)(sqft)(°F)
100 200 300 400 500 600 700 800
FREON: 11
Liquid Inside of Pipe
Heating
Cooling
100° 0° 50°
100° 50° 0°
Transfer Line
Liquid Outside of Pipe
Heating or Cooling
0°—100°
Transfer Line
Inside Diameter of Pipe
Outside Diameter of Pipe
.25" .50" .75" 1.0" 1.5" 2.0" 3.0" 4.0"
Transfer Line
1 2 3 4 5 6 7 8 9 10
Turbulent Velocity Inside of Pipe, (ft)/(sec)
1 2 3 4 5 6 7 8 9 10
Turbulent Velocity Outside of and Normal to Pipe, (ft)/(sec)

Figure 6.28

Freon, 12 (Liquid)

Freon, 12 (liquid) heating or cooling in turbulent flow within a tube or in turbulent flow outside and normal to a single tube.

Equations: Liquid heating in a tube: $Nu = 0.023(Re)^{0.8}(Pr)^{0.4}$
Liquid cooling in a tube: $Nu = 0.023(Re)^{0.8}(Pr)^{0.3}$
Liquid heating or cooling outside and normal to a single tube: $Nu = 0.385(Re)^{0.56}(Pr)^{0.3}$

Text References: Chapter VI; equations 6.5, 6.6, 6.9, 6.12, 6.13, and 6.14.

Extensions: Refer to section 6.5 for extensions to annular spaces, tube bundles, and flow through helical coils.

Special Conditions: For a liquid heating or cooling within a tube, do not use the graph if the velocity is less than 1 fps.

For a liquid flowing outside and normal to a single tube, do not use the graph for velocity less than 1 fps unless the Reynolds number exceeds 100.

Example: Freon, 12 (liquid) is in turbulent flow, at 6 fps velocity, through a tube having an inside diameter of 0.25 inches. The fluid is cooling at a mean temperature of 100 F. The tube is wound in a helical coil having a diameter of 50 inches. Determine the inside film coefficient.*

Solution: The dashed example line on the graph (Fig. 6.29) shows the method of determining the base value of the inside film coefficient for the conditions of flow through a straight tube; this value is read at the top scale as 495. Now refer to Fig. 6.6, enter the bottom scale at 495, and rise to the radial line for a tube-to-coil ratio of 0.25/50 = 0.005. From this intersection move left to the transfer line, then rise to read the corrected film coefficient for flow within the coil as 500 Btu/(hr)(sq ft)(°F).

*__Note:__ To determine other heat transfer coefficients for Freon, 12, use Fig. 6.29 but refer to the examples on the following pages for the appropriate method: Outside film coefficient, page 206; inside film coefficient, page 200; outside film coefficient per lineal foot, page 202; inside film coefficient per lineal foot, use method similar to that for outside film coefficient per lineal foot; overall coefficient, page 208; overall coefficient per lineal foot, page 210.

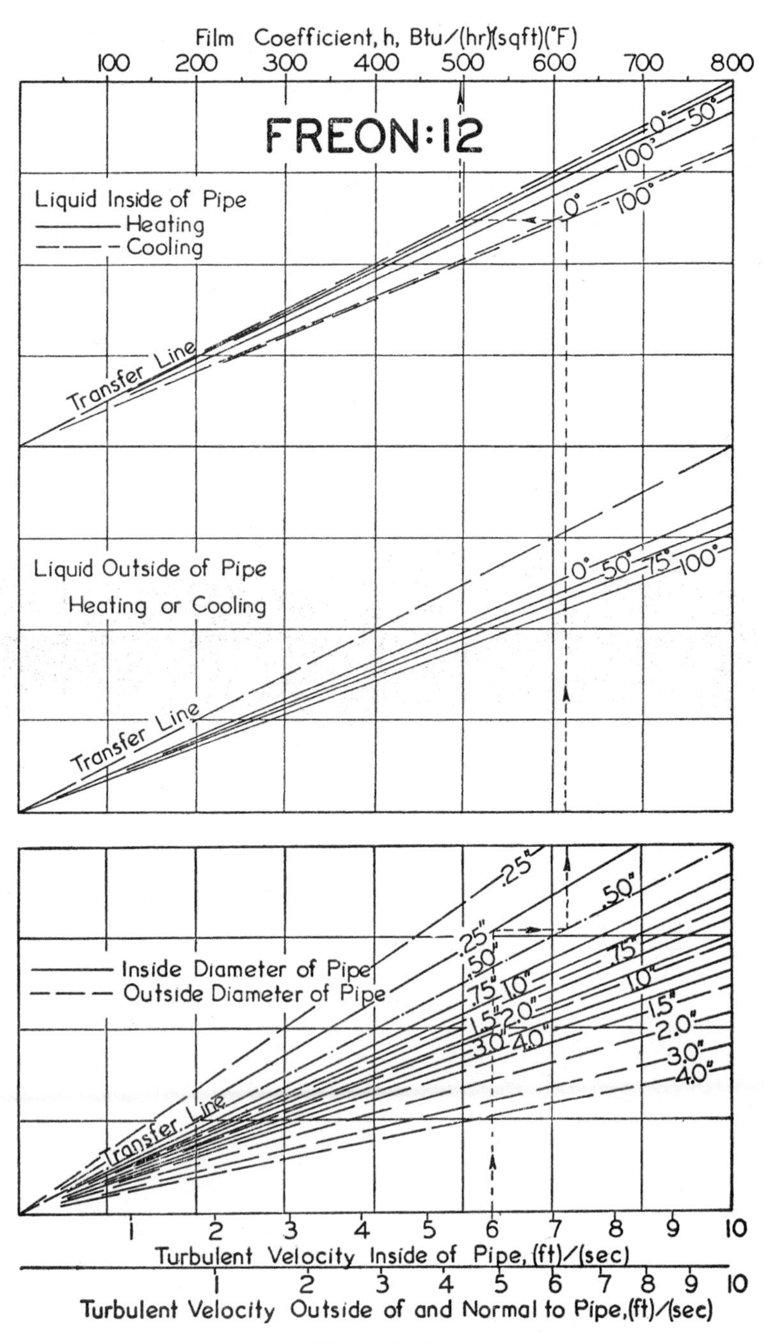
Film Coefficient, h, Btu/(hr)(sqft)(°F)
100 200 300 400 500 600 700 800
FREON:12
Liquid Inside of Pipe
Heating
Cooling
0° 50° 100° 0° 100°
Transfer Line
Liquid Outside of Pipe
Heating or Cooling
0° 50° 75° 100°
Transfer Line
Inside Diameter of Pipe
Outside Diameter of Pipe
.25" .25" .50" .50" .75" .75" 1.0" 1.0" 1.5" 1.5" 2.0" 2.0" 3.0" 3.0" 4.0" 4.0"
Transfer Line
1 2 3 4 5 6 7 8 9 10
Turbulent Velocity Inside of Pipe, (ft)/(sec)
1 2 3 4 5 6 7 8 9 10
Turbulent Velocity Outside of and Normal to Pipe, (ft)/(sec)

Figure 6.29

Freon, 21 (Liquid)

Freon, 21 (liquid) heating or cooling in turbulent flow within a tube or in turbulent flow outside and normal to a single tube.

Equations: Liquid heating in a tube: $Nu = 0.023(Re)^{0.8}(Pr)^{0.4}$
Liquid cooling in a tube: $Nu = 0.023(Re)^{0.8}(Pr)^{0.3}$
Liquid heating or cooling outside and normal to a single tube: $Nu = 0.385(Re)^{0.56}(Pr)^{0.3}$

Text References: Chapter VI; equations 6.5, 6.6, 6.9, 6.12, 6.13, and 6.14.

Extensions: Refer to section 6.5 for extensions to annular spaces, tube bundles, and flow through helical coils.

Special Conditions: For a liquid heating or cooling within a tube, do not use the graph if the velocity is less than 1 fps.

For a liquid flowing outside and normal to a single tube, do not use the graph for velocity less than 1 fps unless the Reynolds number exceeds 100

Example: Freon, 21 (liquid) is heating at a mean temperature of 0 F while flowing at 7 fps outside and normal to a bundle of staggered ¾ inch outside diameter tubes. Determine the outside film coefficient.* Estimate the outside coefficient for a similar, but baffled, tube bundle.

Solution: The base value of the outside film coefficient (for flow normal to a *single* tube) is determined as 515 by following the dashed example line, Fig. 6.30. The corrected value for flow normal to a staggered bundle is 30% greater than the base value (refer to part 6 of section 6.5) hence is 1.3(515) = 670 Btu/(hr)(sq ft)(°F). For a baffled tube bundle (refer to part 6 of section 6.5) the film coefficient would be taken at the base value of 515.

*__Note:__ To determine other heat transfer coefficients for Freon, 21, use Fig. 6.30 but refer to the examples on the following pages for the appropriate method: Inside film coefficient, page 200; outside film coefficient per lineal foot, page 202; inside film coefficient per lineal foot, use method similar to that for outside film coefficient per lineal foot; inside film coefficient for a helical coil, page 212; overall coefficient, page 208; overall coefficient per lineal foot, page 210.

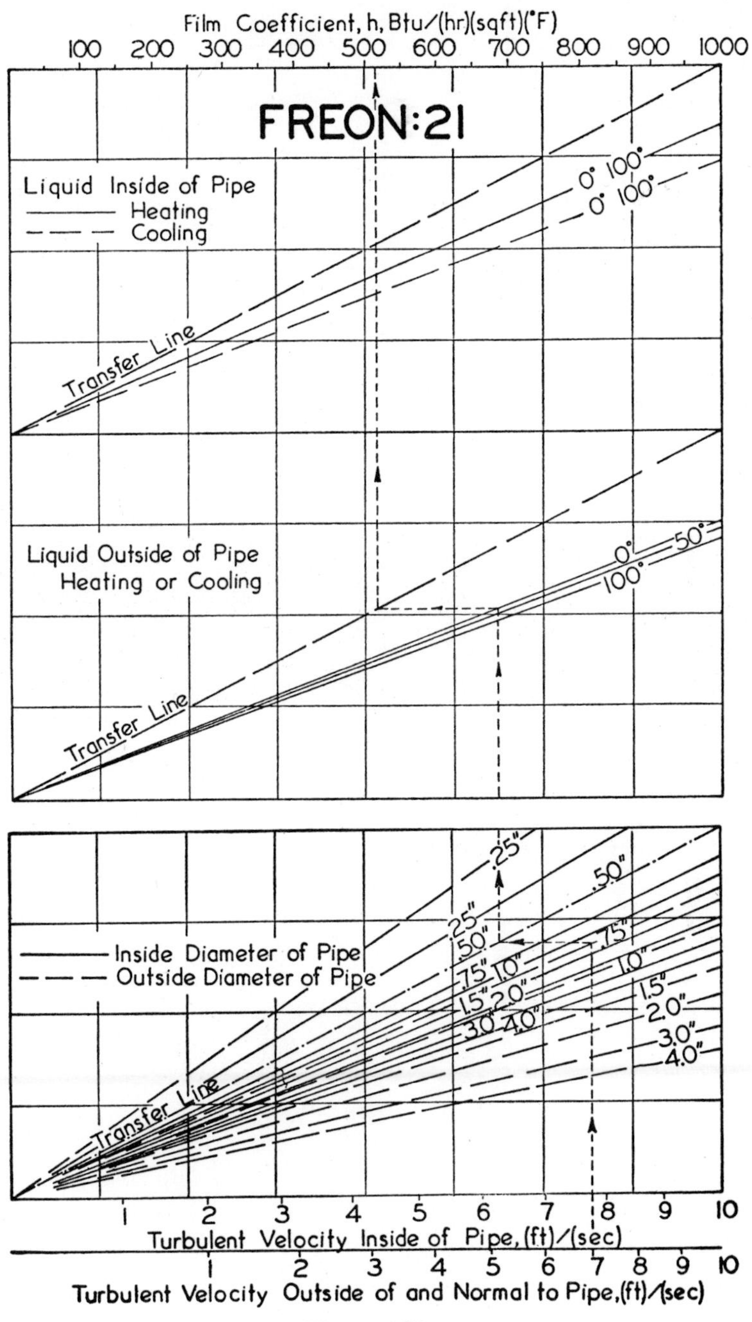
Film Coefficient, h, Btu/(hr)(sqft)(°F)
100 200 300 400 500 600 700 800 900 1000
FREON:21
Liquid Inside of Pipe
Heating
Cooling
0° 100°
0° 100°
Transfer Line
Liquid Outside of Pipe
Heating or Cooling
0° 50°
100°
Transfer Line
Inside Diameter of Pipe
Outside Diameter of Pipe
.25"
.50"
.75"
1.0"
1.5"
2.0"
3.0"
4.0"
Transfer Line
1 2 3 4 5 6 7 8 9 10
Turbulent Velocity Inside of Pipe, (ft)/(sec)
1 2 3 4 5 6 7 8 9 10
Turbulent Velocity Outside of and Normal to Pipe, (ft)/(sec)

Figure 6.30

Freon, 22 (Liquid)

Freon, 22 (liquid) heating or cooling in turbulent flow within a tube or in turbulent flow outside and normal to a single tube.

Equations: Liquid heating in a tube: $Nu = 0.023(Re)^{0.8}(Pr)^{0.4}$
Liquid cooling in a tube: $Nu = 0.023(Re)^{0.8}(Pr)^{0.3}$
Liquid heating or cooling outside and normal to a single tube: $Nu = 0.385(Re)^{0.56}(Pr)^{0.3}$

Text References: Chapter VI; equations 6.5, 6.6, 6.9, 6.12, 6.13, and 6.14.

Extensions: Refer to section 6.5 for extensions to annular spaces, tube bundles, and flow through helical coils.

Special Conditions: For a liquid heating or cooling within a tube, do not use the graph if the velocity is less than 1 fps.

For a liquid flowing outside and normal to a single tube, do not use the graph for velocity less than 1 fps unless the Reynolds number exceeds 100.

Example: Freon, 22 (liquid) is flowing within a 2 inch inside diameter tube at a velocity of 2 fps. The fluid is at a mean temperature of 100 F and is being heated. Determine the inside film coefficient.*

Solution: Enter the bottom scale of the graph (Fig. 6.31) at inside velocity of 2 fps and rise to intersect the solid radial line for a 2 inch inside diameter tube. From this intersection move left to the transfer line and then rise to the top section of the graph where radial lines are given for liquid heating and cooling *inside* a tube. In this section intersect the solid radial for liquid heating at 100 F. From this intersection move left to the transfer line and then rise to the top scale of the graph were read the value of the inside film coefficient as 170 Btu/(hr) (sq ft) (°F).

***Note:** To determine other heat transfer coefficients for Freon, 22, use Fig. 6.31 but refer to the examples on the following pages for the appropriate method: Outside film coefficient, page 214; outside film coefficient per lineal foot, page 202; inside film coefficient per lineal foot, use method similar to that for outside film coefficient per lineal foot; inside film coefficient for a helical coil, page 212; overall coefficient, page 208; overall coefficient per lineal foot, page 210.

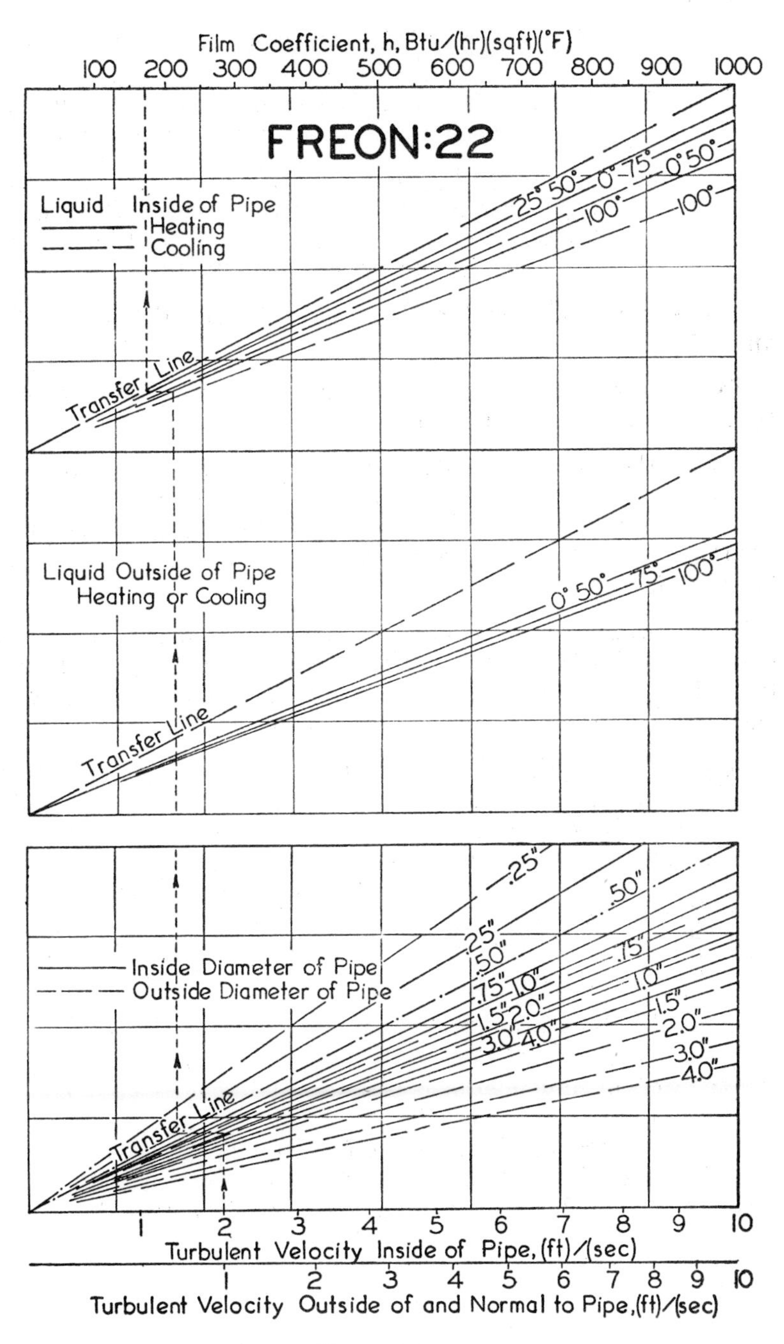
Film Coefficient, h, Btu/(hr)(sqft)(°F)
100 200 300 400 500 600 700 800 900 1000
FREON:22
Liquid Inside of Pipe
Heating
Cooling
25° 50° 0° 75° 0° 50°
100° 100°
Transfer Line
Liquid Outside of Pipe
Heating or Cooling
0° 50° 75° 100°
Transfer Line
Inside Diameter of Pipe
Outside Diameter of Pipe
.25" .50"
.25" .50" .75" 1.0" 1.5" 2.0" 3.0" 4.0"
.75" 1.0" 1.5" 2.0" 3.0" 4.0"
Transfer Line
1 2 3 4 5 6 7 8 9 10
Turbulent Velocity Inside of Pipe, (ft)/(sec)
1 2 3 4 5 6 7 8 9 10
Turbulent Velocity Outside of and Normal to Pipe, (ft)/(sec)

Figure 6.31

Freon, 113 (Liquid)

Freon, 113 (liquid) heating or cooling in turbulent flow within a tube or in turbulent flow outside and normal to a single tube.

Equations: Liquid heating in a tube: $Nu = 0.023(Re)^{0.8}(Pr)^{0.4}$
Liquid cooling in a tube: $Nu = 0.023(Re)^{0.8}(Pr)^{0.3}$
Liquid heating or cooling outside and normal to a single tube: $Nu = 0.385(Re)^{0.56}(Pr)^{0.3}$

Text References: Chapter VI; equations 6.5, 6.6, 6.9, 6.12, 6.13, and 6.14.

Extensions: Refer to section 6.5 for extensions to annular spaces, tube bundles, and flow through helical coils.

Special Conditions: For a liquid heating or cooling within a tube, do not use the graph if the velocity is less than 1 fps.
For a liquid flowing outside and normal to a single tube, do not use the graph for velocity less than 1 fps unless the Reynolds number exceeds 100.

Example: Freon, 113 (liquid) is heating at a mean temperature of 0 F while flowing outside and normal to a 1″ O.D. Type M copper tube. The fluid velocity is 4 fps. Determine the outside film coefficient* in Btu per hour per °F per *lineal foot* of tube.

Solution: The dashed example line on the graph (Fig. 6.32) shows the method of evaluating the outside film coefficient, for the stated conditions, in terms of one square foot of outside surface of the tube. To convert this value, 210 Btu/(hr)(sq ft)(°F), to a lineal basis refer to Fig. 5.6 and, using a method similar to that shown by the dashed example line, enter the graph at h of 210 and come out at the top scale with a film coefficient of 50 Btu per hour per °F per lineal foot of tube.

***Note:** To determine other heat transfer coefficients for Freon, 113, use Fig. 6.32 but refer to the examples on the following pages for the appropriate method: Outside film coefficient, page 214; inside film coefficient, page 216; inside film coefficient per lineal foot, use method similar to that for outside film coefficient per lineal foot; inside film coefficient for a helical coil, page 212; overall coefficient, page 208; overall coefficient per lineal foot, page 210.

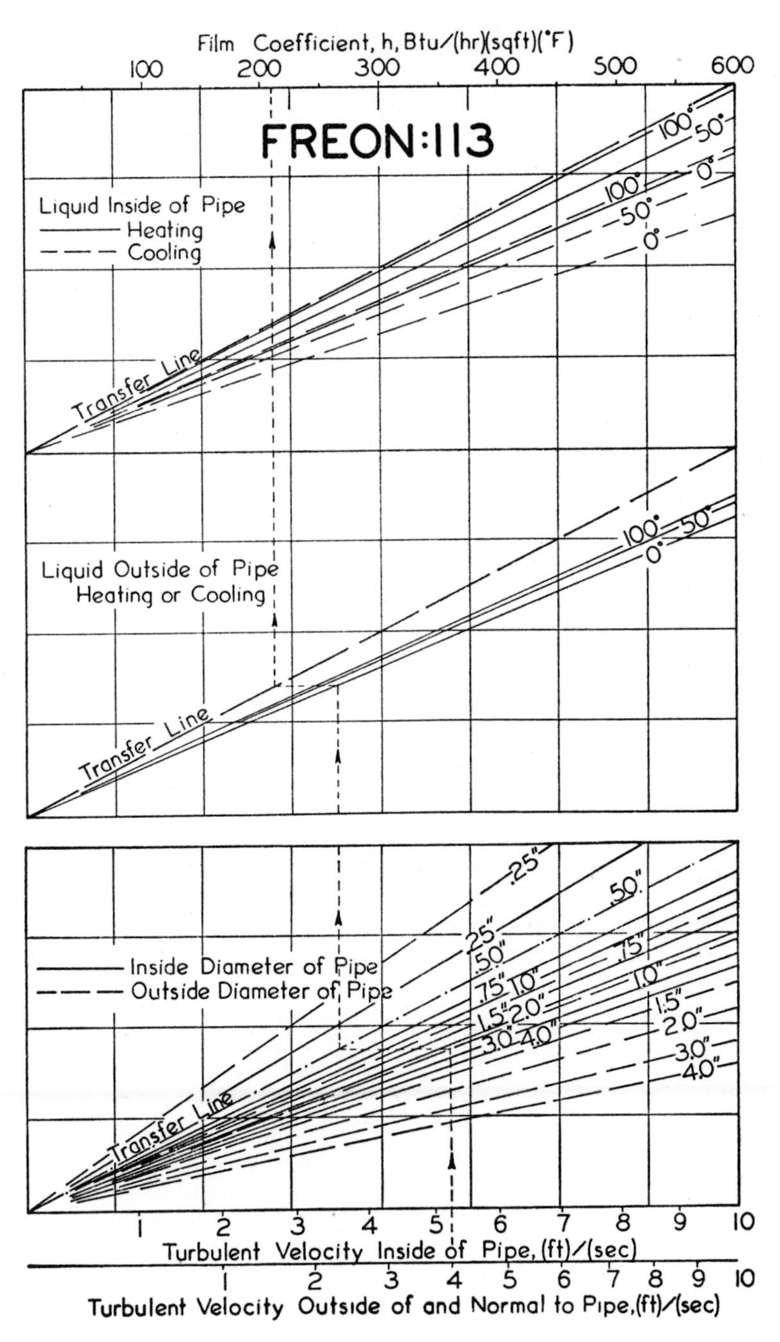
Film Coefficient, h, Btu/(hr)(sqft)(°F)
100
200
300
400
500
600
FREON:113
Liquid Inside of Pipe
Heating
Cooling
100°
50°
0°
100°
50°
0°
Transfer Line
Liquid Outside of Pipe
Heating or Cooling
100°
50°
0°
Transfer Line
Inside Diameter of Pipe
Outside Diameter of Pipe
.25"
.50"
.75"
1.0"
1.5"
2.0"
3.0"
4.0"
.25"
.50"
.75"
1.0"
1.5"
2.0"
3.0"
4.0"
Transfer Line
1 2 3 4 5 6 7 8 9 10
Turbulent Velocity Inside of Pipe, (ft)/(sec)
1 2 3 4 5 6 7 8 9 10
Turbulent Velocity Outside of and Normal to Pipe, (ft)/(sec)

Figure 6.32

Freon, 114 (Liquid)

Freon, 114 (liquid) heating or cooling in turbulent flow within a tube or in turbulent flow outside and normal to a single tube.

Equations: Liquid heating in a tube: $Nu = 0.023(Re)^{0.8}(Pr)^{0.4}$
Liquid cooling in a tube: $Nu = 0.023(Re)^{0.8}(Pr)^{0.3}$
Liquid heating or cooling outside and normal to a single tube: $Nu = 0.385(Re)^{0.56}(Pr)^{0.3}$

Text References: Chapter VI; equations 6.5, 6.6, 6.9, 6.12, 6.13, and 6.14.

Extensions: Refer to section 6.5 for extensions to annular spaces, tube bundles, and flow through helical coils.

Special Conditions: For a liquid heating or cooling within a tube, do not use the graph if the velocity is less than 1 fps.
For a liquid flowing outside and normal to a single tube, do not use the graph for velocity less than 1 fps unless the Reynolds number exceeds 100.

Example: Freon, 114 (liquid) is in turbulent flow, at 6 fps velocity, through a tube having an inside diameter of 0.25 inches. The fluid is cooling at a mean temperature of 60 F. The tube is wound in a helical coil having a diameter of 50 inches. Determine the inside film coefficient.*

Solution: The dashed example line on the graph (Fig. 6.33) shows the method of determining the base value of the inside film coefficient for the conditions of flow through a straight tube; this value is read at the top scale as 430. Now refer to Fig. 6.6, enter the bottom scale at 430 and rise to the radial line for a tube-to-coil ratio of $0.25/50 = 0.005$. From this intersection move left to the transfer line, then rise to read the corrected film coefficient for flow within the coil as 438 Btu/(hr) (sq ft) (°F).

***Note:** To determine other heat transfer coefficients for Freon, 114, use Fig. 6.33 but refer to the examples on the following pages for the appropriate method: Outside film coefficient, page 214; inside film coefficient, page 216; outside film coefficient per lineal foot, page 218; inside film coefficient per lineal foot, use method similar to that for outside film coefficient per lineal foot; overall coefficient, page 208; overall coefficient per lineal foot, page 210.

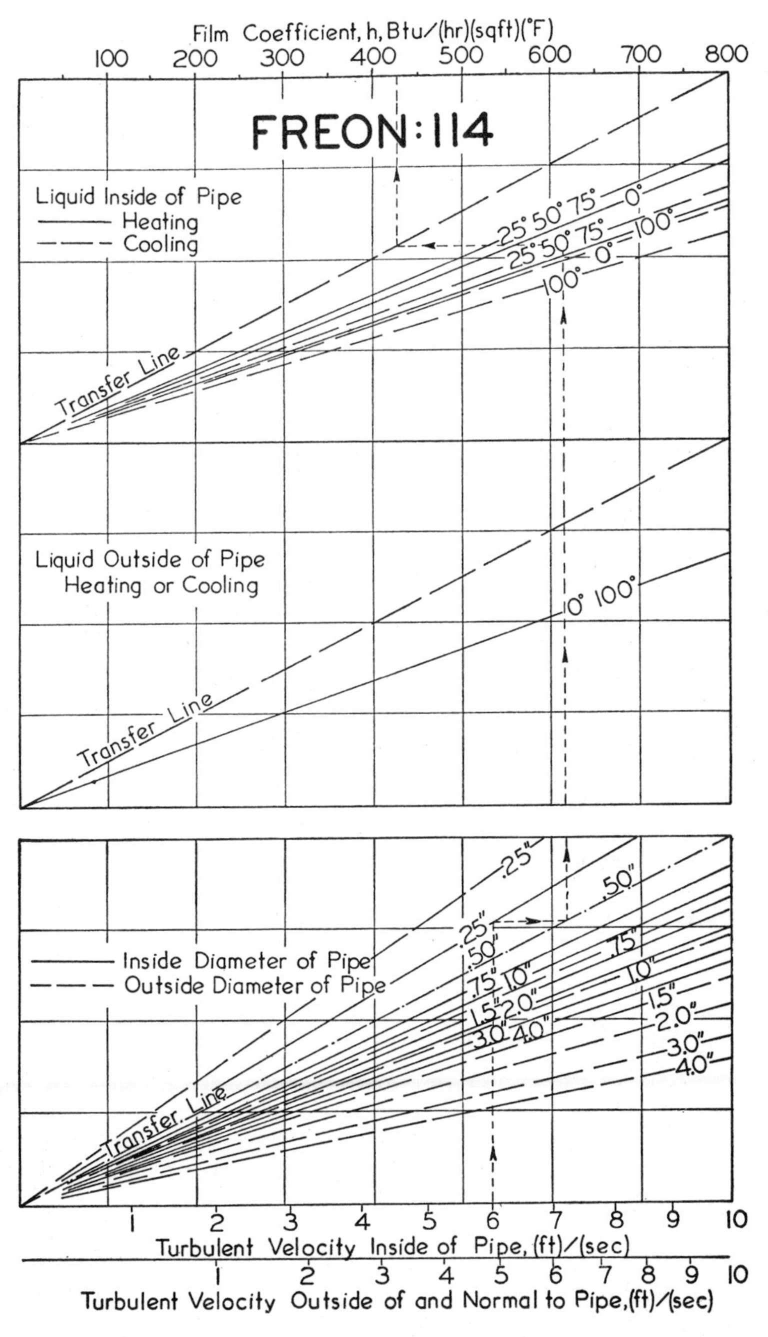
Film Coefficient, h, Btu/(hr)(sqft)(°F)
100 200 300 400 500 600 700 800
FREON:114
Liquid Inside of Pipe
Heating
Cooling
25° 50° 75° 0°
25° 50° 75° 100°
0°
100°
Transfer Line
Liquid Outside of Pipe
Heating or Cooling
0° 100°
Transfer Line
Inside Diameter of Pipe
Outside Diameter of Pipe
.25"
.50"
.75"
1.0"
1.5"
2.0"
3.0"
4.0"
Transfer Line
1 2 3 4 5 6 7 8 9 10
Turbulent Velocity Inside of Pipe, (ft)/(sec)
1 2 3 4 5 6 7 8 9 10
Turbulent Velocity Outside of and Normal to Pipe, (ft)/(sec)

Figure 6.33

Glycerol, 50% (Liquid)

Glycerol, 50% (liquid) heating or cooling in turbulent flow within a tube or in turbulent flow outside and normal to a single tube.

Equations: Liquid heating in a tube: $Nu = 0.023(Re)^{0.8}(Pr)^{0.4}$
Liquid cooling in a tube: $Nu = 0.023(Re)^{0.8}(Pr)^{0.3}$
Liquid heating or cooling outside and normal to a single tube: $Nu = 0.385(Re)^{0.56}(Pr)^{0.3}$

Text References: Chapter VI; equations 6.5, 6.6, 6.9, 6.12, 6.13, and 6.14.

Extensions: Refer to section 6.5 for extensions to annular spaces, tube bundles, and flow through helical coils.

Special Conditions: For a liquid heating or cooling within a tube, do not use the graph unless the value of velocity (fps) times diameter (inches) exceeds 9.7 for 50 F or 0.8 for 250 F.

For a liquid flowing outside and normal to a single tube, do not use the graph for velocity less than 1 fps unless the Reynolds number exceeds 100.

Example: Glycerol, 50% (liquid) is cooling at a mean temperature of 100 F while flowing at 7 fps outside and normal to a bundle of staggered ¾ inch outside diameter tubes. Determine the outside film coefficient.* Estimate the outside coefficient for a similar, but baffled, tube bundle.

Solution: The base value of the outside film coefficient (for flow normal to a *single* tube) is determined as 840 by following the dashed example line, Fig. 6.34. The corrected value for flow normal to a staggered bundle is 30% greater than the base value (refer to part 6 of section 6.5) hence is 1.3(840) = 1090 Btu/(hr) (sq ft) (°F). For a baffled tube bundle (refer to part 6 of section 6.5) the film coefficient would be taken at the base value of 840.

***Note:** To determine other heat transfer coefficients for Glycerol, 50%, use Fig. 6.34 but refer to the examples on the following pages for the appropriate method: Inside film coefficient, page 216; outside film coefficient per lineal foot, page 218; inside film coefficient per lineal foot, use method similar to that for outside film coefficient per lineal foot; inside film coefficient for a helical coil, page 220; overall coefficient, page 208; overall coefficient per lineal foot, page 210.

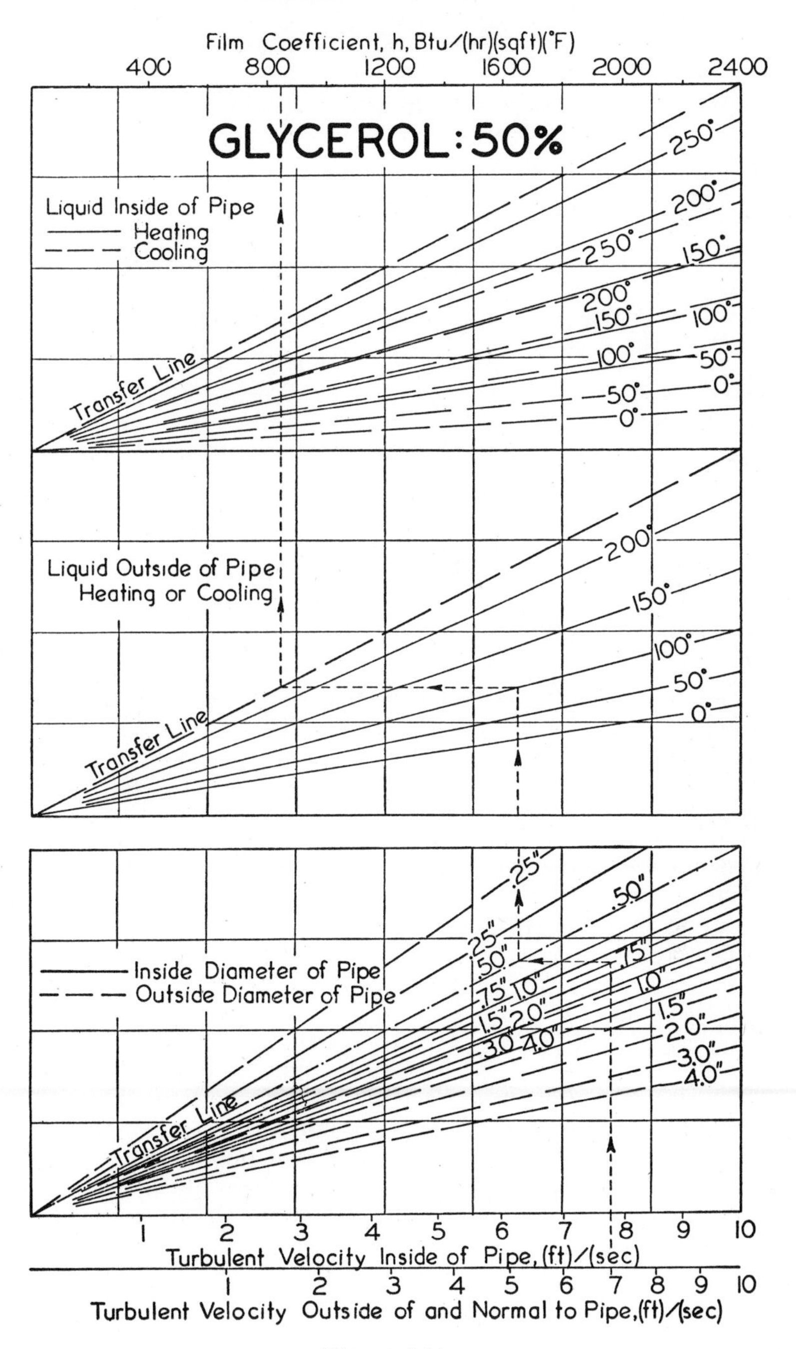

Film Coefficient, h, Btu/(hr)(sqft)(°F)
400
800
1200
1600
2000
2400
GLYCEROL: 50%
Liquid Inside of Pipe
Heating
Cooling
Transfer Line
250°
200°
150°
100°
50°
0°
Liquid Outside of Pipe
Heating or Cooling
Inside Diameter of Pipe
Outside Diameter of Pipe
Turbulent Velocity Inside of Pipe, (ft)/(sec)
Turbulent Velocity Outside of and Normal to Pipe, (ft)/(sec)

Figure 6.34

Heptane (Liquid)

Heptane (liquid) heating or cooling in turbulent flow within a tube or in turbulent flow outside and normal to a single tube.

Equations: Liquid heating in a tube: $Nu = 0.023(Re)^{0.8}(Pr)^{0.4}$
Liquid cooling in a tube: $Nu = 0.023(Re)^{0.8}(Pr)^{0.3}$
Liquid heating or cooling outside and normal to a single tube: $Nu = 0.385(Re)^{0.56}(Pr)^{0.3}$

Text References: Chapter VI; equations 6.5, 6.6, 6.9, 6.12, 6.13, and 6.14.

Extensions: Refer to section 6.5 for extensions to annular spaces, tube bundles, and flow through helical coils.

Special Conditions: For a liquid heating or cooling within a tube, do not use the graph if the velocity is less than 1 fps.

For a liquid flowing outside and normal to a single tube, do not use the graph for velocity less than 1 fps unless the Reynolds number exceeds 100.

Example: Heptane (liquid) is flowing inside a tube of 2″ I.D. at a velocity of 2 fps. The fluid is cooling at a mean temperature of 50 F. If the outside film coefficient is 100 determine the overall coefficient* of heat transfer assuming that the tube is so thin-walled that its thermal resistance is negligible and the difference between inside and outside surface areas can be neglected.

Solution: For the stated conditions the base value of the inside film coefficient is determinable (dashed example line, Fig. 6.35) as 110 Btu/(hr) (sq ft) (°F). Now go to Fig. 5.7 and (by a method similar to that shown by the dashed line) for inside and outside film coefficients of 110 and 100, respectively, read the overall coefficient of heat transfer as 53 Btu/(hr) (sq ft) (°F).

***Note:** To determine other heat transfer coefficients for Heptane, use Fig. 6.35 but refer to the examples on the following pages for the appropriate method: Outside film coefficient, page 222; inside film coefficient, page 216; outside film coefficient per lineal foot, page 218; inside film coefficient per lineal foot, use method similar to that for outside film coefficient per lineal foot; inside film coefficient for a helical coil, page 220; overall coefficient per lineal foot, page 210.

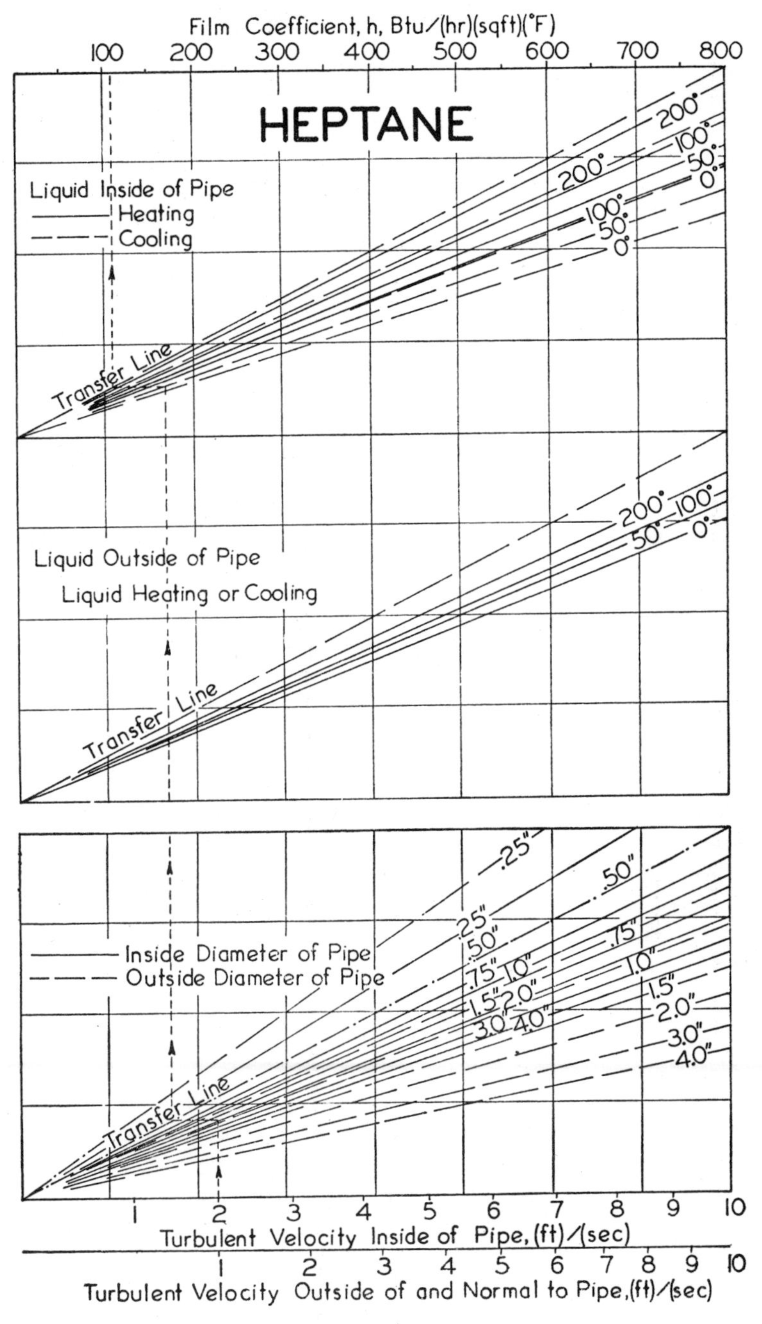
Film Coefficient, h, Btu/(hr)(sqft)(°F)
100 200 300 400 500 600 700 800
HEPTANE
Liquid Inside of Pipe
Heating
Cooling
200°
100°
50°
0°
Transfer Line
Liquid Outside of Pipe
Liquid Heating or Cooling
Transfer Line
Inside Diameter of Pipe
Outside Diameter of Pipe
.25"
.50"
.75"
1.0"
1.5"
2.0"
3.0"
4.0"
Transfer Line
1 2 3 4 5 6 7 8 9 10
Turbulent Velocity Inside of Pipe, (ft)/(sec)
1 2 3 4 5 6 7 8 9 10
Turbulent Velocity Outside of and Normal to Pipe, (ft)/(sec)

Figure 6.35

Hexane (Liquid)

Hexane (liquid) heating or cooling in turbulent flow within a tube or in turbulent flow outside and normal to a single tube.

Equations: Liquid heating in a tube: $Nu = 0.023 (Re)^{0.8} (Pr)^{0.4}$
Liquid cooling in a tube: $Nu = 0.023 (Re)^{0.8} (Pr)^{0.3}$
Liquid heating or cooling outside and normal to a single tube: $Nu = 0.385 (Re)^{0.56} (Pr)^{0.3}$

Text References: Chapter VI; equations 6.5, 6.6, 6.9, 6.12, 6.13, and 6.14.

Extensions: Refer to section 6.5 for extensions to annular spaces, tube bundles, and flow through helical coils.

Special Conditions: For a liquid heating or cooling within a tube, do not use the graph if the velocity is less than 1 fps.

For a liquid flowing outside and normal to a single tube, do not use the graph for velocity less than 1 fps unless the Reynolds number exceeds 100.

Example: Hexane (liquid) is flowing at 4 fps outside and normal to a phosphorized copper tube (Type L) having outside diameter of 1″ and wall thickness of 0.065″. The fluid is heating at 100 F. The inside film coefficient is known as 800 Btu/(hr) (°F) (sq ft of inside surface). Determine the overall coefficient* of heat transfer per *lineal* foot of tube.

Solution: The dashed example line on the graph (Fig. 6.36) determines the outside coefficient as 310. From Fig. 5.5 the inside and outside coefficients, 800 and 310, can be converted to values of 200 and 115, respectively, based on one lineal foot of tube. From Fig. 2.4 the thermal resistance of the tube is 0.00003 (based on outside area), giving a conductance of 33,000 which (Fig. 5.5) becomes 9,000 per lineal foot. The overall coefficient, equation 5.2, is then $U = 1/[1/200 + 1/9{,}000 + 1/115] = 72$ Btu/(hr) (°F) (lineal foot of tube).

***Note:** To determine other heat transfer coefficients for Hexane, use Fig. 6.36 but refer to the examples on the following pages for the appropriate method: Outside film coefficient, page 222; inside film coefficient, page 216; outside film coefficient per lineal foot, page 218; inside film coefficient per lineal foot, use method similar to that for outside film coefficient per lineal foot; inside film coefficient for a helical coil, page 220; overall coefficient, page 224.

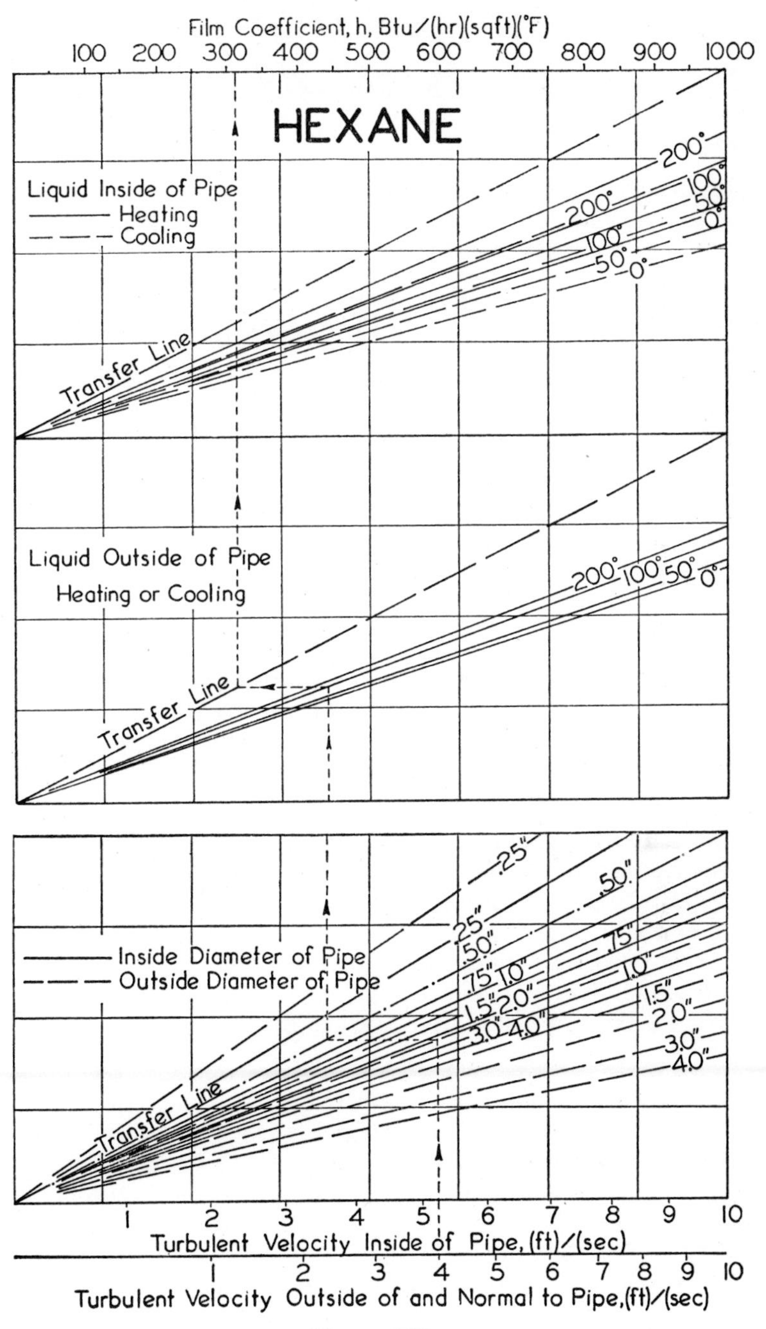

Film Coefficient, h, Btu/(hr)(sqft)(°F)
100 200 300 400 500 600 700 800 900 1000
HEXANE
Liquid Inside of Pipe
Heating
Cooling
200°
100°
50°
0°
200°
100°
50°
0°
Transfer Line
Liquid Outside of Pipe
Heating or Cooling
200° 100° 50° 0°
Transfer Line
Inside Diameter of Pipe
Outside Diameter of Pipe
.25"
.50"
.75"
1.0"
1.5"
2.0"
3.0"
4.0"
.25"
.50"
.75" 1.0"
1.5" 2.0"
3.0" 4.0"
Transfer Line
1 2 3 4 5 6 7 8 9 10
Turbulent Velocity Inside of Pipe, (ft)/(sec)
1 2 3 4 5 6 7 8 9 10
Turbulent Velocity Outside of and Normal to Pipe, (ft)/(sec)

Figure 6.36

Methyl Alcohol, 40% (Liquid)

Methyl Alcohol, 40% (liquid) heating or cooling in turbulent flow within a tube or in turbulent flow outside and normal to a single tube.

Equations: Liquid heating in a tube: $Nu = 0.023(Re)^{0.8}(Pr)^{0.4}$
Liquid cooling in a tube: $Nu = 0.023(Re)^{0.8}(Pr)^{0.3}$
Liquid heating or cooling outside and normal to a single tube: $Nu = 0.385(Re)^{0.56}(Pr)^{0.3}$

Text References: Chapter VI; equations 6.5, 6.6, 6.9, 6.12, 6.13, and 6.14.

Extensions: Refer to section 6.5 for extensions to annular spaces, tube bundles, and flow through helical coils.

Special Conditions: For a liquid heating or cooling within a tube, do not use the graph unless the value of velocity (fps) times diameter (inches) exceeds 5.8 for 50 F or 0.7 for 250 F.

For a liquid flowing outside and normal to a single tube, do not use the graph for velocity less than 1 fps unless the Reynolds number exceeds 100.

Example: Methyl Alcohol, 40% (liquid) is in turbulent flow, at 6 fps velocity, through a tube having an inside diameter of 0.25 inches. The fluid is heating at a mean temperature of 250 F. The tube is wound in a helical coil having a diameter of 50 inches. Determine the inside film coefficient.*

Solution: The dashed example line on the graph (Fig. 6.37) shows the method of determining the base value of the inside film coefficient for the conditions of flow through a straight tube; this value is read at the top scale as 2100. Now referring to Fig. 6.6 it will be noticed that the scale is not large enough to yield the corrected value of film coefficient and it must be calculated by using equation 6.18: $h = 2100(1 + 3.5 \times 0.250/50) = 2135$ Btu/(hr) (sq ft) (°F).

***Note:** To determine other heat transfer coefficients for Methyl Alcohol, 40%, use Fig. 6.37 but refer to the examples on the following pages for the appropriate method: Outside film coefficient, page 222; inside film coefficient, page 216; outside film coefficient per lineal foot, page 218; inside film coefficient per lineal foot, use method similar to that for outside film coefficient per lineal foot; overall coefficient, page 224; overall coefficient per lineal foot, page 226.

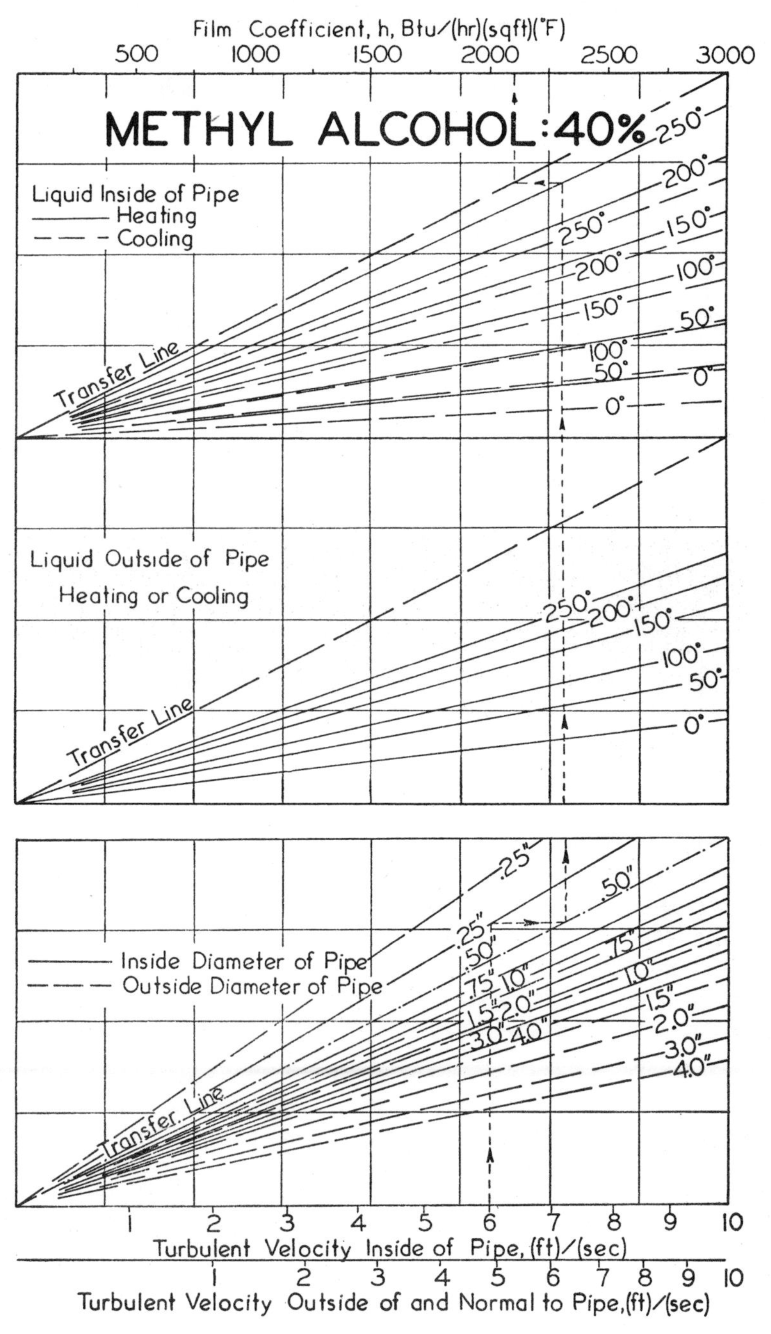
Film Coefficient, h, Btu/(hr)(sqft)(°F)
500 1000 1500 2000 2500 3000
METHYL ALCOHOL:40%
Liquid Inside of Pipe
Heating
Cooling
Transfer Line
250° 200° 150° 100° 50° 0°
Liquid Outside of Pipe
Heating or Cooling
Inside Diameter of Pipe
Outside Diameter of Pipe
.25" .50" .75" 1.0" 1.5" 2.0" 3.0" 4.0"
1 2 3 4 5 6 7 8 9 10
Turbulent Velocity Inside of Pipe, (ft)/(sec)
Turbulent Velocity Outside of and Normal to Pipe, (ft)/(sec)

Figure 6.37

Methyl Alcohol, 90% (Liquid)

Methyl Alcohol, 90% (liquid) heating or cooling in turbulent flow within a tube or in turbulent flow outside and normal to a single tube.

Equations: Liquid heating in a tube: $Nu = 0.023(Re)^{0.8}(Pr)^{0.4}$
Liquid cooling in a tube: $Nu = 0.023(Re)^{0.8}(Pr)^{0.3}$
Liquid heating or cooling outside and normal to a single tube: $Nu = 0.385(Re)^{0.56}(Pr)^{0.3}$

Text References: Chapter VI; equations 6.5, 6.6, 6.9, 6.12, 6.13, and 6.14.

Extensions: Refer to section 6.5 for extensions to annular spaces, tube bundles, and flow through helical coils.

Special Conditions: For a liquid heating or cooling within a tube, do not use the graph if the velocity is less than 1 fps.

For a liquid flowing outside and normal to a single tube, do not use the graph for velocity less than 1 fps unless the Reynolds number exceeds 100.

Example: Methyl Alcohol, 90% (liquid) is flowing within a 2 inch inside diameter tube at a velocity of 2 fps. The fluid is at a mean temperature of 50 F and is being cooled. Determine the inside film coefficient.*

Solution: Enter the bottom scale of the graph (Fig. 6.38) at inside velocity of 2 fps and rise to intersect the solid radial line for a 2 inch inside diameter tube. From this intersection move left to the transfer line and then rise to the top section of the graph where radial lines are given for liquid heating and cooling *inside* a tube. In this section intersect the dashed radial for liquid cooling at 50 F. From this intersection move left to the transfer line and then rise to the top scale of the graph where read the value of the inside film coefficient as 140 Btu/(hr) (sq ft) (°F).

***Note:** To determine other heat transfer coefficients for Methyl Alcohol, 90%, use Fig. 6.38 but refer to the examples on the following pages for the appropriate method: Outside film coefficient, page 222; outside film coefficient per lineal foot, page 218; inside film coefficient per lineal foot, use method similar to that for outside film coefficient per lineal foot; inside film coefficient for a helical coil, page 228; overall coefficient, page 224; overall coefficient per lineal foot, page 226.

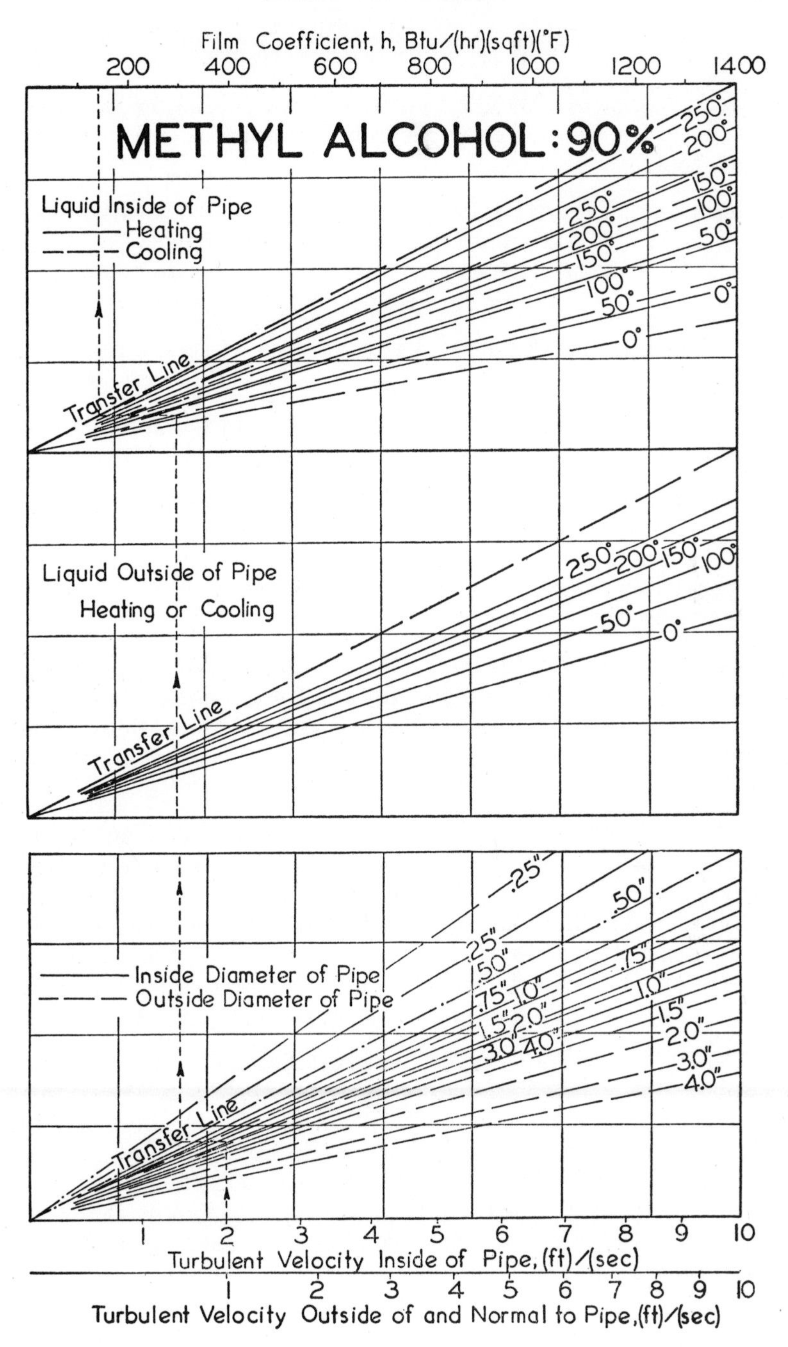
Film Coefficient, h, Btu/(hr)(sqft)(°F)
200
400
600
800
1000
1200
1400
METHYL ALCOHOL: 90%
Liquid Inside of Pipe
Heating
Cooling
250°
200°
150°
100°
50°
0°
Transfer Line
Liquid Outside of Pipe
Heating or Cooling
Inside Diameter of Pipe
Outside Diameter of Pipe
.25"
.50"
.75"
1.0"
1.5"
2.0"
3.0"
4.0"
Turbulent Velocity Inside of Pipe, (ft)/(sec)
Turbulent Velocity Outside of and Normal to Pipe, (ft)/(sec)

Figure 6.38

Methyl Alcohol, 100% (Liquid)

Methyl Alcohol, 100% (liquid) heating or cooling in turbulent flow within a tube or in turbulent flow outside and normal to a single tube.

Equations: Liquid heating in a tube: $Nu = 0.023(Re)^{0.8}(Pr)^{0.4}$
Liquid cooling in a tube: $Nu = 0.023(Re)^{0.8}(Pr)^{0.3}$
Liquid heating or cooling outside and normal to a single tube: $Nu = 0.385(Re)^{0.56}(Pr)^{0.3}$

Text References: Chapter VI; equations 6.5, 6.6, 6.9, 6.12, 6.13, and 6.14.

Extensions: Refer to section 6.5 for extensions to annular spaces, tube bundles, and flow through helical coils.

Special Conditions: For a liquid heating or cooling within a tube, do not use the graph if the velocity is less than 1 fps.

For a liquid flowing outside and normal to a single tube, do not use the graph for velocity less than 1 fps unless the Reynolds number exceeds 100.

Example: Methyl Alcohol, 100% (liquid) is heating at a mean temperature of 50 F while flowing at 7 fps outside and normal to a bundle of staggered ¾ inch outside diameter tubes. Determine the outside film coefficient.* Estimate the outside coefficient for a similar, but baffled, tube bundle.

Solution: The base value of the outside film coefficient (for flow normal to a *single* tube) is determined as 580 by following the dashed example line, Fig. 6.39. The corrected value for flow normal to a staggered bundle is 30% greater than the base value (refer to part 6 of section 6.5) hence is 1.3(580) = 750 Btu/(hr) (sq ft) (°F). For a baffled tube bundle (refer to part 6 of section 6.5) the film coefficient would be taken at the base value of 580.

***Note:** To determine other heat transfer coefficients for Methyl Alcohol, 100%, use Fig. 6.39 but refer to the examples on the following pages for the appropriate method: Inside film coefficient, page 230; outside film coefficient per lineal foot, page 218; inside film coefficient per lineal foot, use method similar to that for outside film coefficient per lineal foot; inside film coefficient for a helical coil, page 228; overall coefficient, page 224; overall coefficient per lineal foot, page 226.

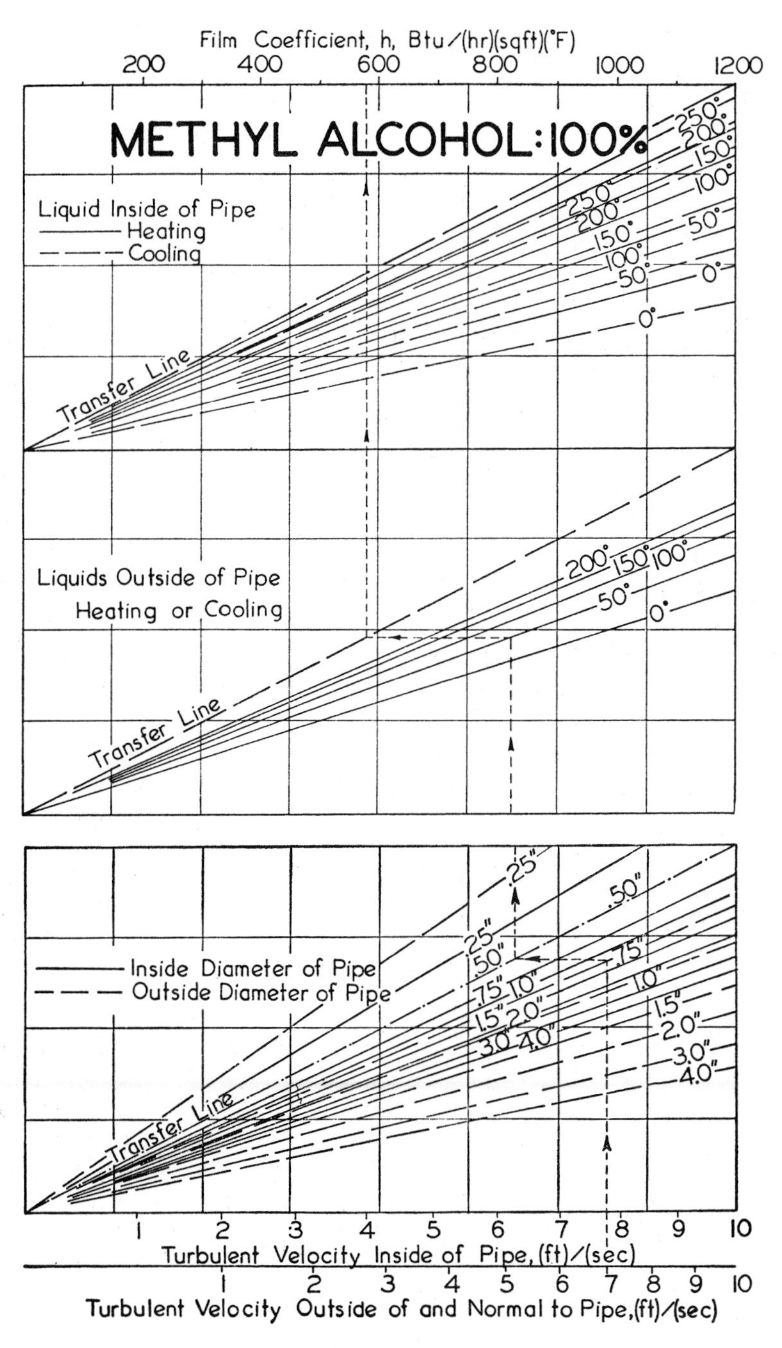
Film Coefficient, h, Btu/(hr)(sqft)(°F)
200 400 600 800 1000 1200
METHYL ALCOHOL: 100%
Liquid Inside of Pipe
Heating
Cooling
250° 200° 150° 100° 50° 0°
Transfer Line
Liquids Outside of Pipe
Heating or Cooling
200° 150° 100° 50° 0°
Transfer Line
Inside Diameter of Pipe
Outside Diameter of Pipe
.25" .50" .75" 1.0" 1.5" 2.0" 3.0" 4.0"
Transfer Line
1 2 3 4 5 6 7 8 9 10
Turbulent Velocity Inside of Pipe, (ft)/(sec)
1 2 3 4 5 6 7 8 9 10
Turbulent Velocity Outside of and Normal to Pipe, (ft)/(sec)

Figure 6.39

Octane, N (Liquid)

Octane, N (liquid) heating or cooling in turbulent flow within a tube or in turbulent flow outside and normal to a single tube.

Equations: Liquid heating in a tube: $Nu = 0.023 (Re)^{0.8} (Pr)^{0.4}$
Liquid cooling in a tube: $Nu = 0.023 (Re)^{0.8} (Pr)^{0.3}$
Liquid heating or cooling outside and normal to a single tube: $Nu = 0.385 (Re)^{0.56} (Pr)^{0.3}$

Text References: Chapter VI; equations 6.5, 6.6, 6.9, 6.12, 6.13, and 6.14.

Extensions: Refer to section 6.5 for extensions to annular spaces, tube bundles, and flow through helical coils.

Special Conditions: For a liquid heating or cooling within a tube, do not use the graph if the velocity is less than 1 fps.

For a liquid flowing outside and normal to a single tube, do not use the graph for velocity less than 1 fps unless the Reynolds number exceeds 100.

Example: Octane, N (liquid) is cooling at a mean temperature of 250 F while flowing outside and normal to a 1″ O.D. Type M copper tube. The fluid velocity is 4 fps. Determine the outside film coefficient* in Btu per hour per °F per *lineal foot* of tube.

Solution: The dashed example line on the graph (Fig. 6.40) shows the method of evaluating the outside film coefficient, for the stated conditions, in terms of one square foot of outside surface of the tube. To convert this value, 310 Btu/(hr) (sq ft) (°F), to a lineal basis refer to Fig. 5.6 and, using a method similar to that shown by the dashed example line, enter the graph at h of 310 and come out at the top scale with a film coefficient of 90 Btu per hour per °F per lineal foot of tube.

***Note:** To determine other heat transfer coefficients for Octane, N, use Fig. 6.40 but refer to the examples on the following pages for the appropriate method: Outside film coefficient, page 232; inside film coefficient, page 230; inside film coefficient per lineal foot, use method similar to that for outside film coefficient per lineal foot; inside film coefficient for a helical coil, page 228; overall coefficient, page 224; overall coefficient per lineal foot, page 226.

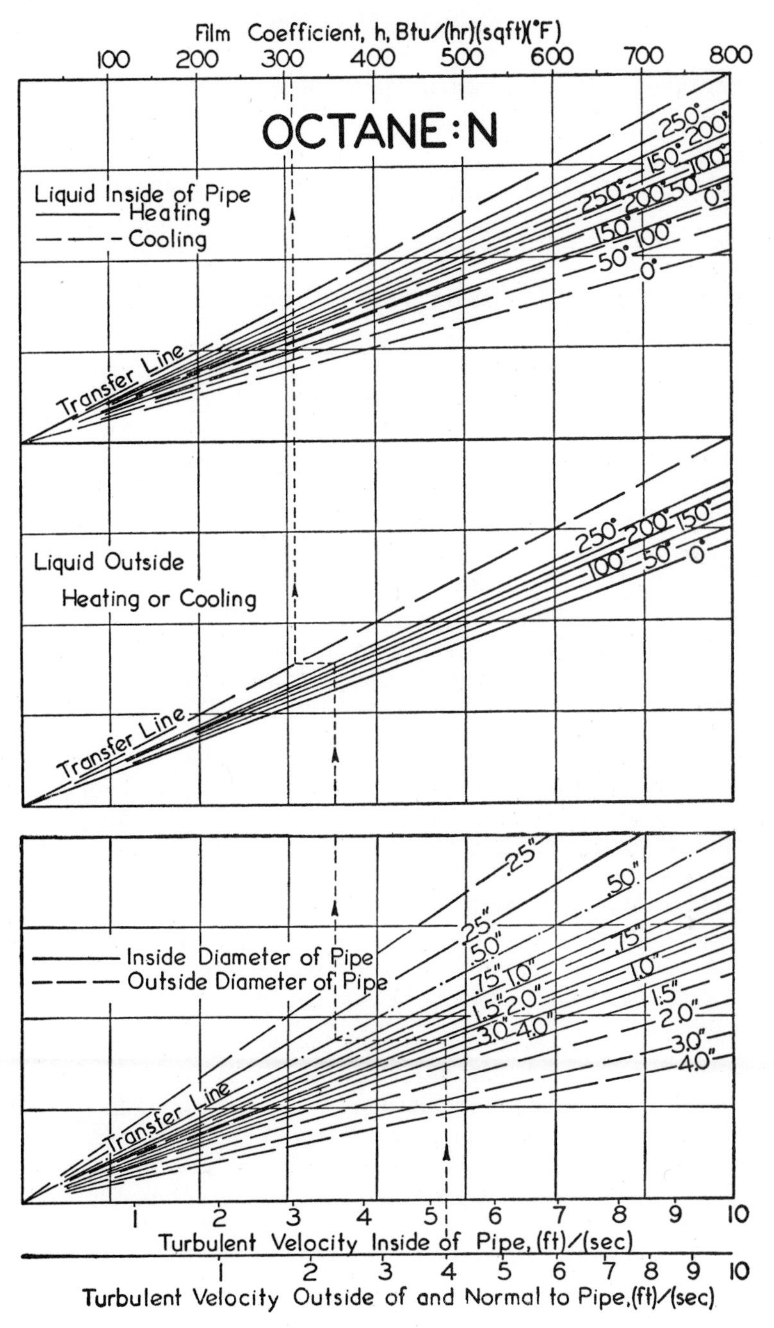
Film Coefficient, h, Btu/(hr)(sqft)(°F)
100 200 300 400 500 600 700 800
OCTANE: N
Liquid Inside of Pipe
Heating
Cooling
250° 200° 150° 100° 50° 0°
Transfer Line
Liquid Outside
Heating or Cooling
250° 200° 150° 100° 50° 0°
Transfer Line
Inside Diameter of Pipe
Outside Diameter of Pipe
.25" .50" .75" 1.0" 1.5" 2.0" 3.0" 4.0"
Transfer Line
1 2 3 4 5 6 7 8 9 10
Turbulent Velocity Inside of Pipe, (ft)/(sec)
1 2 3 4 5 6 7 8 9 10
Turbulent Velocity Outside of and Normal to Pipe, (ft)/(sec)

Figure 6.40

Pentane, N (Liquid)

Pentane, N (liquid) heating or cooling in turbulent flow within a tube or in turbulent flow outside and normal to a single tube.

Equations: Liquid heating in a tube: $Nu = 0.023\,(Re)^{0.8}\,(Pr)^{0.4}$
Liquid cooling in a tube: $Nu = 0.023\,(Re)^{0.8}\,(Pr)^{0.3}$
Liquid heating or cooling outside and normal to a single tube: $Nu = 0.385\,(Re)^{0.56}\,(Pr)^{0.3}$

Text References: Chapter VI; equations 6.5, 6.6, 6.9, 6.12, 6.13, and 6.14.

Extensions: Refer to section 6.5 for extensions to annular spaces, tube bundles, and flow through helical coils.

Special Conditions: For a liquid heating or cooling within a tube, do not use the graph if the velocity is less than 1 fps.

For a liquid flowing outside and normal to a single tube, do not use the graph for velocity less than 1 fps unless the Reynolds number exceeds 100.

Example: Pentane, N (liquid) is in turbulent flow, at 6 fps velocity, through a tube having an inside diameter of 0.25 inches. The fluid is heating at a mean temperature of 100 F. The tube is wound in a helical coil having a diameter of 50 inches. Determine the inside film coefficient.*

Solution: The dashed example line on the graph (Fig. 6.41) shows the method of determining the base value of the inside film coefficient for the conditions of flow through a straight tube; this value is read at the top scale as 620. Now refer to Fig. 6.6, enter the bottom scale at 620, and rise to the radial line for a tube-to-coil ratio of 0.25/50 = 0.005. From this intersection move left to the transfer line, then rise to read the corrected film coefficient for flow within the coil as 630 Btu/(hr) (sq ft) (°F).

***Note:** To determine other heat transfer coefficients for Pentane, N, use Fig. 6.41 but refer to the examples on the following pages for the appropriate method: Outside film coefficient, page 232; inside film coefficient, page 230; outside film coefficient per lineal foot, page 234; inside film coefficient per lineal foot, use method similar to that for outside film coefficient per lineal foot; overall coefficient, page 224; overall coefficient per lineal foot, page 226.

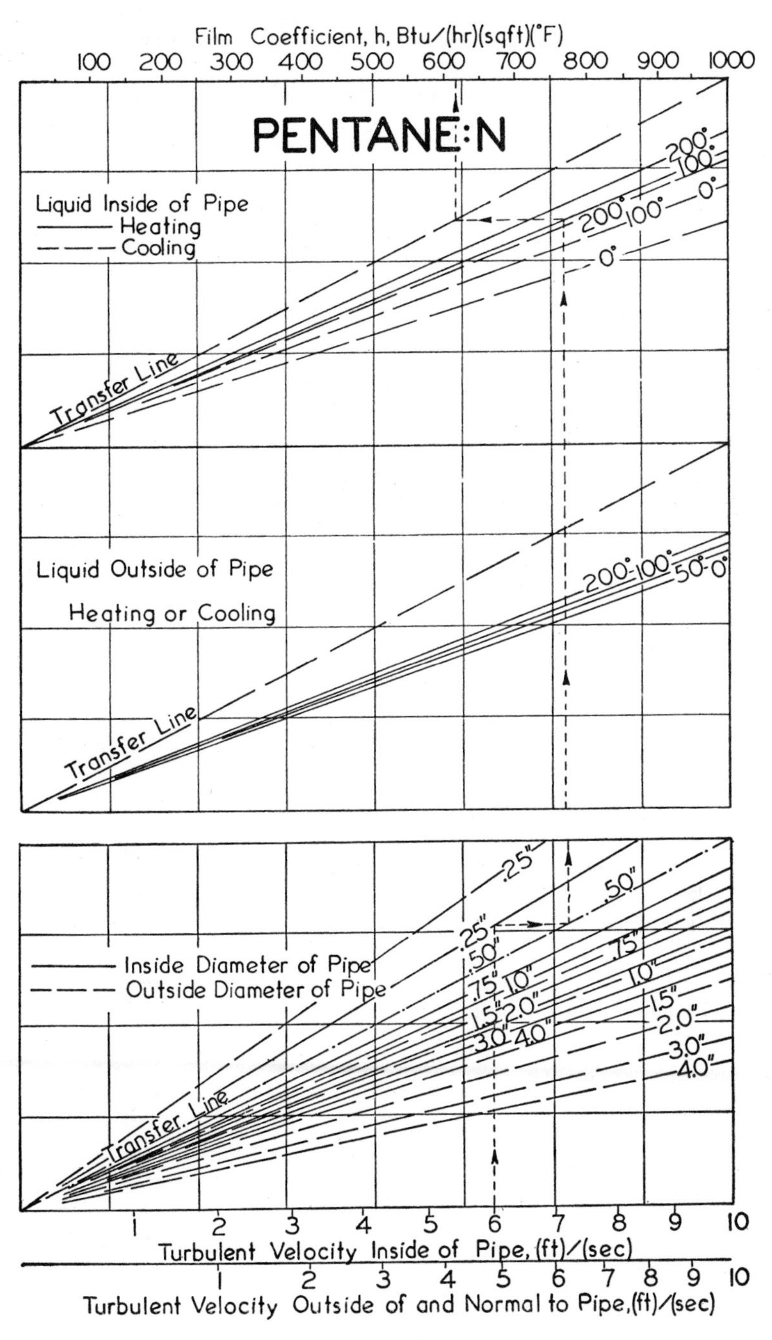
Film Coefficient, h, Btu/(hr)(sqft)(°F)
100 200 300 400 500 600 700 800 900 1000
PENTANE:N
Liquid Inside of Pipe
Heating
Cooling
200° 100° 0°
Transfer Line
Liquid Outside of Pipe
Heating or Cooling
200° 100° 50° 0°
Transfer Line
Inside Diameter of Pipe
Outside Diameter of Pipe
.25" .50" .75" 1.0" 1.5" 2.0" 3.0" 4.0"
Transfer Line
1 2 3 4 5 6 7 8 9 10
Turbulent Velocity Inside of Pipe, (ft)/(sec)
1 2 3 4 5 6 7 8 9 10
Turbulent Velocity Outside of and Normal to Pipe, (ft)/(sec)

Figure 6.41

Petroleum Products, Group I (Liquid)

Petroleum Products, Group I (liquid) heating or cooling in turbulent flow within a tube or in turbulent flow outside and normal to a single tube.

Equations: Liquid heating in a tube: $Nu = 0.023(Re)^{0.8}(Pr)^{0.4}$
Liquid cooling in a tube: $Nu = 0.023(Re)^{0.8}(Pr)^{0.3}$
Liquid heating or cooling outside and normal to a single tube: $Nu = 0.385(Re)^{0.56}(Pr)^{0.3}$

Text References: Chapter VI; equations 6.5, 6.6, 6.9, 6.12, 6.13, and 6.14.

Extensions: Refer to section 6.5 for extensions to annular spaces, tube bundles, and flow through helical coils.

Special Conditions: For a liquid heating or cooling within a tube, do not use the graph unless the value of velocity (fps) exceeds 1.56 for kerosene or 3.0 for diesel oil.

For a liquid flowing outside and normal to a single tube, do not use the graph for velocity less than 1 fps unless the Reynolds number exceeds 100.

Example: Diesel oil (liquid) is cooling while flowing at 7 fps outside and normal to a bundle of staggered 3/4 inch outside diameter tubes. Determine the outside film coefficient.* Estimate the outside coefficient for a similar, but baffled, tube bundle.

Solution: The base value of the outside film coefficient (for flow normal to a *single* tube) is determined as 320 by following the dashed example line, Fig. 6.42. The corrected value for flow normal to a staggered bundle is 30% greater than the base value (refer to part 6 of section 6.5) hence is 1.3(320) = 420 Btu/(hr) (sq ft) (°F). For a baffled tube bundle (refer to part 6 of section 6.5) the film coefficient would be taken at the base value of 320.

***Note:** To determine other heat transfer coefficients for Petroleum Products, Group I, use Fig. 6.42 but refer to the examples on the following pages for the appropriate method: Inside film coefficient, page 230; outside film coefficient per lineal foot, page 234; inside film coefficient per lineal foot, use method similar to that for outside film coefficient per lineal foot; inside film coefficient for a helical coil, page 236; overall coefficient, page 224; overall coefficient per lineal foot, page 226.

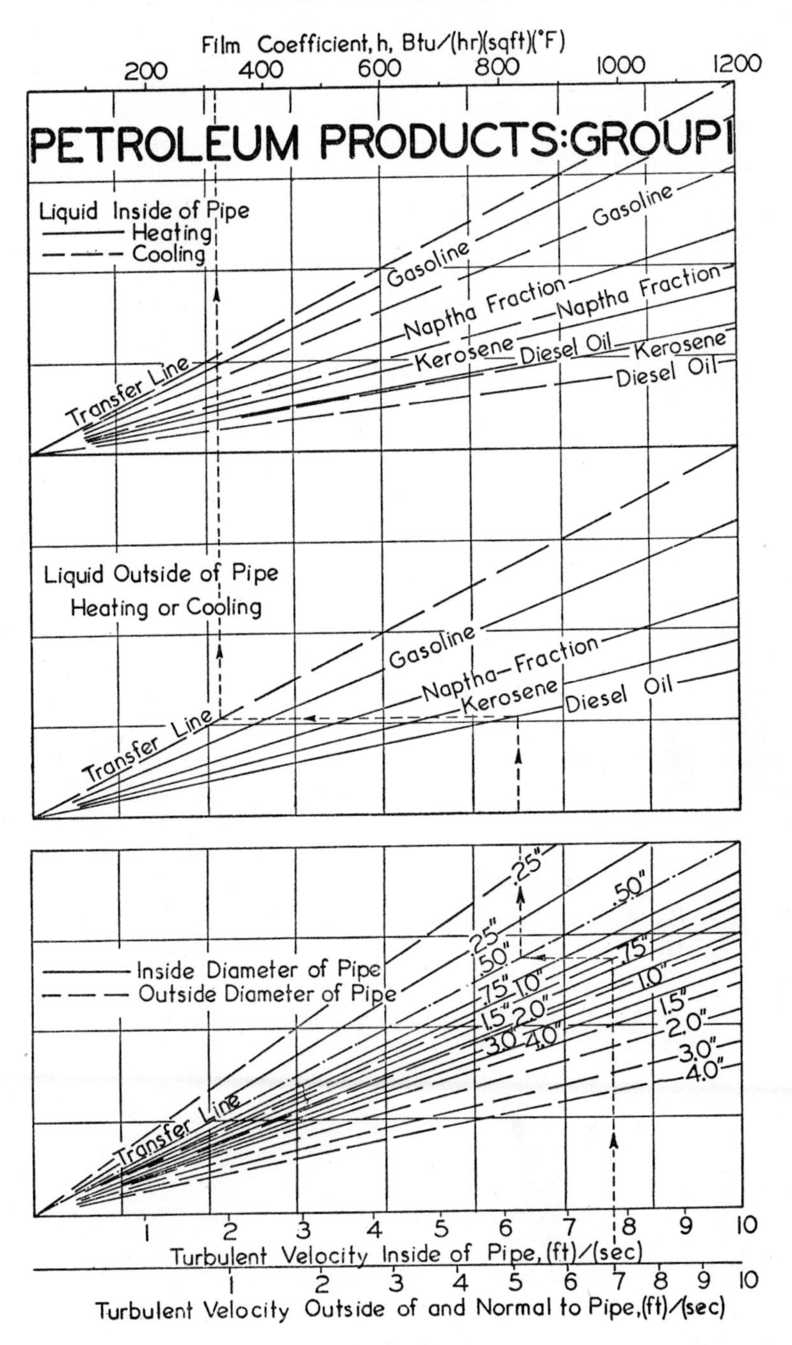

Film Coefficient, h, Btu/(hr)(sqft)(°F)
200
400
600
800
1000
1200
PETROLEUM PRODUCTS:GROUP I
Liquid Inside of Pipe
Heating
Cooling
Gasoline
Gasoline
Naptha Fraction
Naptha Fraction
Kerosene
Diesel Oil
Kerosene
Diesel Oil
Transfer Line
Liquid Outside of Pipe
Heating or Cooling
Gasoline
Naptha–Fraction
Kerosene
Diesel Oil
Transfer Line
Inside Diameter of Pipe
Outside Diameter of Pipe
.25"
.50"
.75"
1.0"
1.5"
2.0"
3.0"
4.0"
Transfer Line
1
2
3
4
5
6
7
8
9
10
Turbulent Velocity Inside of Pipe, (ft)/(sec)
Turbulent Velocity Outside of and Normal to Pipe, (ft)/(sec)

Figure 6.42

Petroleum Products, Group II (Liquid)

Petroleum Products, Group II (liquid) heating or cooling in turbulent flow within a tube or in turbulent flow outside and normal to a single tube.

Equations: Liquid heating in a tube: $Nu = 0.023(Re)^{0.8}(Pr)^{0.4}$
Liquid cooling in a tube: $Nu = 0.023(Re)^{0.8}(Pr)^{0.3}$
Liquid heating or cooling outside and normal to a single tube: $Nu = 0.385(Re)^{0.56}(Pr)^{0.3}$

Text References: Chapter VI; equations 6.5, 6.6, 6.9, 6.12, 6.13, and 6.14.

Extensions: Refer to section 6.5 for extensions to annular spaces, tube bundles, and flow through helical coils.

Special Conditions: For a liquid heating or cooling within a tube, do not use the graph unless the value of velocity (fps) exceeds 1.23 for naphtha or 2.95 for crude oil.

For a liquid flowing outside and normal to a single tube, do not use the graph for velocity less than 1 fps unless the Reynolds number exceeds 100.

Example: Mid-continent crude oil (liquid) is flowing inside a tube of 2″ I.D. at a velocity of 2 fps. The fluid is cooling. If the outside film coefficient is 25 determine the overall coefficient* of heat transfer assuming that the tube is so thin-walled that its thermal resistance is negligible and the difference between inside and outside surface areas can be neglected.

Solution: For the stated conditions the base value of the inside film coefficient is determinable (dashed example line, Fig. 6.43) as 55 Btu/(hr) (sq ft) (°F). Now go to Fig. 5.7 and (by a method similar to that shown by the dashed line) for inside and outside film coefficients of 55 and 25, respectively, read the overall coefficient of heat transfer as 16 Btu/(hr) (sq ft) (°F).

***Note:** To determine other heat transfer coefficients for Petroleum Products, Group II, use Fig. 6.43 but refer to the examples on the following pages for the appropriate method: Outside film coefficient, page 238; inside film coefficient, page 230; outside film coefficient per lineal foot, page 234; inside film coefficient per lineal foot, use method similar to that for outside film coefficient per lineal foot; inside film coefficient for a helical coil, page 236; overall coefficient per lineal foot, page 226.

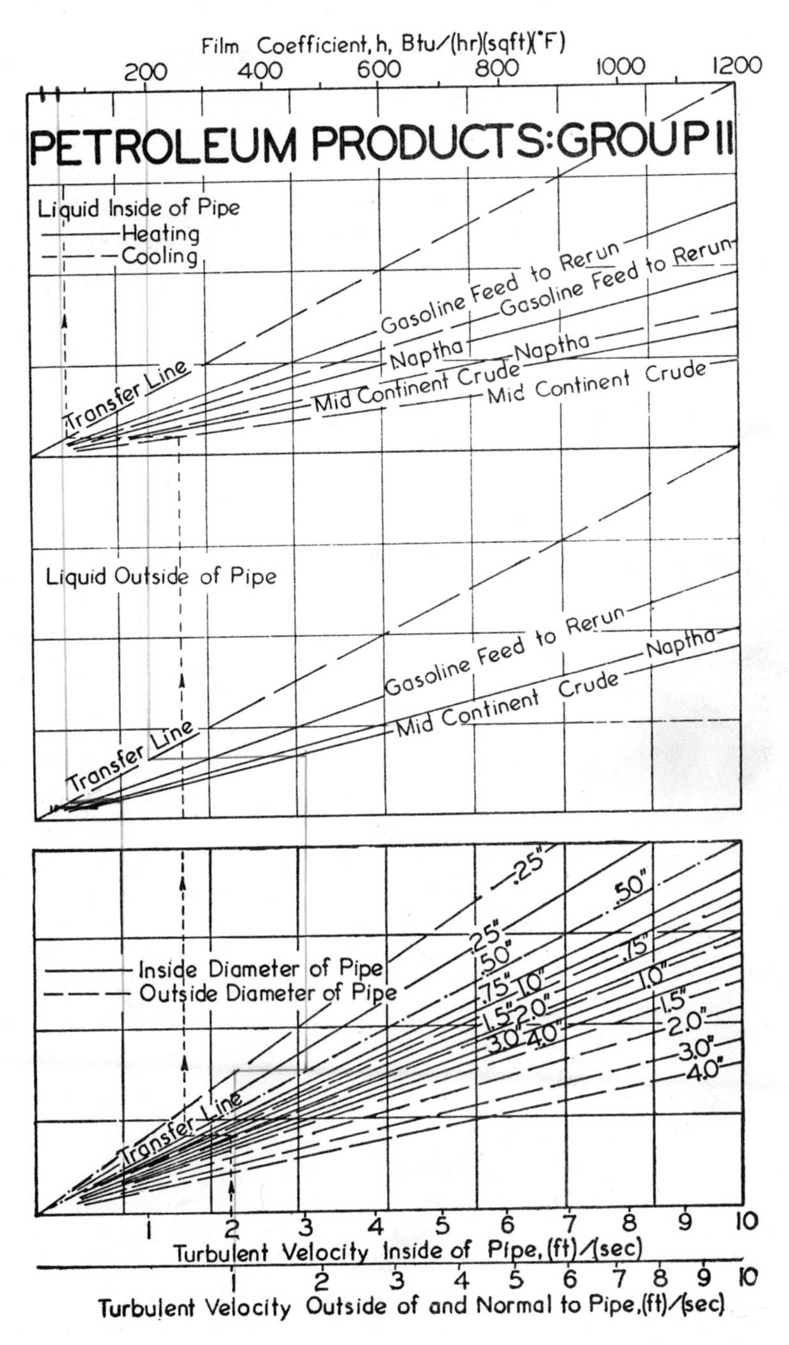
Film Coefficient, h, Btu/(hr)(sqft)(°F)
200
400
600
800
1000
1200
PETROLEUM PRODUCTS: GROUP II
Liquid Inside of Pipe
Heating
Cooling
Gasoline Feed to Rerun
Gasoline Feed to Rerun
Naptha
Naptha
Mid Continent Crude
Mid Continent Crude
Transfer Line
Liquid Outside of Pipe
Gasoline Feed to Rerun
Naptha
Mid Continent Crude
Transfer Line
Inside Diameter of Pipe
Outside Diameter of Pipe
Transfer Line
1 2 3 4 5 6 7 8 9 10
Turbulent Velocity Inside of Pipe, (ft)/(sec)
1 2 3 4 5 6 7 8 9 10
Turbulent Velocity Outside of and Normal to Pipe, (ft)/(sec)

Figure 6.43

Propyl Alcohol, Iso (Liquid)

Propyl Alcohol, Iso (liquid) heating or cooling in turbulent flow within a tube or in turbulent flow outside and normal to a single tube.

Equations: Liquid heating in a tube: $Nu = 0.023(Re)^{0.8}(Pr)^{0.4}$
Liquid cooling in a tube: $Nu = 0.023(Re)^{0.8}(Pr)^{0.3}$
Liquid heating or cooling outside and normal to a single tube: $Nu = 0.385(Re)^{0.56}(Pr)^{0.3}$

Text References: Chapter VI; equations 6.5, 6.6, 6.9, 6.12, 6.13, and 6.14.

Extensions: Refer to section 6.5 for extensions to annular spaces, tube bundles, and flow through helical coils.

Special Conditions: For a liquid heating or cooling within a tube, do not use the graph unless the value of velocity (fps) times diameter (inches) exceeds 5.4 for 50 F or 0.6 for 250 F.

For a liquid flowing outside and normal to a single tube, do not use the graph for velocity less than 1 fps unless the Reynolds number exceeds 100.

Example: Propyl Alcohol, Iso (liquid) is flowing at 4 fps outside and normal to a phosphorized copper tube (Type L) having outside diameter of 1″ and wall thickness of 0.065″. The fluid is cooling at 150 F. The inside film coefficient is known to be 800 Btu/(hr) (°F) (sq ft of inside surface). Determine the overall coefficient* of heat transfer per *lineal* foot of tube.

Solution: The dashed example line on the graph (Fig. 6.44) determines the outside coefficient as 305. From Fig. 5.5 the inside and outside coefficients, 800 and 305, can be converted to values of 200 and 112, respectively, based on one lineal foot of tube. From Fig. 2.4 the thermal resistance of the tube is 0.00003 (based on outside area), giving a conductance of 33,000 which (Fig. 5.5) becomes 9,000 per lineal foot. The overall coefficient, equation 5.2, is then $U = 1/[1/200 + 1/9{,}000 + 1/112] = 71$ Btu/(hr) (°F) (lineal foot of tube).

***Note:** To determine other heat transfer coefficients for Propyl Alcohol, Iso, use Fig. 6.44 but refer to the examples on the following pages for the appropriate method: Outside film coefficient, page 238; inside film coefficient, page 230; outside film coefficient per lineal foot, page 234; inside film coefficient per lineal foot, use method similar to that for outside film coefficient per lineal foot; inside film coefficient for a helical coil, page 236; overall coefficient, page 240.

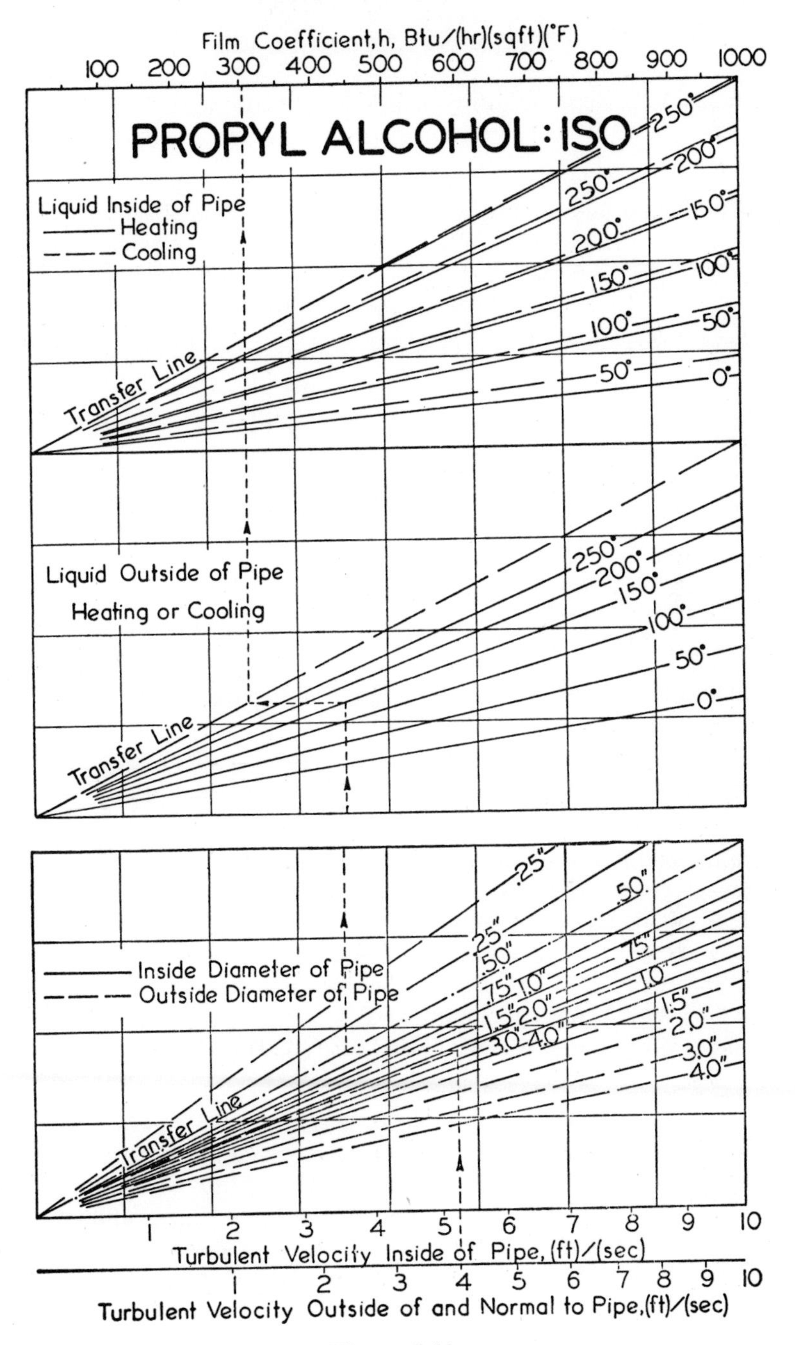
Film Coefficient, h, Btu/(hr)(sqft)(°F)
100 200 300 400 500 600 700 800 900 1000
PROPYL ALCOHOL: ISO
Liquid Inside of Pipe
Heating
Cooling
Transfer Line
250° 200° 150° 100° 50° 0°
Liquid Outside of Pipe
Heating or Cooling
Inside Diameter of Pipe
Outside Diameter of Pipe
.25" .50" .75" 1.0" 1.5" 2.0" 3.0" 4.0"
1 2 3 4 5 6 7 8 9 10
Turbulent Velocity Inside of Pipe, (ft)/(sec)
Turbulent Velocity Outside of and Normal to Pipe, (ft)/(sec)

Figure 6.44

Sugar Solutions (Liquid)

Sugar Solutions (liquid) heating or cooling in turbulent flow within a tube or in turbulent flow outside and normal to a single tube.

Equations: Liquid heating in a tube: $Nu = 0.023 (Re)^{0.8} (Pr)^{0.4}$
Liquid cooling in a tube: $Nu = 0.023 (Re)^{0.8} (Pr)^{0.3}$
Liquid heating or cooling outside and normal to a single tube: $Nu = 0.385 (Re)^{0.56} (Pr)^{0.3}$

Text References: Chapter VI; equations 6.5, 6.6, 6.9, 6.12, 6.13, and 6.14.

Extensions: Refer to section 6.5 for extensions to annular spaces, tube bundles, and flow through helical coils.

Special Conditions: For a liquid heating or cooling within a tube, do not use the graph unless the value of velocity (fps) exceeds 0.26 for 10% or 0.68 for 40% sucrose.

For a liquid flowing outside and normal to a single tube, do not use the graph for velocity less than 1 fps unless the Reynolds number exceeds 100.

Example: A Sugar Solution (liquid) is in turbulent flow, at 6 fps velocity, through a tube having an inside diameter of 0.25 inches. The solution is of 10% sucrose concentration and is cooling at 60 F. The tube is wound in a helical coil having a diameter of 50 inches. Determine the inside film coefficient.*

Solution: The dashed example line on the graph (Fig. 6.45) shows the method of determining the base value of the inside film coefficient for the conditions of flow through a straight tube; this value is read at the top scale as 1140. Now referring to Fig. 6.6 it will be noticed that the scale is not large enough to yield the corrected value of film coefficient and it must be calculated by using equation 6.18: $h = 1140 (1 + 3.5 \times 0.250/50) = 1160$ Btu/(hr) (sq ft) (°F).

*__Note:__ To determine other heat transfer coefficients for Sugar Solutions, use Fig. 6.45 but refer to the examples on the following pages for the appropriate method: Outside film coefficient, page 238; inside film coefficient, page 230; outside film coefficient per lineal foot, page 234; inside film coefficient per lineal foot, use method similar to that for outside film coefficient per lineal foot; overall coefficient, page 240; overall coefficient per lineal foot, page 242.

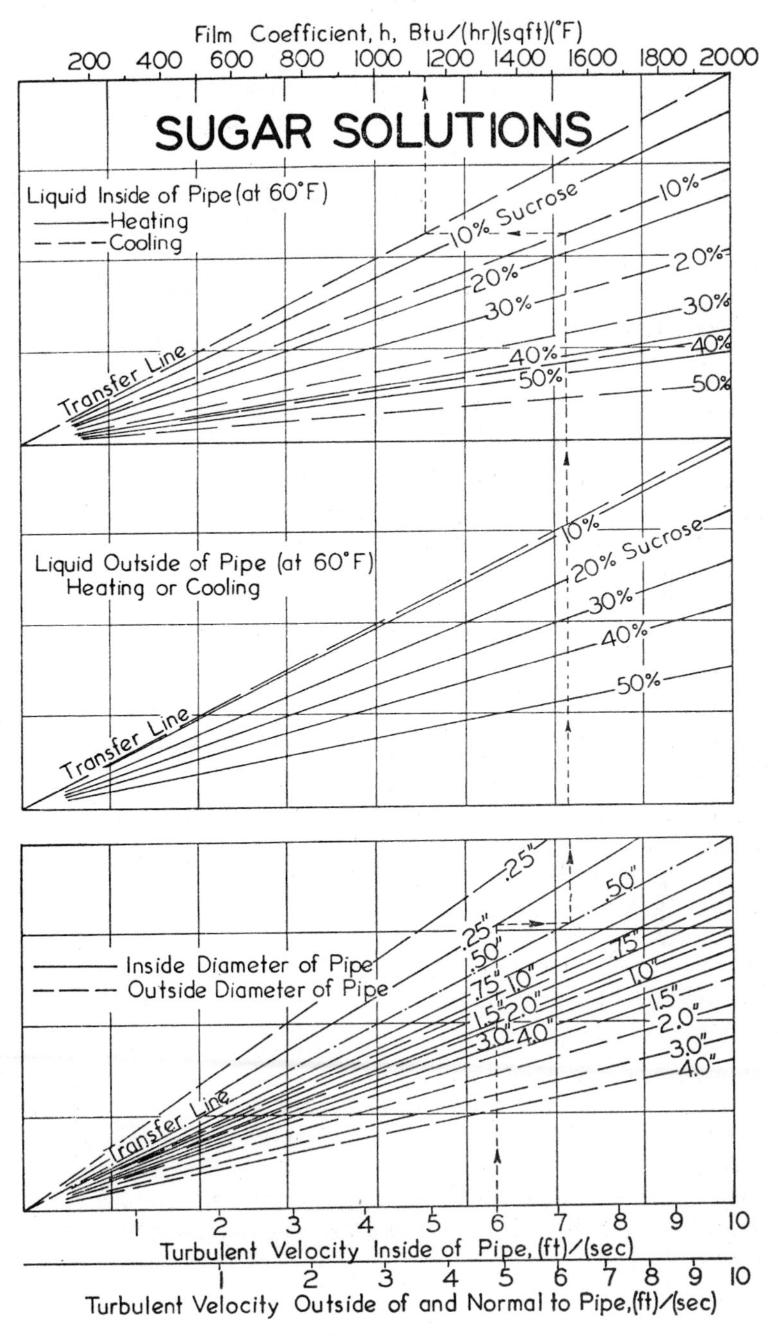
Film Coefficient, h, Btu/(hr)(sqft)(°F)
200 400 600 800 1000 1200 1400 1600 1800 2000
SUGAR SOLUTIONS
Liquid Inside of Pipe (at 60°F)
Heating
Cooling
10% Sucrose
10%
20%
30%
40%
50%
Transfer Line
Liquid Outside of Pipe (at 60°F)
Heating or Cooling
10%
20% Sucrose
30%
40%
50%
Transfer Line
Inside Diameter of Pipe
Outside Diameter of Pipe
.25"
.50"
.75"
1.0"
1.5"
2.0"
3.0"
4.0"
Transfer Line
1 2 3 4 5 6 7 8 9 10
Turbulent Velocity Inside of Pipe, (ft)/(sec)
1 2 3 4 5 6 7 8 9 10
Turbulent Velocity Outside of and Normal to Pipe, (ft)/(sec)

Figure 6.45

Sulfur Dioxide (Liquid)

Sulfur Dioxide (liquid) heating or cooling in turbulent flow within a tube or in turbulent flow outside and normal to a single tube.

Equations: Liquid heating in a tube: $Nu = 0.023(Re)^{0.8}(Pr)^{0.4}$
Liquid cooling in a tube: $Nu = 0.023(Re)^{0.8}(Pr)^{0.3}$
Liquid heating or cooling outside and normal to a single tube: $Nu = 0.385(Re)^{0.56}(Pr)^{0.3}$

Text References: Chapter VI; equations 6.5, 6.6, 6.9, 6.12, 6.13, and 6.14.

Extensions: Refer to section 6.5 for extensions to annular spaces, tube bundles, and flow through helical coils.

Special Conditions: For a liquid heating or cooling within a tube, do not use the graph if the velocity is less than 1 fps.

For a liquid flowing outside and normal to a single tube, do not use the graph for velocity less than 1 fps unless the Reynolds number exceeds 100.

Example: Sulfur Dioxide (liquid) is heating at a mean temperature of 0 F while flowing at 7 fps outside and normal to a bundle of staggered ¾ inch outside diameter tubes. Determine the outside film coefficient.* Estimate the outside coefficient for a similar, but baffled, tube bundle.

Solution: The base value of the outside film coefficient (for flow normal to a *single* tube) is determined as 870 by following the dashed example line, Fig. 6.46. The corrected value for flow normal to a staggered bundle is 30% greater than the base value (refer to part 6 of section 6.5) hence is 1.3(870) = 1130 Btu/(hr) (sq ft) (°F). For a baffled tube bundle (refer to part 6 of section 6.5) the film coefficient would be taken at the base value of 870.

***Note:** To determine other heat transfer coefficients for Sulfur Dioxide, use Fig. 6.46 but refer to the examples on the following pages for the appropriate method: Inside film coefficient, page 230; outside film coefficient per lineal foot, page 234; inside film coefficient per lineal foot, use method similar to that for outside film coefficient per lineal foot; inside film coefficient for a helical coil, page 244; overall coefficient, page 240; overall coefficient per lineal foot, page 242.

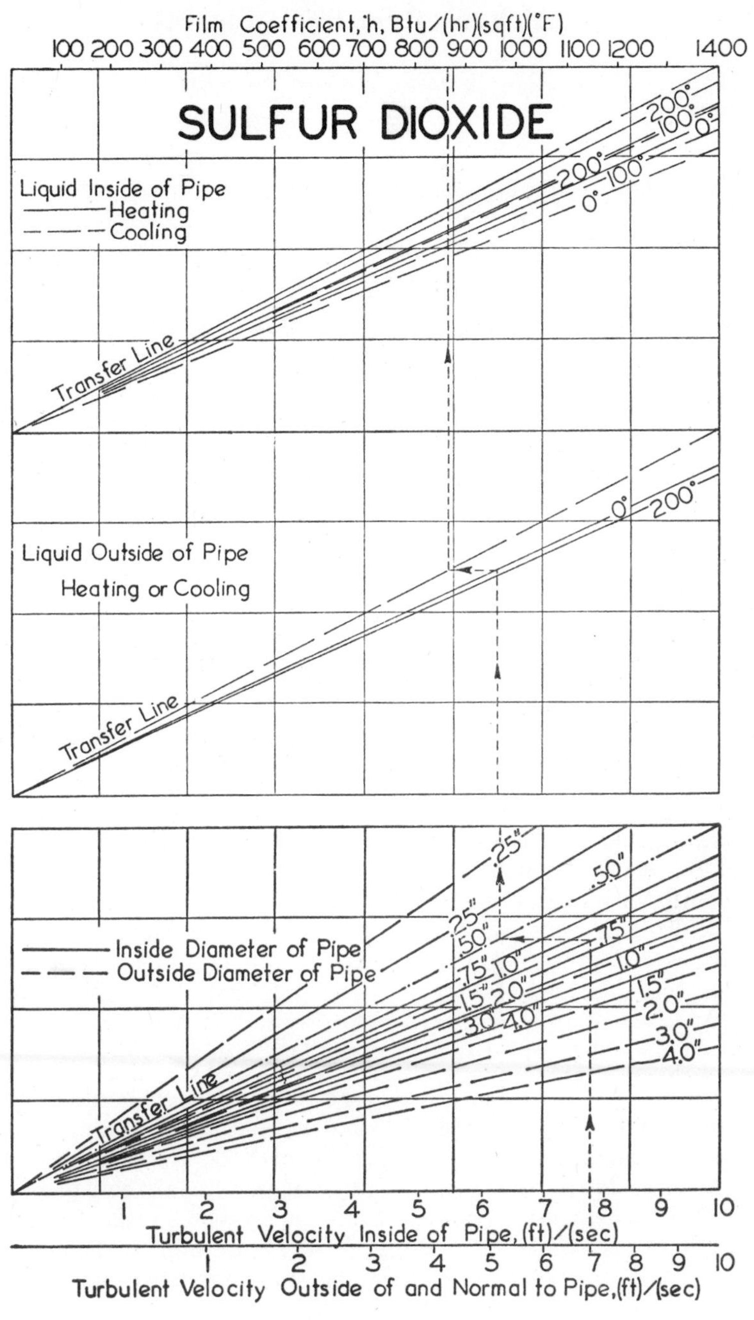
Film Coefficient, h, Btu/(hr)(sqft)(°F)
100 200 300 400 500 600 700 800 900 1000 1100 1200 1400
SULFUR DIOXIDE
Liquid Inside of Pipe
Heating
Cooling
200° 100° 0°
200° 100° 0°
Transfer Line
Liquid Outside of Pipe
Heating or Cooling
0° 200°
Transfer Line
Inside Diameter of Pipe
Outside Diameter of Pipe
.25" .50" .75" 1.0" 1.5" 2.0" 3.0" 4.0"
Transfer Line
1 2 3 4 5 6 7 8 9 10
Turbulent Velocity Inside of Pipe, (ft)/(sec)
1 2 3 4 5 6 7 8 9 10
Turbulent Velocity Outside of and Normal to Pipe, (ft)/(sec)

Figure 6.46

Sulphuric Acid, 60% (Liquid)

Sulfuric Acid, 60% (liquid) heating or cooling in turbulent flow within a tube or in turbulent flow outside and normal to a single tube.

Equations: Liquid heating in a tube: $Nu = 0.023(Re)^{0.8}(Pr)^{0.4}$
Liquid cooling in a tube: $Nu = 0.023(Re)^{0.8}(Pr)^{0.3}$
Liquid heating or cooling outside and normal to a single tube: $Nu = 0.385(Re)^{0.56}(Pr)^{0.3}$

Text References: Chapter VI; equations 6.5, 6.6, 6.9, 6.12, 6.13, and 6.14.

Extensions: Refer to section 6.5 for extensions to annular spaces, tube bundles, and flow through helical coils.

Special Conditions: For a liquid heating or cooling within a tube, do not use the graph unless the value of velocity (fps) times diameter (inches) exceeds 6.5 for 50 F or 1.7 for 250 F.

For a liquid flowing outside and normal to a single tube, do not use the graph for velocity less than 1 fps unless the Reynolds number exceeds 100.

Example: Sulfuric Acid, 60% (liquid) is flowing within a 2 inch inside diameter tube at a velocity of 2 fps. The fluid is at a mean temperature of 200 F and is being heated. Determine the inside film coefficient.*

Solution: Enter the bottom scale of the graph (Fig. 6.47) at inside velocity of 2 fps and rise to intersect the solid radial line for a 2 inch inside diameter tube. From this intersection move left to the transfer line and then rise to the top section of the graph where radial lines are given for liquid heating and cooling *inside* a tube. In this section intersect the solid radial for liquid heating at 200 F. From this intersection move left to the transfer line and then rise to the top scale of the graph where read the value of the inside film coefficient as 165 Btu/(hr) (sq ft) (°F).

***Note:** To determine other heat transfer coefficients for Sulphuric Acid, 60%, use Fig. 6.47 but refer to the examples on the following pages for the appropriate method: Outside film coefficient, page 246; outside film coefficient per lineal foot, page 234; inside film coefficient per lineal foot, use method similar to that for outside film coefficient per lineal foot; inside film coefficient for a helical coil, page 244; overall coefficient, page 240; overall coefficient per lineal foot, page 242.

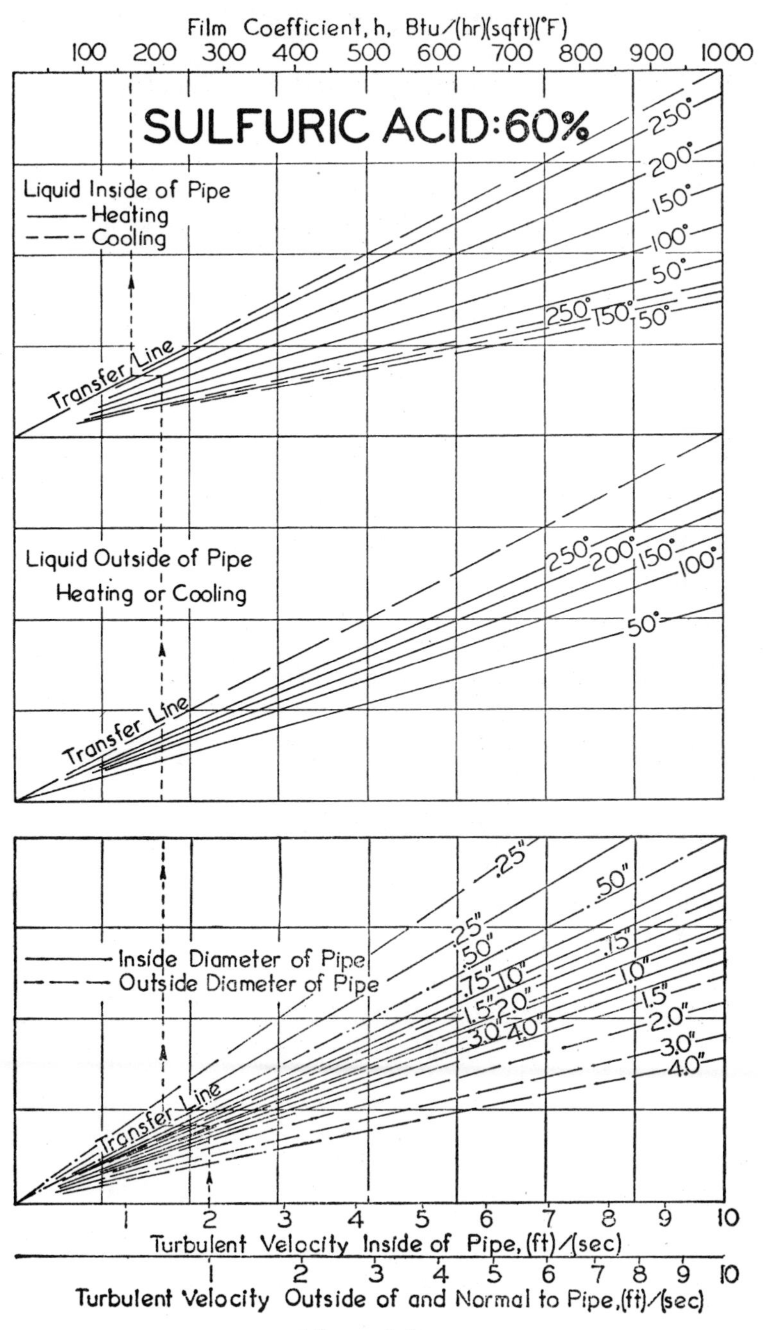
Film Coefficient, h, Btu/(hr)(sqft)(°F)
100 200 300 400 500 600 700 800 900 1000
SULFURIC ACID: 60%
Liquid Inside of Pipe
Heating
Cooling
250°
200°
150°
100°
50°
250° 150° 50°
Transfer Line
Liquid Outside of Pipe
Heating or Cooling
250° 200° 150° 100°
50°
Transfer Line
Inside Diameter of Pipe
Outside Diameter of Pipe
.25"
.50"
.25"
.50"
.75" 1.0"
1.5" 2.0"
3.0" 4.0"
.75"
1.0"
1.5"
2.0"
3.0"
4.0"
Transfer Line
1 2 3 4 5 6 7 8 9 10
Turbulent Velocity Inside of Pipe, (ft)/(sec)
1 2 3 4 5 6 7 8 9 10
Turbulent Velocity Outside of and Normal to Pipe, (ft)/(sec)

Figure 6.47

Toluene (Liquid)

Toluene (liquid) heating or cooling in turbulent flow within a tube or in turbulent flow outside and normal to a single tube.

Equations: Liquid heating in a tube: $Nu = 0.023(Re)^{0.8}(Pr)^{0.4}$
Liquid cooling in a tube: $Nu = 0.023(Re)^{0.8}(Pr)^{0.3}$
Liquid heating or cooling outside and normal to a single tube: $Nu = 0.385(Re)^{0.56}(Pr)^{0.3}$

Text References: Chapter VI; equations 6.5, 6.6, 6.9, 6.12, 6.13, and 6.14.

Extensions: Refer to section 6.5 for extensions to annular spaces, tube bundles, and flow through helical coils.

Special Conditions: For a liquid heating or cooling within a tube, do not use the graph if the velocity is less than 1 fps.

For a liquid flowing outside and normal to a single tube, do not use the graph for velocity less than 1 fps unless the Reynolds number exceeds 100.

Example: Toluene (liquid) is cooling at a mean temperature of 200 F while flowing outside and normal to a 1″ O.D. Type M copper tube. The fluid velocity is 4 fps. Determine the outside film coefficient* in Btu per hour per °F per *lineal foot* of tube.

Solution: The dashed example line on the graph (Fig. 6.48) shows the method of evaluating the outside film coefficient, for the stated conditions, in terms of one square foot of outside surface of the tube. To convert this value, 325 Btu/(hr) (sq ft) (°F), to a lineal basis refer to Fig. 5.6 and, using a method similar to that shown by the dashed example line, enter the graph at *h* of 325 and come out at the top scale with a film coefficient of 96 Btu per hour per °F per lineal foot of tube.

***Note:** To determine other heat transfer coefficients for Toluene, use Fig. 6.48 but refer to the examples on the following pages for the appropriate method: Outside film coefficient, page 246; inside film coefficient, page 248; inside film coefficient per lineal foot, use method similar to that for outside film coefficient per lineal foot; inside film coefficient for a helical coil, page 244; overall coefficient, page 240; overall coefficient per lineal foot, page 242.

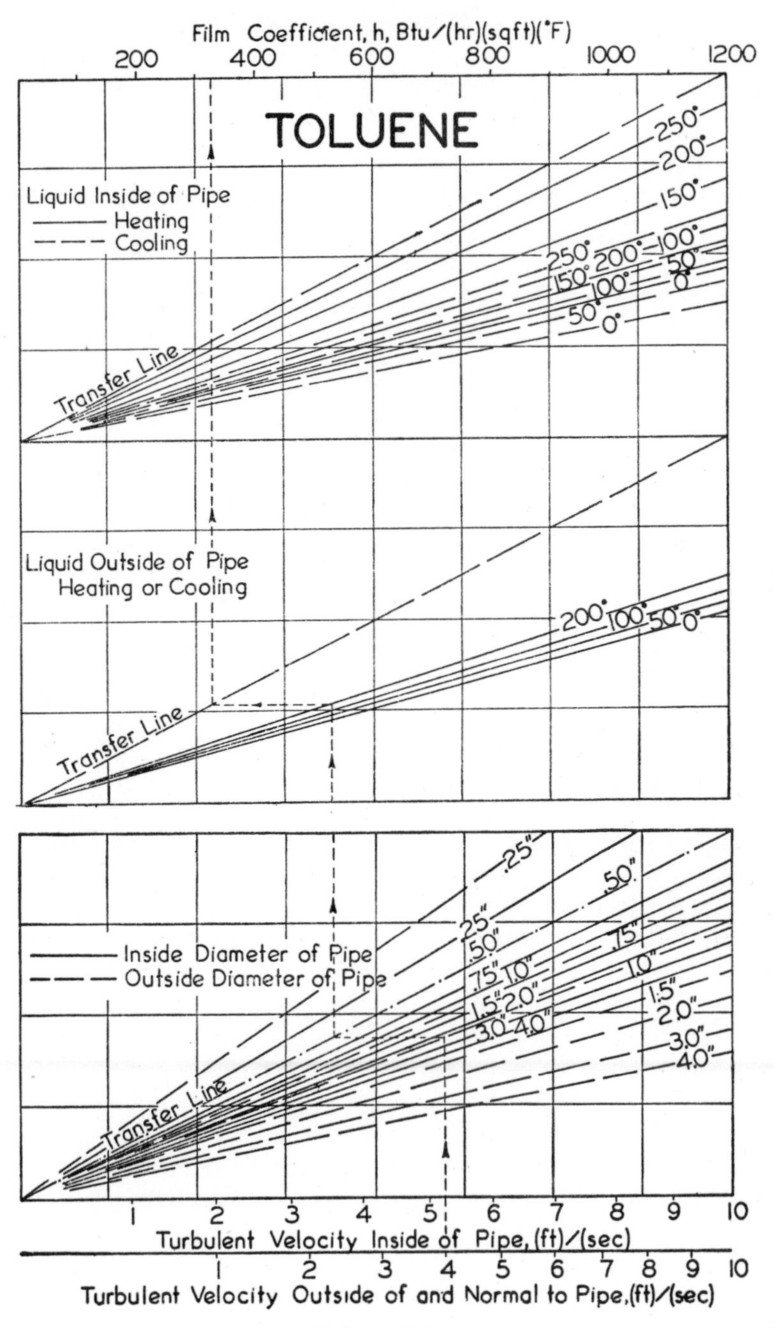

Film Coefficient, h, Btu/(hr)(sqft)(°F)
200
400
600
800
1000
1200
TOLUENE
Liquid Inside of Pipe
Heating
Cooling
250°
200°
150°
100°
50°
0°
Transfer Line
Liquid Outside of Pipe
Heating or Cooling
Inside Diameter of Pipe
Outside Diameter of Pipe
.25"
.50"
.75"
1.0"
1.5"
2.0"
3.0"
4.0"
Turbulent Velocity Inside of Pipe, (ft)/(sec)
Turbulent Velocity Outside of and Normal to Pipe, (ft)/(sec)

Figure 6.48

Water (Liquid)

Water (liquid) heating or cooling in turbulent flow within a tube or in turbulent flow outside and normal to a single tube.

Equations: Liquid heating in a tube: $Nu = 0.023(Re)^{0.8}(Pr)^{0.4}$
Liquid cooling in a tube: $Nu = 0.023(Re)^{0.8}(Pr)^{0.3}$
Liquid heating or cooling outside and normal to a single tube: $Nu = 0.385(Re)^{0.56}(Pr)^{0.3}$

Text References: Chapter VI; equations 6.5, 6.6, 6.9, 6.12, 6.13, and 6.14.

Extensions: Refer to section 6.5 for extensions to annular spaces, tube bundles, and flow through helical coils.

Special Conditions: For a liquid heating or cooling within a tube, do not use the graph if the velocity is less than 1 fps.

For a liquid flowing outside and normal to a single tube, do not use the graph for velocity less than 1 fps unless the Reynolds number exceeds 100.

Example: Water (liquid) is in turbulent flow, at 6 fps velocity, through a tube having an inside diameter of 0.25 inches. The fluid is heating at a mean temperature of 200 F. The tube is wound in a helical coil having a diameter of 50 inches. Determine the inside film coefficient.*

Solution: The dashed example line on the graph (Fig. 6.49) shows the method of determining the base value of the inside film coefficient for the conditions of flow through a straight tube; this value is read at the top scale as 2500. Now referring to Fig. 6.6 it will be noticed the scale is not large enough to yield the corrected value of film coefficient and it must be calculated by using equation 6.18: $h = 2500(1 + 3.5 \times 0.250/50) = 2545$ Btu/(hr) (sq ft) (°F).

***Note:** To determine other heat transfer coefficients for Water, use Fig. 6.49 but refer to the examples on the following pages for the appropriate method: Outside film coefficient, page 246; inside film coefficient, page 248; outside film coefficient per lineal foot, page 250; inside film coefficient per lineal foot, use method similar to that for outside film coefficient per lineal foot; overall coefficient, page 240; overall coefficient per lineal foot, page 242.

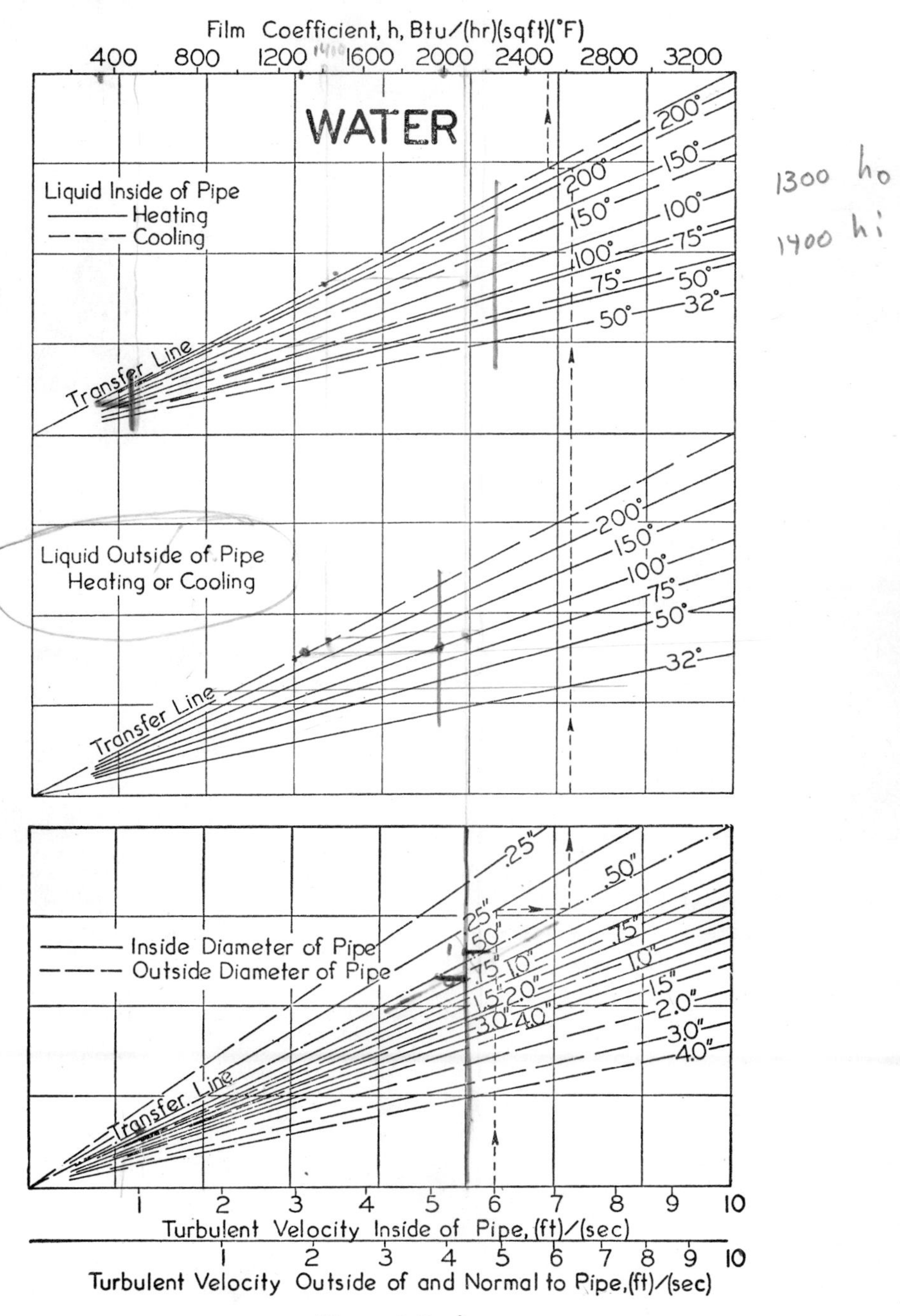
Film Coefficient, h, Btu/(hr)(sqft)(°F)
400 800 1200 1600 2000 2400 2800 3200
WATER
Liquid Inside of Pipe
Heating
Cooling
200° 150° 100° 75° 50° 32°
Transfer Line
Liquid Outside of Pipe
Heating or Cooling
Inside Diameter of Pipe
Outside Diameter of Pipe
.25" .50" .75" 1.0" 1.5" 2.0" 3.0" 4.0"
1 2 3 4 5 6 7 8 9 10
Turbulent Velocity Inside of Pipe, (ft)/(sec)
Turbulent Velocity Outside of and Normal to Pipe, (ft)/(sec)
1300 ho
1400 hi

Figure 6.49

Acetone (Vapor)

Acetone (vapor) heating or cooling in turbulent flow within a tube or in turbulent flow outside and normal to a single tube.

Equations: Gas or vapor heating or cooling within a tube:
$Nu = 0.023(Re)^{0.8}(Pr)^{0.4}$
Gas or vapor heating or cooling outside and normal to a single tube: $Nu = 0.385(Re)^{0.56}(Pr)^{0.3}$

Text References: Chapter VI; equations 6.5, 6.9, 6.12, and 6.14.

Extensions: Refer to section 6.5 for extensions to annular spaces, tube bundles, and flow through helical coils.

Special Conditions: For a gas or vapor heating or cooling within a tube, do not use the graph unless the weight velocity, $V\rho$ (ft/sec) (lb/cu ft), exceeds 0.5 at 1 atmosphere, 2 at 10 atmospheres, or 3.0 at 20 atmospheres.

For a gas or vapor flowing outside and normal to a single tube, do not use the graph for $V\rho$ less than 0.1 unless the Reynolds number exceeds 100.

Example: Acetone (vapor) is being heated while flowing within a tube having an inside diameter of 1/4 inch. The weight velocity is 10 (ft/sec) (lb/cu ft) and the mean temperature is 300 F. Determine the value of the inside film coefficient.*

Solution: Enter the bottom of the graph (Fig. 6.50) at a weight velocity of 10 and rise to intersect the radial line for a tube of 1/4″ inside diameter. From this intersection move right to intersect the transfer line, then rise to the group of radials for fluid inside; intersect the radial for a temperature of 300 F then move left to the transfer line and from this intersection rise to read the answer at the top scale as 43 Btu/(hr) (sq ft) (°F).

*__Note:__ To determine other heat transfer coefficients for Acetone, use Fig. 6.50 but refer to the examples on the following pages for the appropriate method: Outside film coefficient, page 256; outside film coefficient per lineal foot, page 260; inside film coefficient per lineal foot, use method similar to that for outside film coefficient per lineal foot; inside film coefficient for a double-pipe exchanger, page 258.

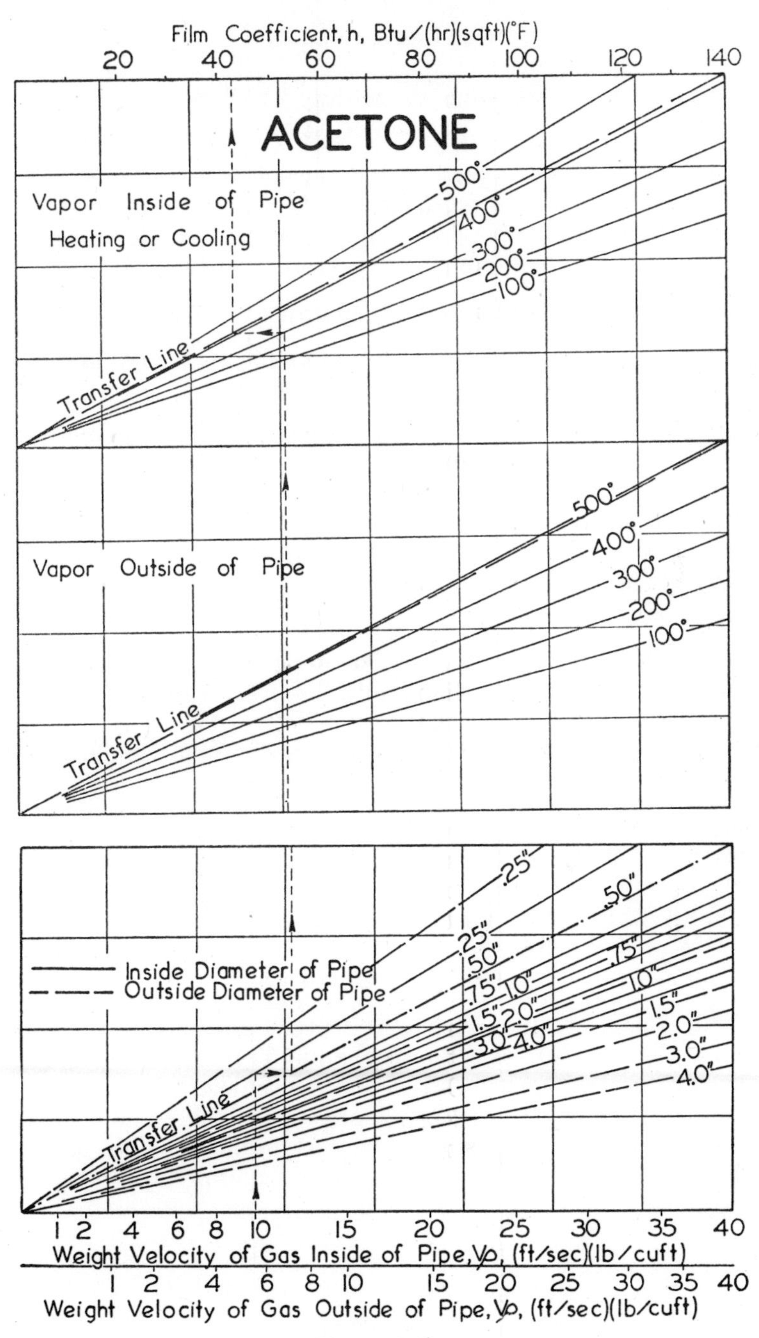

Film Coefficient, h, Btu/(hr)(sqft)(°F)
20 40 60 80 100 120 140
ACETONE
Vapor Inside of Pipe
Heating or Cooling
500°
400°
300°
200°
100°
Transfer Line
Vapor Outside of Pipe
500°
400°
300°
200°
100°
Transfer Line
Inside Diameter of Pipe
Outside Diameter of Pipe
.25"
.50"
.25"
.50"
.75"
1.0"
.75"
1.0"
1.5"
2.0"
3.0"
4.0"
1.5"
2.0"
3.0"
4.0"
Transfer Line
1 2 4 6 8 10 15 20 25 30 35 40
Weight Velocity of Gas Inside of Pipe, Vρ, (ft/sec)(lb/cuft)
1 2 4 6 8 10 15 20 25 30 35 40
Weight Velocity of Gas Outside of Pipe, Vρ, (ft/sec)(lb/cuft)

Figure 6.50

Acetylene (Gas)

Acetylene (gas) heating or cooling in turbulent flow within a tube or in turbulent flow outside and normal to a single tube.

Equations: Gas or vapor heating or cooling within a tube:

$$Nu = 0.023(Re)^{0.8}(Pr)^{0.4}$$

Gas or vapor heating or cooling outside and normal to a single tube: $Nu = 0.385(Re)^{0.56}(Pr)^{0.3}$

Text References: Chapter VI; equations 6.5, 6.9, 6.12, and 6.14.

Extensions: Refer to section 6.5 for extensions to annular spaces, tube bundles, and flow through helical coils.

Special Conditions: For a gas or vapor heating or cooling within a tube, do not use the graph unless the weight velocity, $V\rho$ (ft/sec) (lb/cu ft), exceeds 0.5 at 1 atmosphere, 2 at 10 atmospheres, or 3.0 at 20 atmospheres.

For a gas or vapor flowing outside and normal to a single tube, do not use the graph for $V\rho$ less than 0.1 unless the Reynolds number exceeds 100.

Example: Acetylene (gas) is flowing outside and normal to a bundle of staggered 2 inch outside diameter tubes. The weight velocity through the narrowest section between tubes is 2 (ft/sec) (lb/cu ft) and the mean temperature of the gas, which is being cooled, is 0 F. Determine the outside film coefficient.*

Solution: The dashed example line on the graph (Fig. 6.51) shows that, for the stated conditions, the film coefficient for flow normal to a single tube would be 9. For flow across a staggered tube bundle the base value of the outside coefficient is raised by 30% (refer to part 6 of section 6.5) hence for this case the corrected coefficient is $1.3 \times 9 = 12$ Btu/(hr) (sq ft) (°F).

*__Note:__ To determine other heat transfer coefficients for Acetylene, use Fig. 6.51 but refer to the examples on the following pages for the appropriate method: Inside film coefficient, page 254; outside film coefficient per lineal foot, page 260; inside film coefficient per lineal foot, use method similar to that for outside film coefficient per lineal foot; inside film coefficient for a double-pipe exchanger, page 258.

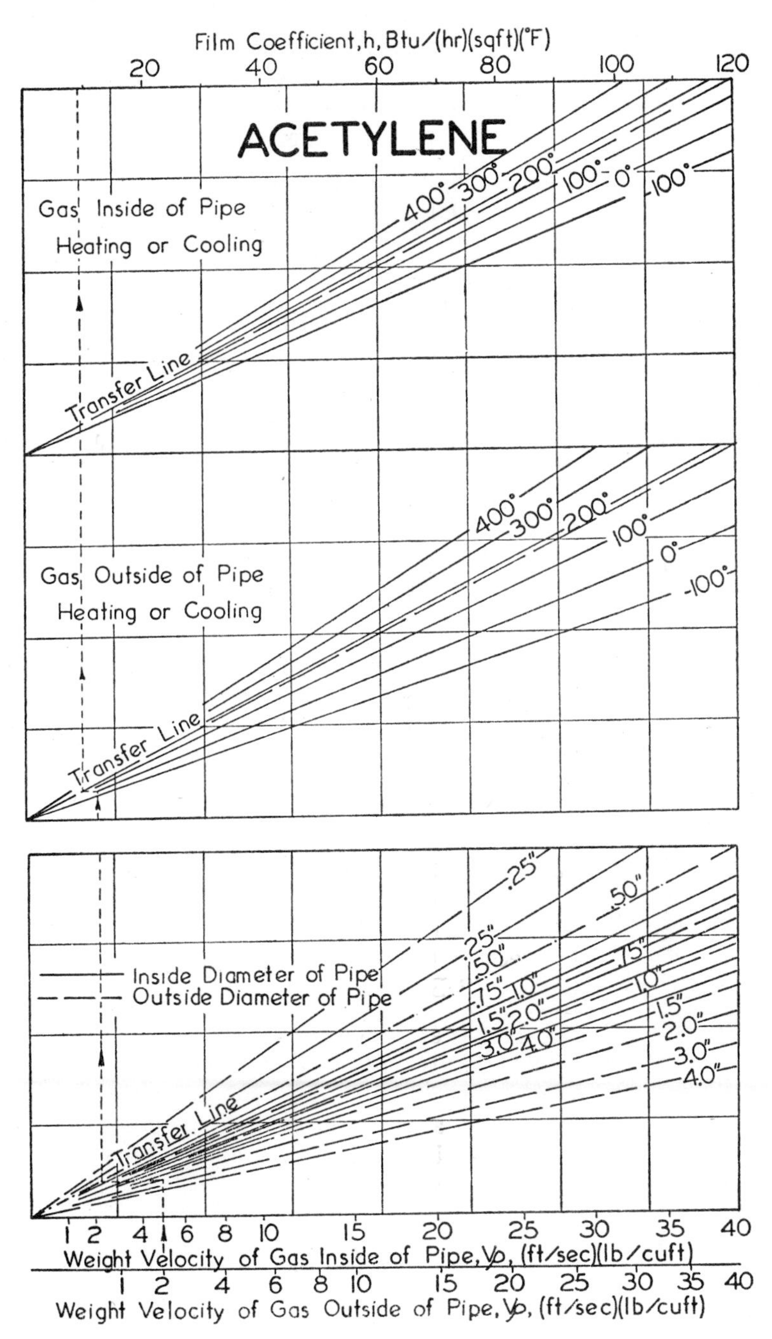
Film Coefficient, h, Btu/(hr)(sqft)(°F)
20
40
60
80
100
120
ACETYLENE
Gas Inside of Pipe
Heating or Cooling
400° 300° 200° 100° 0° -100°
Transfer Line
Gas Outside of Pipe
Heating or Cooling
400° 300° 200° 100° 0° -100°
Transfer Line
Inside Diameter of Pipe
Outside Diameter of Pipe
.25" .50" .75" 1.0" 1.5" 2.0" 3.0" 4.0"
.25" .50" .75" 1.0" 1.5" 2.0" 3.0" 4.0"
Transfer Line
1 2 4 6 8 10 15 20 25 30 35 40
Weight Velocity of Gas Inside of Pipe, Vρ, (ft/sec)(lb/cuft)
1 2 4 6 8 10 15 20 25 30 35 40
Weight Velocity of Gas Outside of Pipe, Vρ, (ft/sec)(lb/cuft)

Figure 6.51

Air (Gas)

Air (gas) heating or cooling in turbulent flow within a tube or in turbulent flow outside and normal to a single tube.

Equations: Gas or vapor heating or cooling within a tube:

$$Nu = 0.023\,(Re)^{0.8}\,(Pr)^{0.4}$$

Gas or vapor heating or cooling outside and normal to a single tube: $Nu = 0.385\,(Re)^{0.56}\,(Pr)^{0.3}$

Text References: Chapter VI; equations 6.5, 6.9, 6.12, and 6.14.

Extensions: Refer to section 6.5 for extensions to annular spaces, tube bundles, and flow through helical coils.

Special Conditions: For a gas or vapor heating or cooling within a tube, do not use the graph unless the weight velocity, $V\rho$ (ft/sec) (lb/cu ft), exceeds 0.5 at 1 atmosphere, 2 at 10 atmospheres, or 3.0 at 20 atmospheres.

For a gas or vapor flowing outside and normal to a single tube, do not use the graph for $V\rho$ less than 0.1 unless the Reynolds number exceeds 100.

Example: Air (gas) at 0 F is being cooled while flowing through an annular space in a double-pipe heat exchanger for which the equivalent inside diameter (equation 6.16) is 1 inch. The weight velocity is 30 (ft/sec) (lb/cu ft). Determine the inside film coefficient.*

Solution: The film coefficient is directly determinable from the graph as indicated by the dashed example line, Fig. 6.52. The resultant value, 58, is the film coefficient for the outside of the inner pipe of the annular exchanger and its units are Btu per hour per °F per square foot of outer surface of the inner pipe.

***Note:** To determine other heat transfer coefficients for Air, use Fig. 6.52 but refer to the examples on the following pages for the appropriate method: Outside film coefficient, page 256; inside film coefficient, page 254; outside film coefficient per lineal foot, page 260; inside film coefficient per lineal foot, use method similar to that for outside film coefficient per lineal foot.

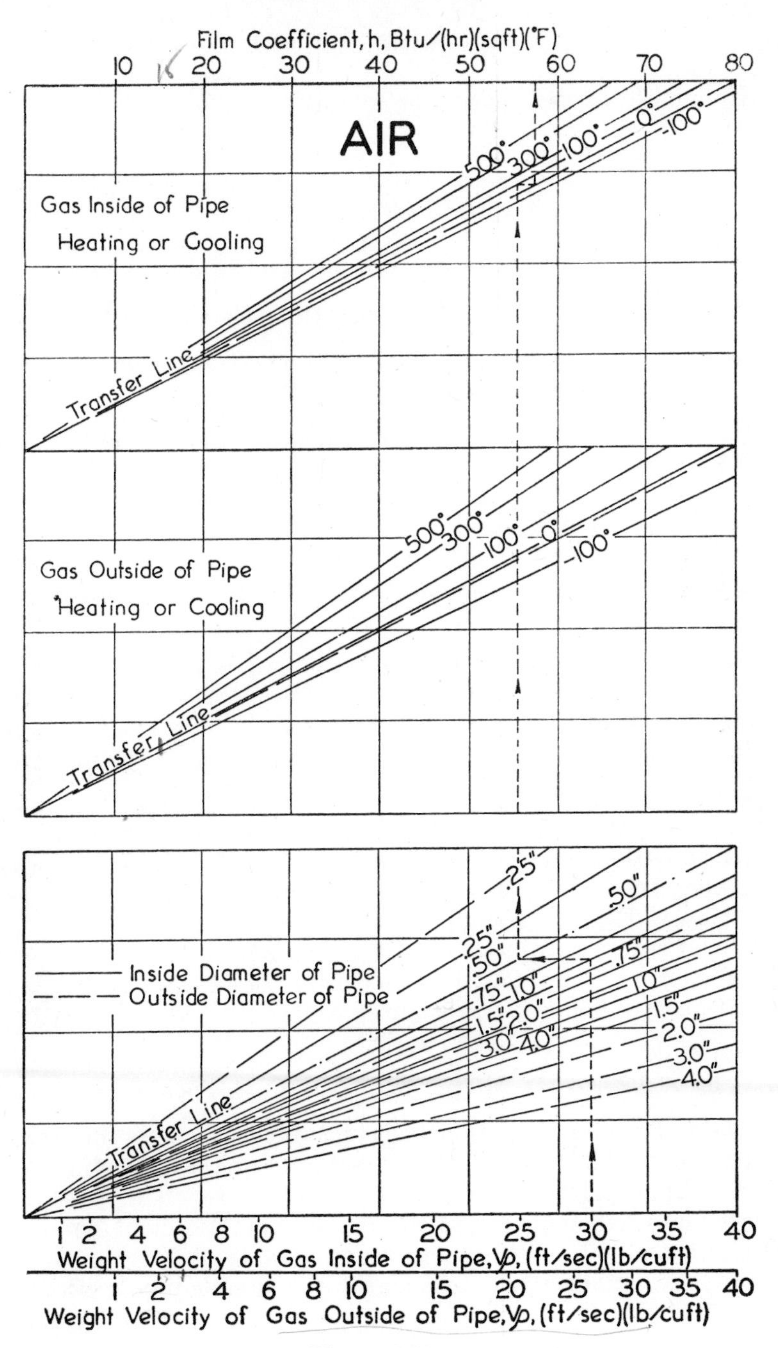
Film Coefficient, h, Btu/(hr)(sqft)(°F)
10 20 30 40 50 60 70 80
AIR
Gas Inside of Pipe
Heating or Cooling
500° 300° 100° 0° -100°
Transfer Line
Gas Outside of Pipe
Heating or Cooling
500° 300° 100° 0° -100°
Transfer Line
Inside Diameter of Pipe
Outside Diameter of Pipe
.25" .50" .75" 1.0" 1.5" 2.0" 3.0" 4.0"
Transfer Line
1 2 4 6 8 10 15 20 25 30 35 40
Weight Velocity of Gas Inside of Pipe, Vρ, (ft/sec)(lb/cuft)
1 2 4 6 8 10 15 20 25 30 35 40
Weight Velocity of Gas Outside of Pipe, Vρ, (ft/sec)(lb/cuft)

Figure 6.52

Ammonia (Vapor)

Ammonia (vapor) heating or cooling in turbulent flow within a tube or in turbulent flow outside and normal to a single tube.

Equations: Gas or vapor heating or cooling within a tube:
$Nu = 0.023\,(Re)^{0.8}(Pr)^{0.4}$
Gas or vapor heating or cooling outside and normal to a single tube: $Nu = 0.385\,(Re)^{0.56}(Pr)^{0.3}$

Text References: Chapter VI; equations 6.5, 6.9, 6.12, and 6.14.

Extensions: Refer to section 6.5 for extensions to annular spaces, tube bundles, and flow through helical coils.

Special Conditions: For a gas or vapor heating or cooling within a tube, do not use the graph unless the weight velocity, $V\rho$ (ft/sec) (lb/cu ft), exceeds 0.5 at 1 atmosphere, 2 at 10 atmospheres, or 3.0 at 20 atmospheres.

For a gas or vapor flowing outside and normal to a single tube, do not use the graph for $V\rho$ less than 0.1 unless the Reynolds number exceeds 100.

Example: Ammonia (vapor) is heating at —100 F while flowing outside and normal to a ¾″ Type K copper tube; the weight velocity is 20 (ft/sec) (lb/cu ft). Determine the film coefficient per lineal foot of tube.*

Solution: The dashed example line on the graph (Fig. 6.53) shows the method of evaluating the outside film coefficient, for the stated conditions, in terms of one square foot of outside surface of the tube. To convert this value, 52 Btu/(hr) (sq ft) (°F), to a lineal basis Fig. 5.4 would ordinarily be used. However, in this case, the entering value of 52 Btu/(hr) (sq ft) (°F) would be at the low end of the scale where accurate use of the graph is difficult. Equation 5.9 is therefore used,

$$h_o' = h_o A_{o_L}$$
$$= 52 \times 0.229 = 12 \text{ Btu per hour per °F per lineal foot of tube}$$

***Note:** To determine other heat transfer coefficients for Ammonia, use Fig. 6.53 but refer to the examples on the following pages for the appropriate method: Outside film coefficient, page 256; inside film coefficient, page 254; inside film coefficient per lineal foot, use method similar to that for outside film coefficient per lineal foot; inside film coefficient for a double-pipe exchanger, page 258.

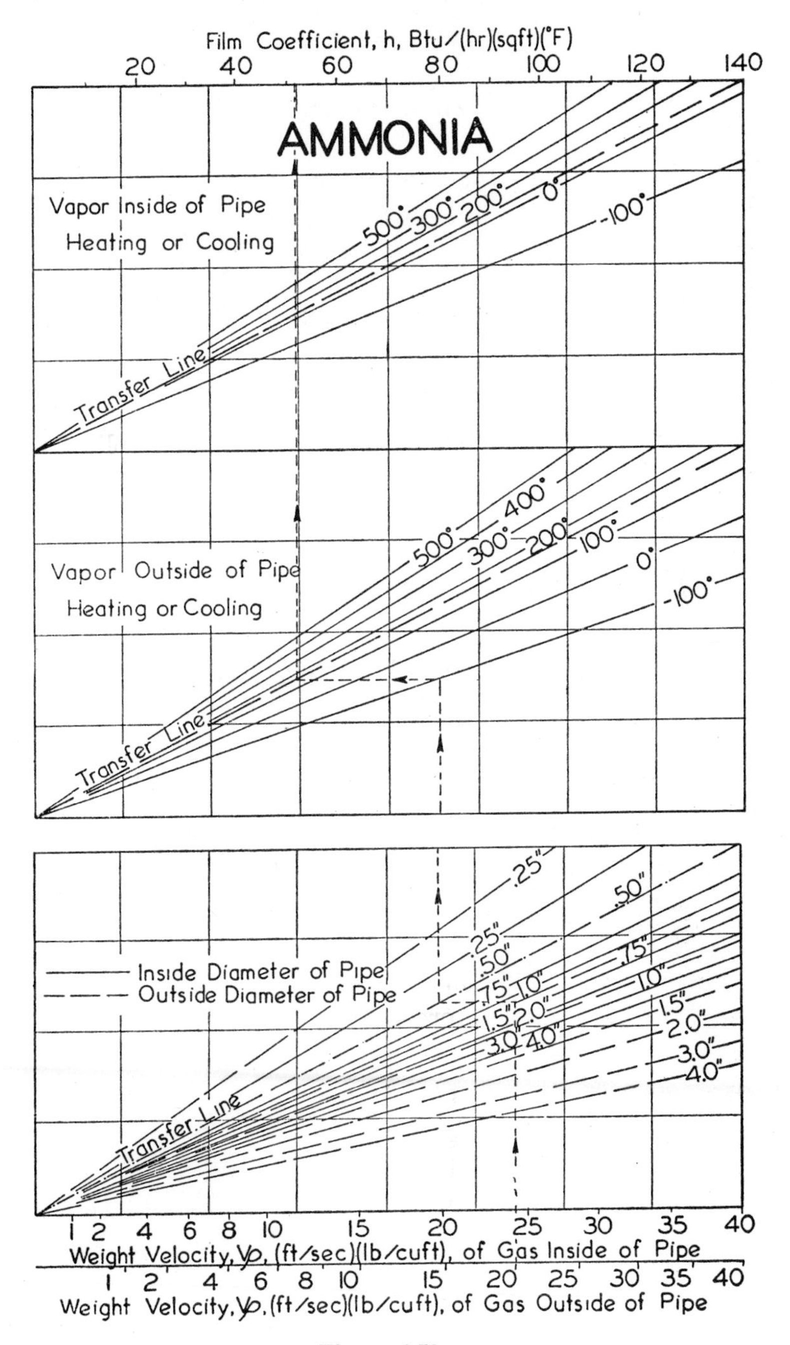
Film Coefficient, h, Btu/(hr)(sqft)(°F)
20 40 60 80 100 120 140
AMMONIA
Vapor Inside of Pipe
Heating or Cooling
500° 300° 200° 0° -100°
Transfer Line
Vapor Outside of Pipe
Heating or Cooling
500° 400° 300° 200° 100° 0° -100°
Transfer Line
Inside Diameter of Pipe
Outside Diameter of Pipe
.25" .50" .75" 1.0" 1.5" 2.0" 3.0" 4.0"
Transfer Line
1 2 4 6 8 10 15 20 25 30 35 40
Weight Velocity, Vρ, (ft/sec)(lb/cuft), of Gas Inside of Pipe
1 2 4 6 8 10 15 20 25 30 35 40
Weight Velocity, Vρ, (ft/sec)(lb/cuft), of Gas Outside of Pipe

Figure 6.53

Benzene (Vapor)

Benzene (vapor) heating or cooling in turbulent flow within a tube or in turbulent flow outside and normal to a single tube.

Equations: Gas or vapor heating or cooling within a tube:
$Nu = 0.023 (Re)^{0.8} (Pr)^{0.4}$
Gas or vapor heating or cooling outside and normal to a single tube: $Nu = 0.385 (Re)^{0.56} (Pr)^{0.3}$

Text References: Chapter VI; equations 6.5, 6.9, 6.12, and 6.14.

Extensions: Refer to section 6.5 for extensions to annular spaces, tube bundles, and flow through helical coils.

Special Conditions: For a gas or vapor heating or cooling within a tube, do not use the graph unless the weight velocity, $V\rho$ (ft/sec) (lb/cu ft), exceeds 0.5 at 1 atmosphere, 2 at 10 atmospheres, or 3.0 at 20 atmospheres.

For a gas or vapor flowing outside and normal to a single tube, do not use the graph for $V\rho$ less than 0.1 unless the Reynolds number exceeds 100.

Example: Benzene (vapor) is being heated while flowing within a tube having an inside diameter of ¼ inch. The weight velocity is 10 (ft/sec) (lb/cu ft) and the mean temperature is 100 F. Determine the value of the inside film coefficient.*

Solution: Enter the bottom of the graph (Fig. 6.54) at a weight velocity of 10 and rise to intersect the radial line for a tube of ¼″ inside diameter. From this intersection move right to intersect the transfer line, then rise to the group of radials for fluid inside; intersect the radial for a temperature of 100 F then move left to the transfer line and from this intersection rise to read the answer at the top scale as 28 Btu/(hr) (sq ft) (°F).

***Note:** To determine other heat transfer coefficients for Benzene, use Fig. 6.54 but refer to the examples on the following pages for the appropriate method: Outside film coefficient, page 256; outside film coefficient per lineal foot, page 260; inside film coefficient per lineal foot, use method similar to that for outside film coefficient per lineal foot; inside film coefficient for a double-pipe exchanger, page 258.

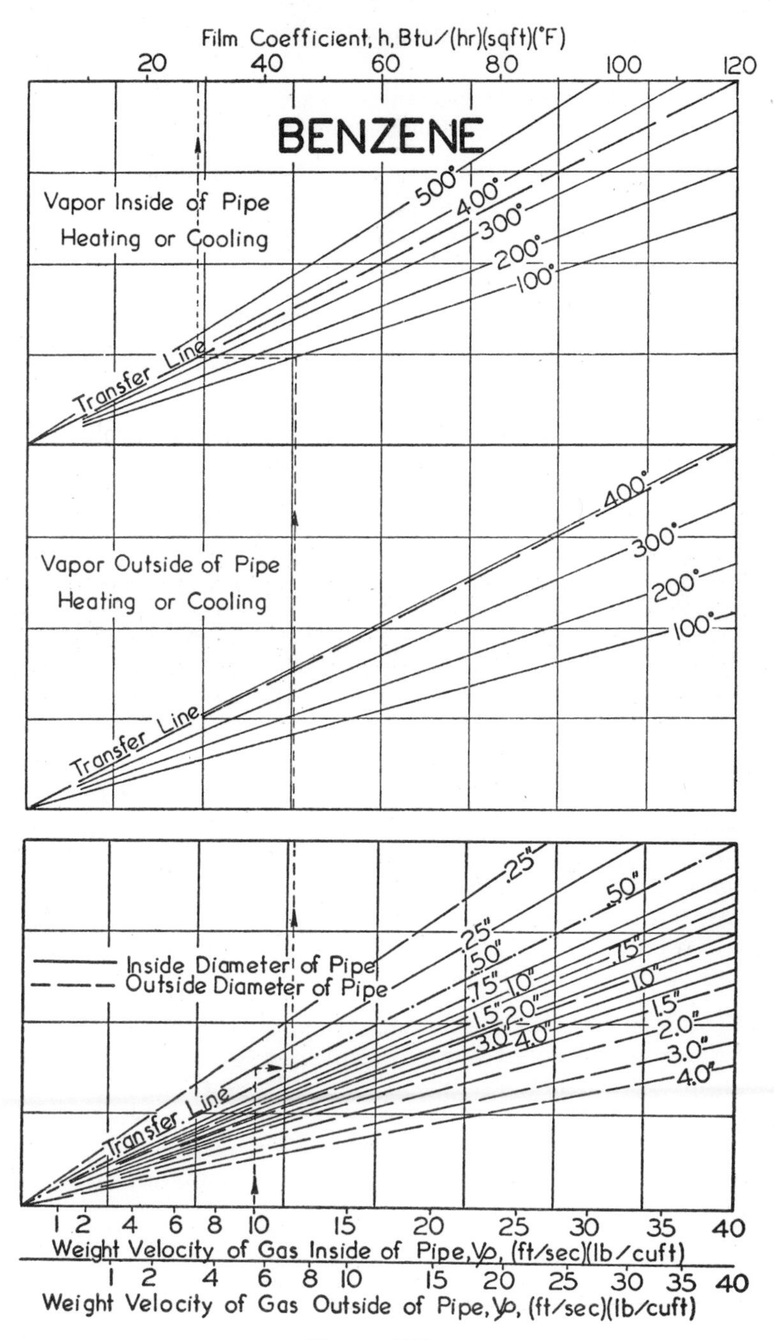
Film Coefficient, h, Btu/(hr)(sqft)(°F)
20
40
60
80
100
120
BENZENE
Vapor Inside of Pipe
Heating or Cooling
500°
400°
300°
200°
100°
Transfer Line
Vapor Outside of Pipe
Heating or Cooling
400°
300°
200°
100°
Transfer Line
Inside Diameter of Pipe
Outside Diameter of Pipe
.25"
.50"
.75"
1.0"
1.5"
2.0"
3.0"
4.0"
Transfer Line
1 2 4 6 8 10 15 20 25 30 35 40
Weight Velocity of Gas Inside of Pipe, Vρ, (ft/sec)(lb/cuft)
1 2 4 6 8 10 15 20 25 30 35 40
Weight Velocity of Gas Outside of Pipe, Vρ, (ft/sec)(lb/cuft)

Figure 6.54

Butane (Gas)

Butane (gas) heating or cooling in turbulent flow within a tube or in turbulent flow outside and normal to a single tube.

Equations: Gas or vapor heating or cooling within a tube:
$$Nu = 0.023\,(Re)^{0.8}\,(Pr)^{0.4}$$
Gas or vapor heating or cooling outside and normal to a single tube: $Nu = 0.385\,(Re)^{0.56}\,(Pr)^{0.3}$

Text References: Chapter VI; equations 6.5, 6.9, 6.12, and 6.14.

Extensions: Refer to section 6.5 for extensions to annular spaces, tube bundles, and flow through helical coils.

Special Conditions: For a gas or vapor heating or cooling within a tube, do not use the graph unless the weight velocity, $V\rho$ (ft/sec) (lb/cu ft), exceeds 0.5 at 1 atmosphere, 2 at 10 atmospheres, or 3.0 at 20 atmospheres.

For a gas or vapor flowing outside and normal to a single tube, do not use the graph for $V\rho$ less than 0.1 unless the Reynolds number exceeds 100.

Example: Butane (gas) is flowing outside and normal to a bundle of staggered 2 inch outside diameter tubes. The weight velocity through the narrowest section between tubes is 2 (ft/sec) (lb/cu ft) and the mean temperature of the gas, which is being cooled, is 100 F. Determine the outside film coefficient.

Solution: The dashed example line on the graph (Fig. 6.55) shows that, for the stated conditions, the film coefficient for flow normal to a single tube would be 10. For flow across a staggered tube bundle the base value of the outside coefficient is raised by 30% (refer to part 6 of section 6.5) hence for this case the corrected coefficient is $1.3 \times 10 = 13$ Btu/(hr) (sq ft) (°F).

*__Note:__ To determine other heat transfer coefficients for Butane, use Fig. 6.55 but refer to the examples on the following pages for the appropriate method: Inside film coefficient, page 262; outside film coefficient per lineal foot, page 260; inside film coefficient per lineal foot, use method similar to that for outside film coefficient per lineal foot; inside film coefficient for a double-pipe exchanger, page 258.

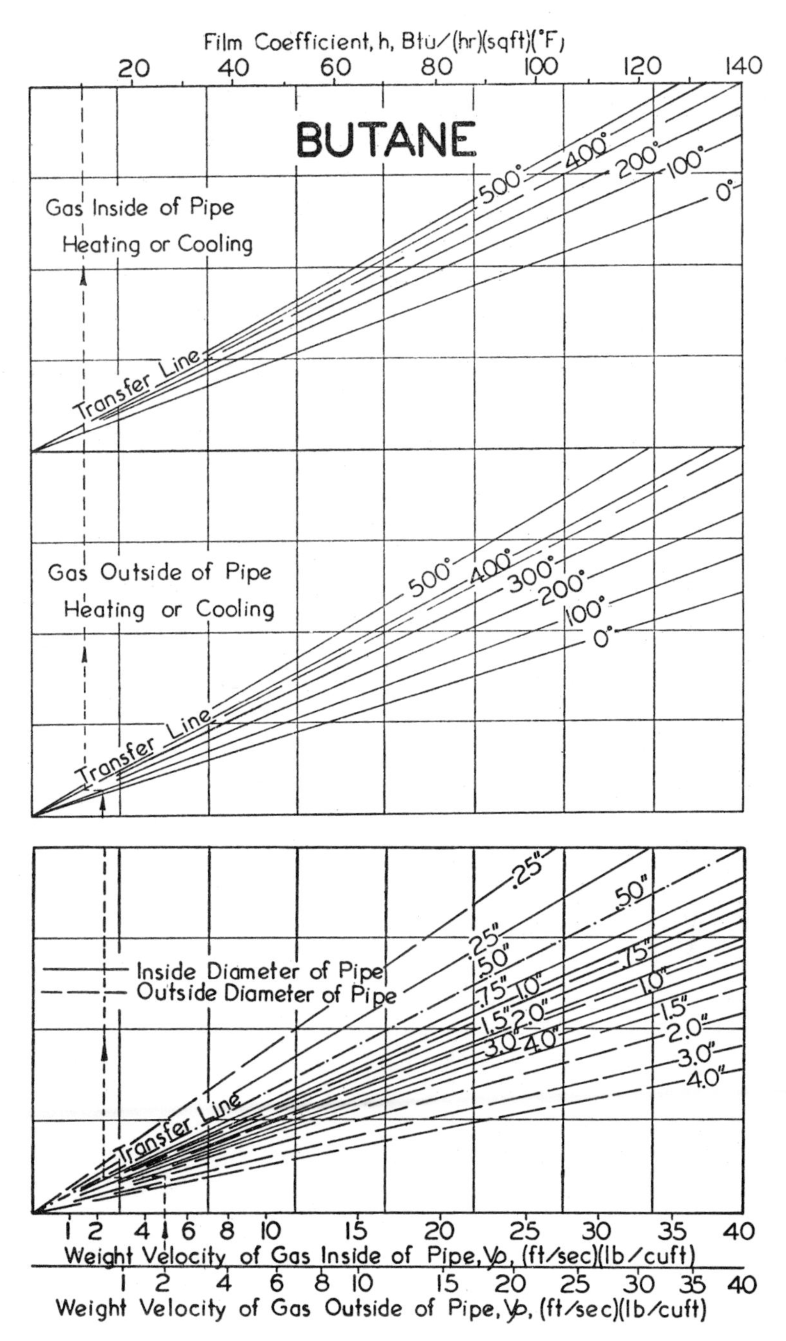
Film Coefficient, h, Btu/(hr)(sqft)(°F)
20 40 60 80 100 120 140
BUTANE
Gas Inside of Pipe
Heating or Cooling
500° 400° 200° 100° 0°
Transfer Line
Gas Outside of Pipe
Heating or Cooling
500° 400° 300° 200° 100° 0°
Transfer Line
Inside Diameter of Pipe
Outside Diameter of Pipe
.25" .50" .75" 1.0" 1.5" 2.0" 3.0" 4.0"
Transfer Line
1 2 4 6 8 10 15 20 25 30 35 40
Weight Velocity of Gas Inside of Pipe, Vρ, (ft/sec)(lb/cuft)
1 2 4 6 8 10 15 20 25 30 35 40
Weight Velocity of Gas Outside of Pipe, Vρ, (ft/sec)(lb/cuft)

Figure 6.55

Carbon Dioxide (Gas)

Carbon Dioxide (gas) heating or cooling in turbulent flow within a tube or in turbulent flow outside and normal to a single tube.

Equations: Gas or vapor heating or cooling within a tube:
$Nu = 0.023\,(Re)^{0.8}\,(Pr)^{0.4}$
Gas or vapor heating or cooling outside and normal to a single tube: $Nu = 0.385\,(Re)^{0.56}\,(Pr)^{0.3}$

Text References: Chapter VI; equations 6.5, 6.9, 6.12, and 6.14.

Extensions: Refer to section 6.5 for extensions to annular spaces, tube bundles, and flow through helical coils.

Special Conditions: For a gas or vapor heating or cooling within a tube, do not use the graph unless the weight velocity, $V\rho$ (ft/sec) (lb/cu ft), exceeds 0.5 at 1 atmosphere, 2 at 10 atmospheres, or 3.0 at 20 atmospheres.

For a gas or vapor flowing outside and normal to a single tube, do not use the graph for $V\rho$ less than 0.1 unless the Reynolds number exceeds 100.

Example: Carbon Dioxide (gas) at −100 F is being cooled while flowing through an annular space in a double-pipe heat exchanger for which the equivalent inside diameter (equation 6.16) is 1 inch. The weight velocity is 30 (ft/sec) (lb/cu ft). Determine the inside film coefficient.*

Solution: The film coefficient is directly determinable from the graph as indicated by the dashed example line, Fig. 6.56. The resultant value, 39, is the film coefficient for the outside of the inner pipe of the annular exchanger and its units are Btu per hour per °F per square foot of outer surface of the inner pipe.

***Note:** To determine other heat transfer coefficients for Carbon Dioxide, use Fig. 6.56 but refer to the examples on the following pages for the appropriate method: Outside film coefficient, page 264; inside film coefficient, page 262; outside film coefficient per lineal foot, page 260; inside film coefficient per lineal foot, use method similar to that for outside film coefficient per lineal foot.

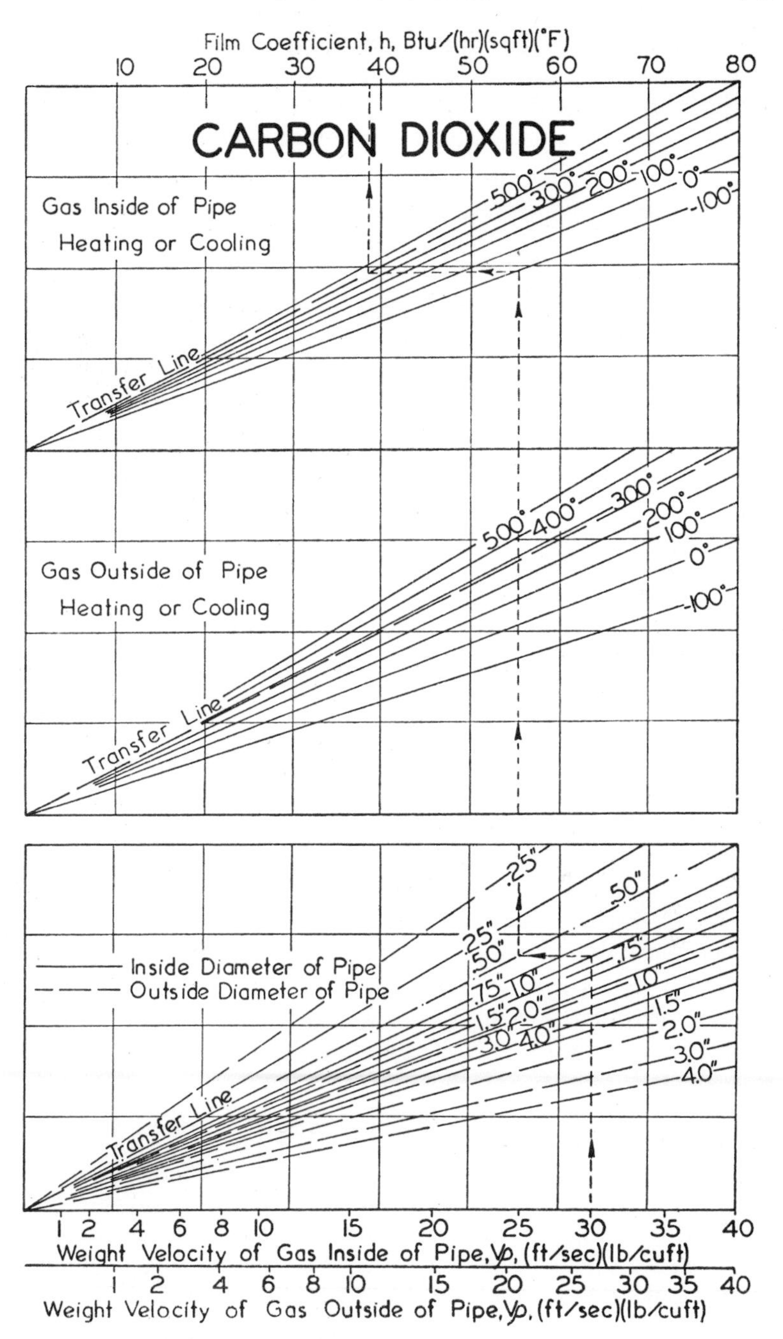

Film Coefficient, h, Btu/(hr)(sqft)(°F)
10 20 30 40 50 60 70 80
CARBON DIOXIDE
Gas Inside of Pipe
Heating or Cooling
500° 300° 200° 100° 0° -100°
Transfer Line
Gas Outside of Pipe
Heating or Cooling
500° 400° 300° 200° 100° 0° -100°
Transfer Line
Inside Diameter of Pipe
Outside Diameter of Pipe
.25" .50" .75" 1.0" 1.5" 2.0" 3.0" 4.0"
.25" .50" .75" 1.0" 1.5" 2.0" 3.0" 4.0"
Transfer Line
1 2 4 6 8 10 15 20 25 30 35 40
Weight Velocity of Gas Inside of Pipe, Vρ, (ft/sec)(lb/cuft)
1 2 4 6 8 10 15 20 25 30 35 40
Weight Velocity of Gas Outside of Pipe, Vρ, (ft/sec)(lb/cuft)

Figure 6.56

Carbon Monoxide (Gas)

Carbon Monoxide (gas) heating or cooling in turbulent flow within a tube or in turbulent flow outside and normal to a single tube.

Equations: Gas or vapor heating or cooling within a tube:
$$Nu = 0.023\,(Re)^{0.8}\,(Pr)^{0.4}$$
Gas or vapor heating or cooling outside and normal to a single tube: $Nu = 0.385\,(Re)^{0.56}\,(Pr)^{0.3}$

Text References: Chapter VI; equations 6.5, 6.9, 6.12, and 6.14.

Extensions: Refer to section 6.5 for extensions to annular spaces, tube bundles, and flow through helical coils.

Special Conditions: For a gas or vapor heating or cooling within a tube, do not use the graph unless the weight velocity, $V\rho$ (ft/sec) (lb/cu ft), exceeds 0.5 at 1 atmosphere, 2 at 10 atmospheres, or 3.0 at 20 atmospheres.

For a gas or vapor flowing outside and normal to a single tube, do not use the graph for $V\rho$ less than 0.1 unless the Reynolds number exceeds 100.

Example: Carbon Monoxide (gas) is heating at 200 F while flowing outside and normal to a ¾″ Type K copper tube; the weight velocity is 20 (ft/sec) (lb/cu ft). Determine the film coefficient per lineal foot of tube.*

Solution: The dashed example line on the graph (Fig. 6.57) shows the method of evaluating the outside film coefficient, for the stated conditions, in terms of one square foot of outside surface of the tube. To convert this value, 53 Btu/(hr) (sq ft) (°F), to a lineal basis Fig. 5.4 would ordinarily be used. However, in this case, the entering value of 53 Btu/(hr) (sq ft) (°F) would be at the low end of the scale where accurate use of the graph is difficult. Equation 5.9 is therefore used,

$$h_o' = h_o A_{o_L}$$
$$= 53 \times 0.229 = 12 \text{ Btu per hour per °F per lineal foot of tube}$$

***Note:** To determine other heat transfer coefficients for Carbon Monoxide, use Fig. 6.57 but refer to the examples on the following pages for the appropriate method: Outside film coefficient, page 264; inside film coefficient, page 262; inside film coefficient per lineal foot, use method similar to that for outside film coefficient per lineal foot; inside film coefficient for a double-pipe exchanger, page 266.

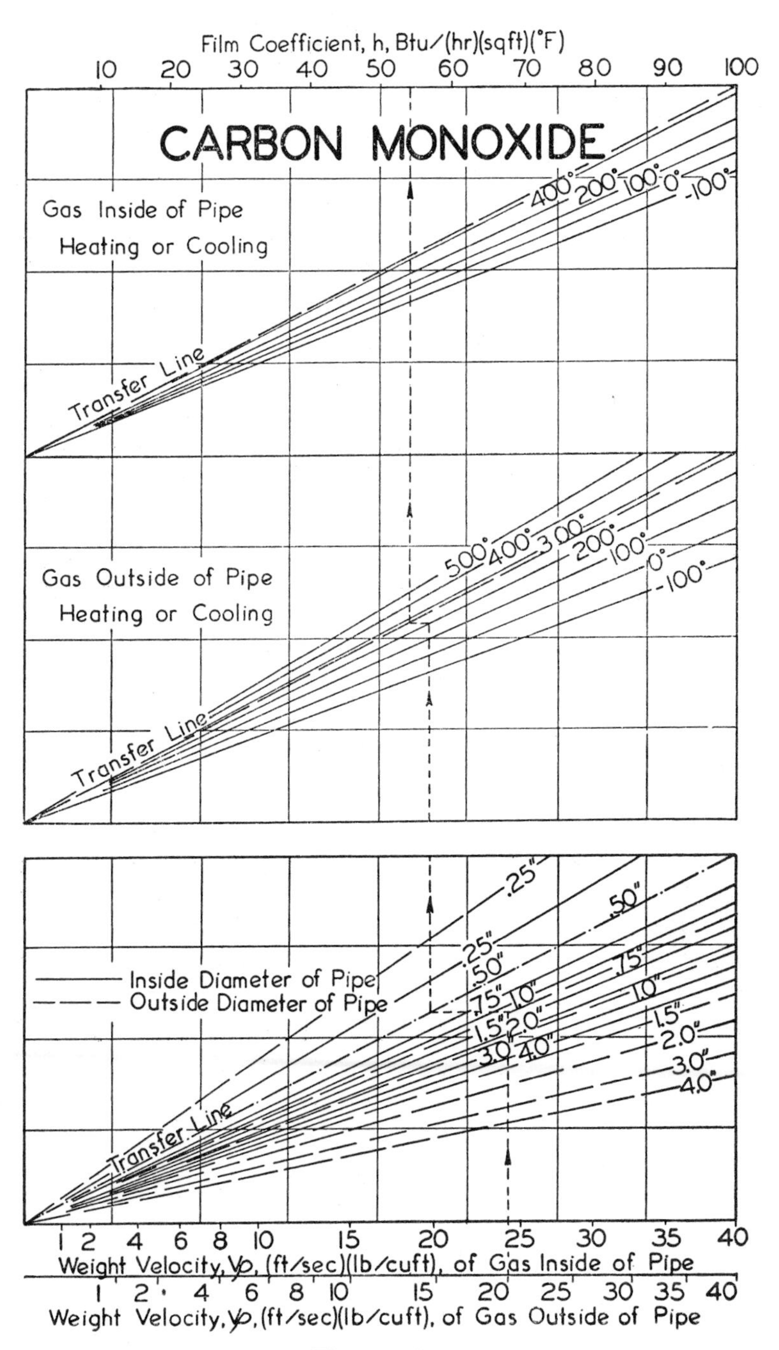
Film Coefficient, h, Btu/(hr)(sqft)(°F)
10 20 30 40 50 60 70 80 90 100
CARBON MONOXIDE
Gas Inside of Pipe
Heating or Cooling
400° 200° 100° 0° -100°
Transfer Line
Gas Outside of Pipe
Heating or Cooling
500° 400° 300° 200° 100° 0° -100°
Transfer Line
Inside Diameter of Pipe
Outside Diameter of Pipe
.25" .50" .75" 1.0" 1.5" 2.0" 3.0" 4.0"
.25" .50" .75" 1.0" 1.5" 2.0" 3.0" 4.0"
Transfer Line
1 2 4 6 8 10 15 20 25 30 35 40
Weight Velocity, Vρ, (ft/sec)(lb/cuft), of Gas Inside of Pipe
1 2 4 6 8 10 15 20 25 30 35 40
Weight Velocity, Vρ, (ft/sec)(lb/cuft), of Gas Outside of Pipe

Figure 6.57

Chlorine (Vapor)

Chlorine (vapor) heating or cooling in turbulent flow within a tube or in turbulent flow outside and normal to a single tube.

Equations: Gas or vapor heating or cooling within a tube:
$$Nu = 0.023(Re)^{0.8}(Pr)^{0.4}$$
Gas or vapor heating or cooling outside and normal to a single tube: $Nu = 0.385(Re)^{0.56}(Pr)^{0.3}$

Text References: Chapter VI; equations 6.5, 6.9, 6.12, and 6.14.

Extensions: Refer to section 6.5 for extensions to annular spaces, tube bundles, and flow through helical coils.

Special Conditions: For a gas or vapor heating or cooling within a tube, do not use the graph unless the weight velocity, $V\rho$ (ft/sec) (lb/cu ft), exceeds 0.5 at 1 atmosphere, 2 at 10 atmospheres, or 3.0 at 20 atmospheres.

For a gas or vapor flowing outside and normal to a single tube, do not use the graph for $V\rho$ less than 0.1 unless the Reynolds number exceeds 100.

Example: Chlorine (vapor) is being heated while flowing within a tube having an inside diameter of 1/4 inch. The weight velocity is 10 (ft/sec) (lb/cu ft) and the mean temperature is 500 F. Determine the value of the inside film coefficient.*

Solution: Enter the bottom of the graph (Fig. 6.58) at a weight velocity of 10 and rise to intersect the radial line for a tube of 1/4″ inside diameter. From this intersection move right to intersect the transfer line, then rise to the group of radials for fluid inside; intersect the radial for a temperature of 500 F then move right to the transfer line and from this intersection rise to read the answer at the top scale as 16 Btu/(hr) (sq ft) (°F).

***Note:** To determine other heat transfer coefficients for Chlorine, use Fig. 6.58 but refer to the examples on the following pages for the appropriate method: Outside film coefficient, page 264; outside film coefficient per lineal foot, page 268; inside film coefficient per lineal foot, use method similar to that for outside film coefficient per lineal foot; inside film coefficient for a double-pipe exchanger, page 266.

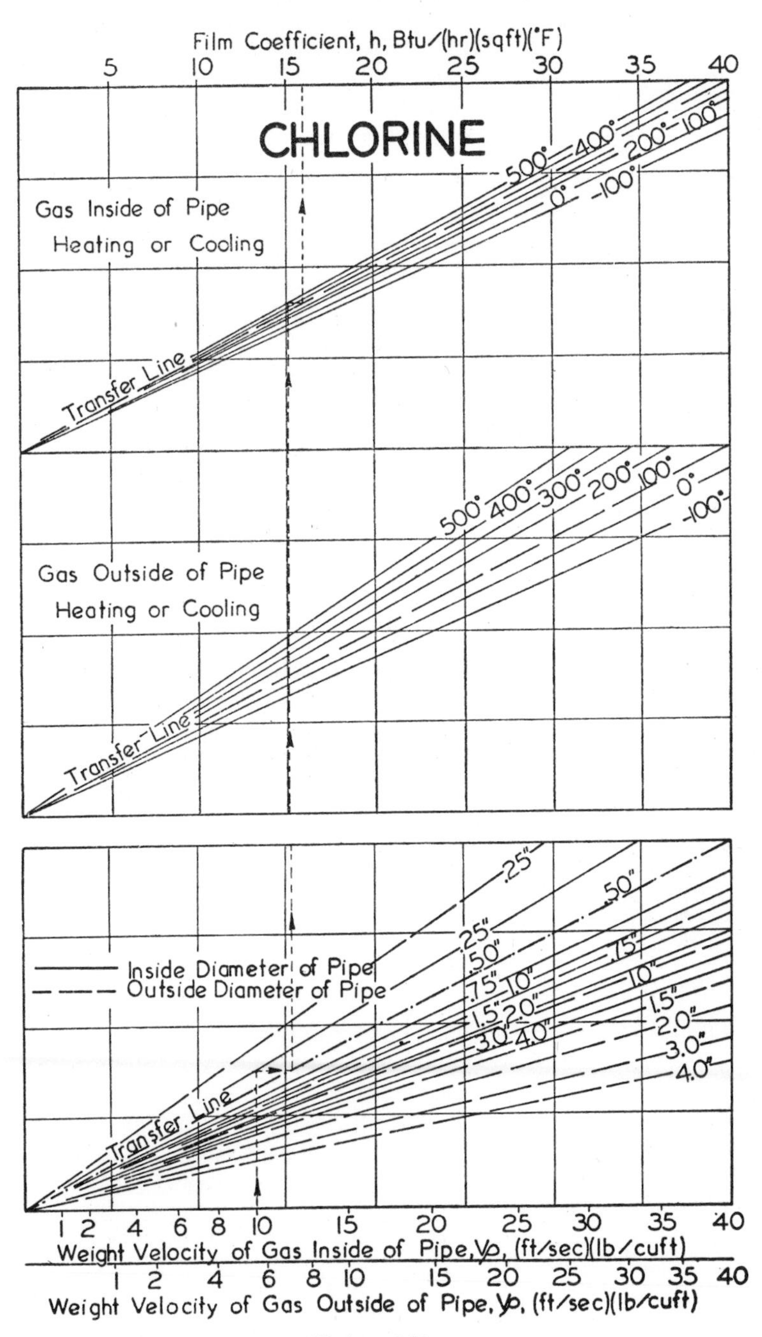
Film Coefficient, h, Btu/(hr)(sqft)(°F)
5 10 15 20 25 30 35 40
CHLORINE
Gas Inside of Pipe
Heating or Cooling
500° 400° 200° 100° 0° -100°
Transfer Line
Gas Outside of Pipe
Heating or Cooling
500° 400° 300° 200° 100° 0° -100°
Transfer Line
Inside Diameter of Pipe
Outside Diameter of Pipe
.25" .50" .75" 1.0" 1.5" 2.0" 3.0" 4.0"
Transfer Line
1 2 4 6 8 10 15 20 25 30 35 40
Weight Velocity of Gas Inside of Pipe, Vρ, (ft/sec)(lb/cuft)
1 2 4 6 8 10 15 20 25 30 35 40
Weight Velocity of Gas Outside of Pipe, Vρ, (ft/sec)(lb/cuft)

Figure 6.58

Chloroform (Vapor)

Chloroform (vapor) heating or cooling in turbulent flow within a tube or in turbulent flow outside and normal to a single tube.

Equations: Gas or vapor heating or cooling within a tube:

$$Nu = 0.023 (Re)^{0.8} (Pr)^{0.4}$$

Gas or vapor heating or cooling outside and normal to a single tube: $Nu = 0.385 (Re)^{0.56} (Pr)^{0.3}$

Text References: Chapter VI; equations 6.5, 6.9, 6.12, and 6.14.

Extensions: Refer to section 6.5 for extensions to annular spaces, tube bundles, and flow through helical coils.

Special Conditions: For a gas or vapor heating or cooling within a tube, do not use the graph unless the weight velocity, $V\rho$ (ft/sec) (lb/cu ft), exceeds 0.5 at 1 atmosphere, 2 at 10 atmospheres, or 3.0 at 20 atmospheres.

For a gas or vapor flowing outside and normal to a single tube, do not use the graph for $V\rho$ less than 0.1 unless the Reynolds number exceeds 100.

Example: Chloroform (vapor) is flowing outside and normal to a bundle of staggered 2 inch outside diameter tubes. The weight velocity through the narrowest section between tubes is 2 (ft/sec) (lb/cu ft) and the mean temperature of the fluid, which is being cooled, is 100 F. Determine the outside film coefficient.*

Solution: The dashed example line on the graph (Fig. 6.59) shows that, for the stated conditions, the film coefficient for flow normal to a single tube would be 4. For flow across a staggered tube bundle the base value of the outside coefficient is raised by 30% (refer to part 6 of section 6.5) hence for this case the corrected coefficient is $1.3 \times 4 = 5.2$ Btu/(hr) (sq ft) (°F).

***Note:** To determine other heat transfer coefficients for Chloroform, use Fig. 6.59 but refer to the examples on the following pages for the appropriate method: Inside film coefficient, page 270; outside film coefficient per lineal foot, page 268; inside film coefficient per lineal foot, use method similar to that for outside film coefficient per lineal foot; inside film coefficient for a double-pipe exchanger, page 266.

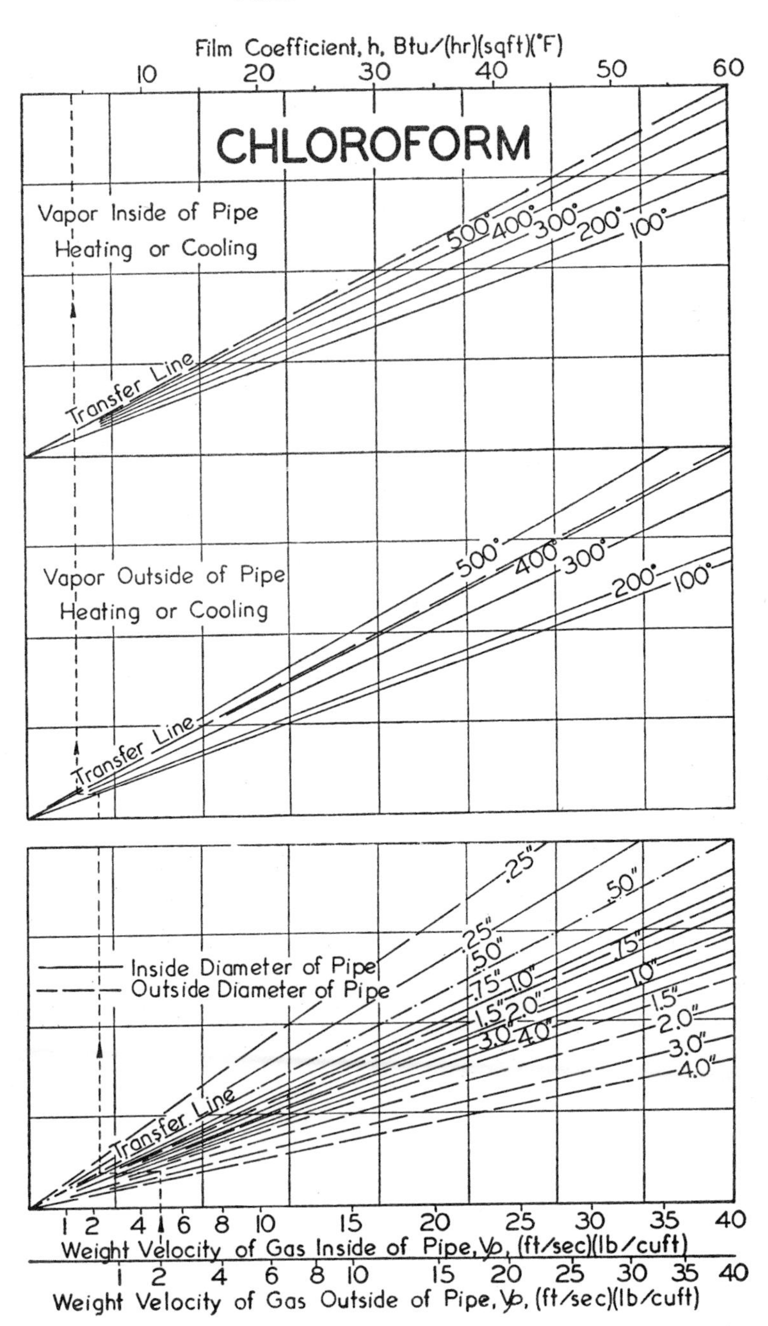
Film Coefficient, h, Btu/(hr)(sqft)(°F)
10 20 30 40 50 60
CHLOROFORM
Vapor Inside of Pipe
Heating or Cooling
500° 400° 300° 200° 100°
Transfer Line
Vapor Outside of Pipe
Heating or Cooling
500° 400° 300° 200° 100°
Transfer Line
Inside Diameter of Pipe
Outside Diameter of Pipe
.25" .50" .25" .50" .75" 1.0" 1.5" 2.0" 3.0" 4.0" .75" 1.0" 1.5" 2.0" 3.0" 4.0"
Transfer Line
1 2 4 6 8 10 15 20 25 30 35 40
Weight Velocity of Gas Inside of Pipe, Vρ, (ft/sec)(lb/cuft)
1 2 4 6 8 10 15 20 25 30 35 40
Weight Velocity of Gas Outside of Pipe, Vρ, (ft/sec)(lb/cuft)

Figure 6.59

Ethane (Vapor)

Ethane (vapor) heating or cooling in turbulent flow within a tube or in turbulent flow outside and normal to a single tube.

Equations: Gas or vapor heating or cooling within a tube:

$$Nu = 0.023\,(Re)^{0.8}\,(Pr)^{0.4}$$

Gas or vapor heating or cooling outside and normal to a single tube: $Nu = 0.385\,(Re)^{0.56}\,(Pr)^{0.3}$

Text References: Chapter VI; equations 6.5, 6.9, 6.12, and 6.14.

Extensions: Refer to section 6.5 for extensions to annular spaces, tube bundles, and flow through helical coils.

Special Conditions: For a gas or vapor heating or cooling within a tube, do not use the graph unless the weight velocity, $V\rho$ (ft/sec) (lb/cu ft), exceeds 0.5 at 1 atmosphere, 2 at 10 atmospheres, or 3.0 at 20 atmospheres.

For a gas or vapor flowing outside and normal to a single tube, do not use the graph for $V\rho$ less than 0.1 unless the Reynolds number exceeds 100.

Example: Ethane (vapor) at 0 F is being cooled while flowing through an annular space in a double-pipe heat exchanger for which the equivalent inside diameter (equation 6.16) is 1 inch. The weight velocity is 30 ft (ft/sec) (lb/cu ft). Determine the inside film coefficient.*

Solution: The film coefficient is directly determinable from the graph as indicated by the dashed example line, Fig. 6.60. The resultant value, 72, is the film coefficient for the outside of the inner pipe of the annular exchanger and its units are Btu per hour per °F per square foot of outer surface of the inner pipe.

***Note:** To determine other heat transfer coefficients for Ethane, use Fig. 6.60 but refer to the examples on the following pages for the appropriate method: Outside film coefficient, page 272; inside film coefficient, page 270; outside film coefficient per lineal foot, page 268; inside film coefficient per lineal foot, use method similar to that for outside film coefficient per lineal foot.

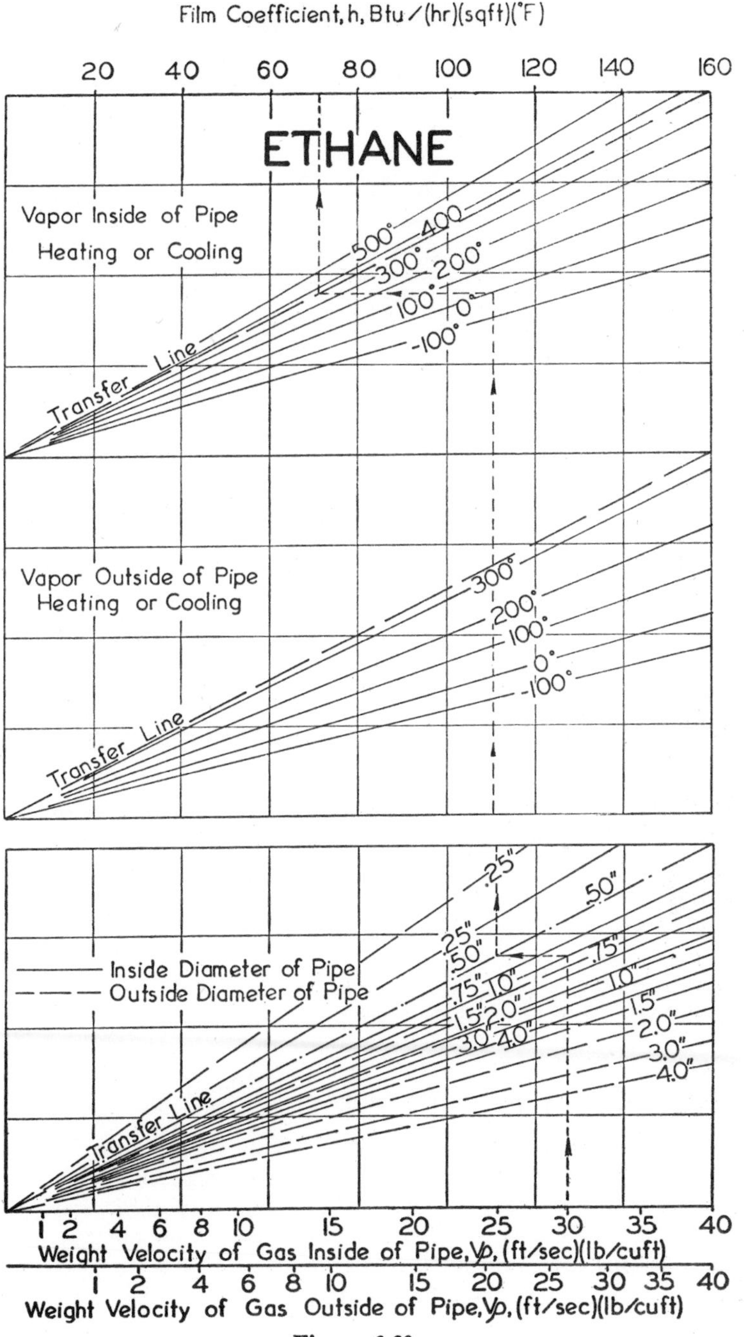

Film Coefficient, h, Btu/(hr)(sqft)(°F)
20 40 60 80 100 120 140 160
ETHANE
Vapor Inside of Pipe
Heating or Cooling
500° 400°
300° 200°
100° 0°
-100°
Transfer Line
Vapor Outside of Pipe
Heating or Cooling
300°
200°
100°
0°
-100°
Transfer Line
Inside Diameter of Pipe
Outside Diameter of Pipe
.25"
.50"
.75"
1.0"
1.5"
2.0"
3.0"
4.0"
Transfer Line
1 2 4 6 8 10 15 20 25 30 35 40
Weight Velocity of Gas Inside of Pipe, Vρ, (ft/sec)(lb/cuft)
1 2 4 6 8 10 15 20 25 30 35 40
Weight Velocity of Gas Outside of Pipe, Vρ, (ft/sec)(lb/cuft)

Figure 6.60

Ethyl Acetate (Vapor)

Ethyl Acetate (vapor) heating or cooling in turbulent flow within a tube or in turbulent flow outside and normal to a single tube.

Equations: Gas or vapor heating or cooling within a tube:
$$Nu = 0.023\,(Re)^{0.8}\,(Pr)^{0.4}$$
Gas or vapor heating or cooling outside and normal to a single tube: $Nu = 0.385\,(Re)^{0.56}\,(Pr)^{0.3}$

Text References: Chapter VI; equations 6.5, 6.9, 6.12, and 6.14.

Extensions: Refer to section 6.5 for extensions to annular spaces, tube bundles, and flow through helical coils.

Special Conditions: For a gas or vapor heating or cooling within a tube, do not use the graph unless the weight velocity, $V\rho$ (ft/sec) (lb/cu ft), exceeds 0.5 at 1 atmosphere, 2 at 10 atmospheres, or 3.0 at 20 atmospheres.

For a gas or vapor flowing outside and normal to a single tube, do not use the graph for $V\rho$ less than 0.1 unless the Reynolds number exceeds 100.

Example: Ethyl Acetate (vapor) is heating at 400 F while flowing outside and normal to a ¾″ Type K copper tube; the weight velocity is 20 (ft/sec) (lb/cu ft). Determine the film coefficient per lineal foot of tube.*

Solution: The dashed example line on the graph (Fig. 6.61) shows the method of evaluating the outside film coefficient, for the stated conditions, in terms of one square foot of outside surface of the tube. To convert this value, 65 Btu/(hr) (sq ft) (°F), to a lineal basis Fig. 5.4 would ordinarily be used. However, in this case, the entering value of 65 Btu/(hr) (sq ft) (°F) would be at the low end of the scale where accurate use of the graph is difficult. Equation 5.9 is therefore used,

$$h_o' = h_o A_{o_L}$$
$$= 65 \times 0.229 = 15 \text{ Btu per hour per °F per lineal foot of tube}$$

***Note:** To determine other heat transfer coefficients for Ethyl Acetate, use Fig. 6.61 but refer to the examples on the following pages for the appropriate method: Outside film coefficient, page 272; inside film coefficient, page 270; inside film coefficient per lineal foot, use method similar to that for outside film coefficient per lineal foot; inside film coefficient for a double-pipe exchanger, page 274.

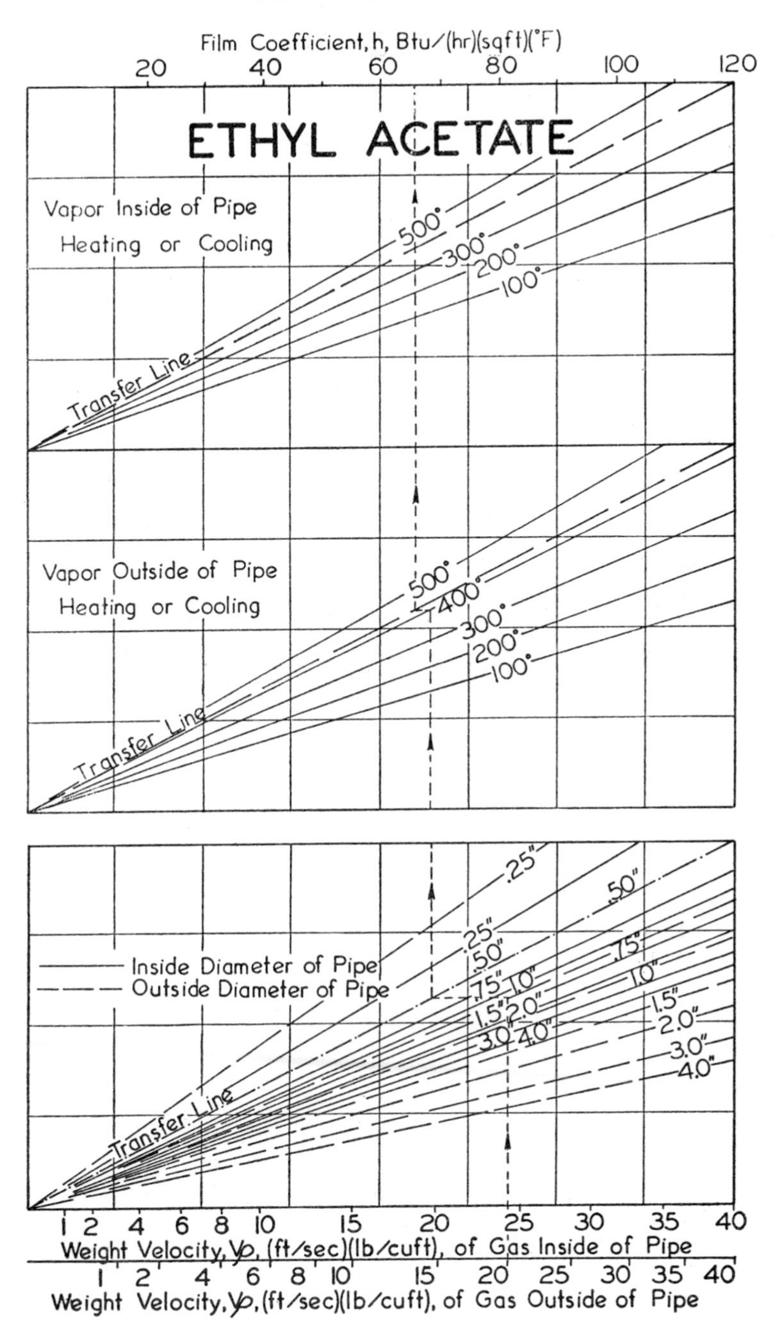
Film Coefficient, h, Btu/(hr)(sqft)(°F)
20
40
60
80
100
120
ETHYL ACETATE
Vapor Inside of Pipe
Heating or Cooling
500°
300°
200°
100°
Transfer Line
Vapor Outside of Pipe
Heating or Cooling
500°
400°
300°
200°
100°
Transfer Line
.25"
.50"
Inside Diameter of Pipe
Outside Diameter of Pipe
.75"
1.0"
1.5"
2.0"
3.0"
4.0"
Transfer Line
1 2 4 6 8 10 15 20 25 30 35 40
Weight Velocity, Vρ, (ft/sec)(lb/cuft), of Gas Inside of Pipe
1 2 4 6 8 10 15 20 25 30 35 40
Weight Velocity, Vρ, (ft/sec)(lb/cuft), of Gas Outside of Pipe

Figure 6.61

Ethyl Alcohol (Vapor)

Ethyl Alcohol (vapor) heating or cooling in turbulent flow within a tube or in turbulent flow outside and normal to a single tube.

Equations: Gas or vapor heating or cooling within a tube:
$Nu = 0.023(Re)^{0.8}(Pr)^{0.4}$
Gas or vapor heating or cooling outside and normal to a single tube: $Nu = 0.385(Re)^{0.56}(Pr)^{0.3}$

Text References: Chapter VI; equations 6.5, 6.9, 6.12, and 6.14.

Extensions: Refer to section 6.5 for extensions to annular spaces, tube bundles, and flow through helical coils.

Special Conditions: For a gas or vapor heating or cooling within a tube, do not use the graph unless the weight velocity, $V\rho$ (ft/sec) (lb/cu ft), exceeds 0.5 at 1 atmosphere, 2 at 10 atmospheres, or 3.0 at 20 atmospheres.

For a gas or vapor flowing outside and normal to a single tube, do not use the graph for $V\rho$ less than 0.1 unless the Reynolds number exceeds 100.

Example: Ethyl Alcohol (vapor) is being heated while flowing within a tube having an inside diameter of 1/4 inch. The weight velocity is 10 (ft/sec) (lb/cu ft) and the mean temperature is 500 F. Determine the value of the inside film coefficient.*

Solution: Enter the bottom of the graph (Fig. 6.62) at a weight velocity of 10 and rise to intersect the radial line for a tube of 1/4″ inside diameter. From this intersection move right to intersect the transfer line, then rise to the group of radials for fluid inside; intersect the radial for a temperature of 500 F then move right to the transfer line and from this intersection rise to read the answer at the top scale as 50 Btu/(hr) (sq ft) (°F).

***Note:** To determine other heat transfer coefficients for Ethyl Alcohol, use Fig. 6.62 but refer to the examples on the following pages for the appropriate method: Outside film coefficient, page 272; outside film coefficient per lineal foot, page 276; inside film coefficient per lineal foot, use method similar to that for outside film coefficient per lineal foot; inside film coefficient for a double-pipe exchanger, page 274.

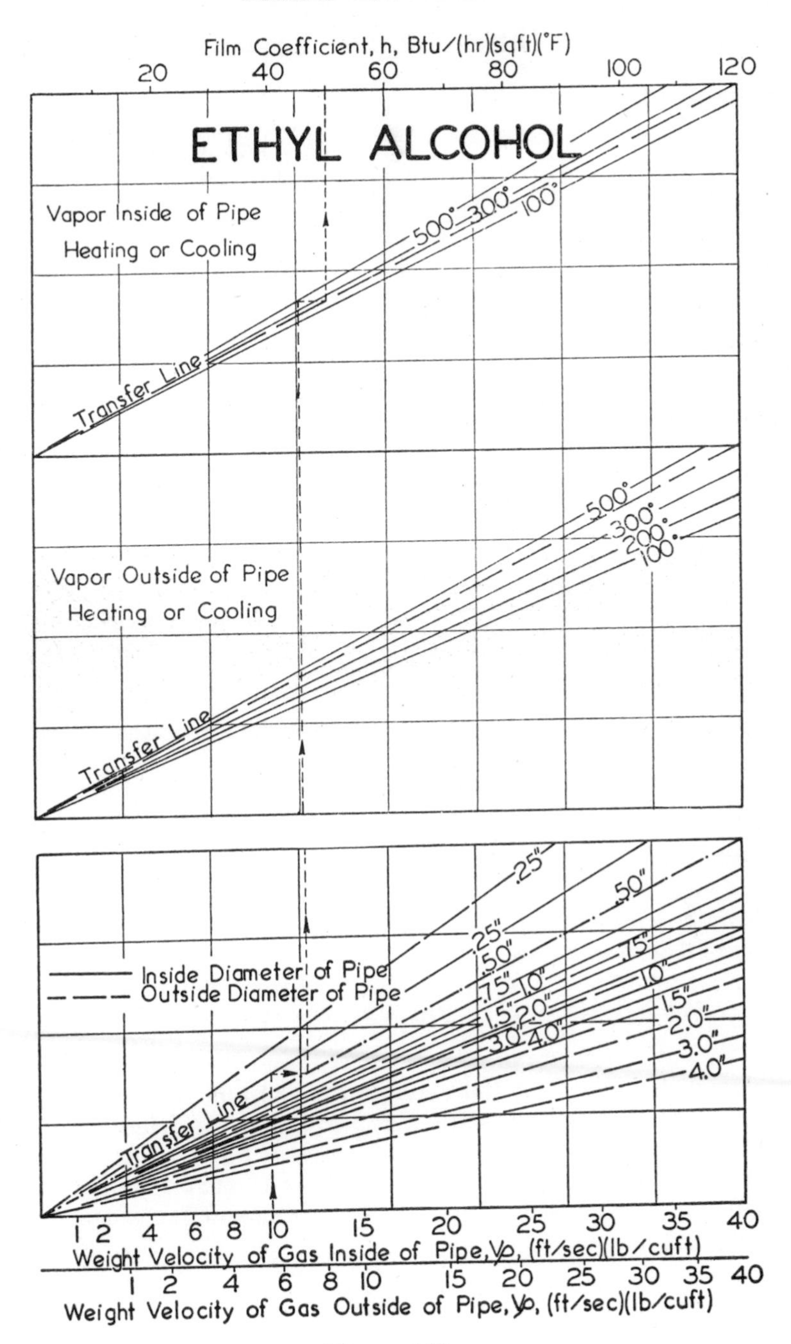
Film Coefficient, h, Btu/(hr)(sqft)(°F)
20 40 60 80 100 120
ETHYL ALCOHOL
Vapor Inside of Pipe
Heating or Cooling
500° 300° 100°
Transfer Line
Vapor Outside of Pipe
Heating or Cooling
500° 300° 200° 100°
Transfer Line
Inside Diameter of Pipe
Outside Diameter of Pipe
.25" .50" .75" 1.0" 1.5" 2.0" 3.0" 4.0"
Transfer Line
1 2 4 6 8 10 15 20 25 30 35 40
Weight Velocity of Gas Inside of Pipe, Vρ, (ft/sec)(lb/cuft)
1 2 4 6 8 10 15 20 25 30 35 40
Weight Velocity of Gas Outside of Pipe, Vρ, (ft/sec)(lb/cuft)

Figure 6.62

Ethyl Chloride (Vapor)

Ethyl Chloride (vapor) heating or cooling in turbulent flow within a tube or in turbulent flow outside and normal to a single tube.

Equations: Gas or vapor heating or cooling within a tube:

$$Nu = 0.023\,(Re)^{0.8}\,(Pr)^{0.4}$$

Gas or vapor heating or cooling outside and normal to a single tube: $Nu = 0.385\,(Re)^{0.56}\,(Pr)^{0.3}$

Text References: Chapter VI; equations 6.5, 6.9, 6.12, and 6.14.

Extensions: Refer to section 6.5 for extensions to annular spaces, tube bundles, and flow through helical coils.

Special Conditions: For a gas or vapor heating or cooling within a tube, do not use the graph unless the weight velocity, $V\rho$ (ft/sec) (lb/cu ft), exceeds 0.5 at 1 atmosphere, 2 at 10 atmospheres, or 3.0 at 20 atmospheres.

For a gas or vapor flowing outside and normal to a single tube, do not use the graph for $V\rho$ less than 0.1 unless the Reynolds number exceeds 100.

Example: Ethyl Chloride (vapor) is flowing outside and normal to a bundle of staggered 2 inch outside diameter tubes. The weight velocity through the narrowest section between tubes is 2 (ft/sec) (lb/cu ft) and the mean temperature of the vapor, which is being cooled, is 350 F. Determine the outside film coefficient.*

Solution: The dashed example line on the graph (Fig. 6.63) shows that, for the stated conditions, the film coefficient for flow normal to a single tube would be 8. For flow across a staggered tube bundle the base value of the outside coefficient is raised by 30% (refer to part 6 of section 6.5) hence for this case the corrected coefficient is $1.3 \times 8 = 10$ Btu/(hr) (sq ft) (°F).

*__Note:__ To determine other heat transfer coefficients for Ethyl Chloride, use Fig. 6.63 but refer to the examples on the following pages for the appropriate method: Inside film coefficient, page 278; outside film coefficient per lineal foot, page 276; inside film coefficient per lineal foot, use method similar to that for outside film coefficient per lineal foot; inside film coefficient for a double-pipe exchanger, page 274.

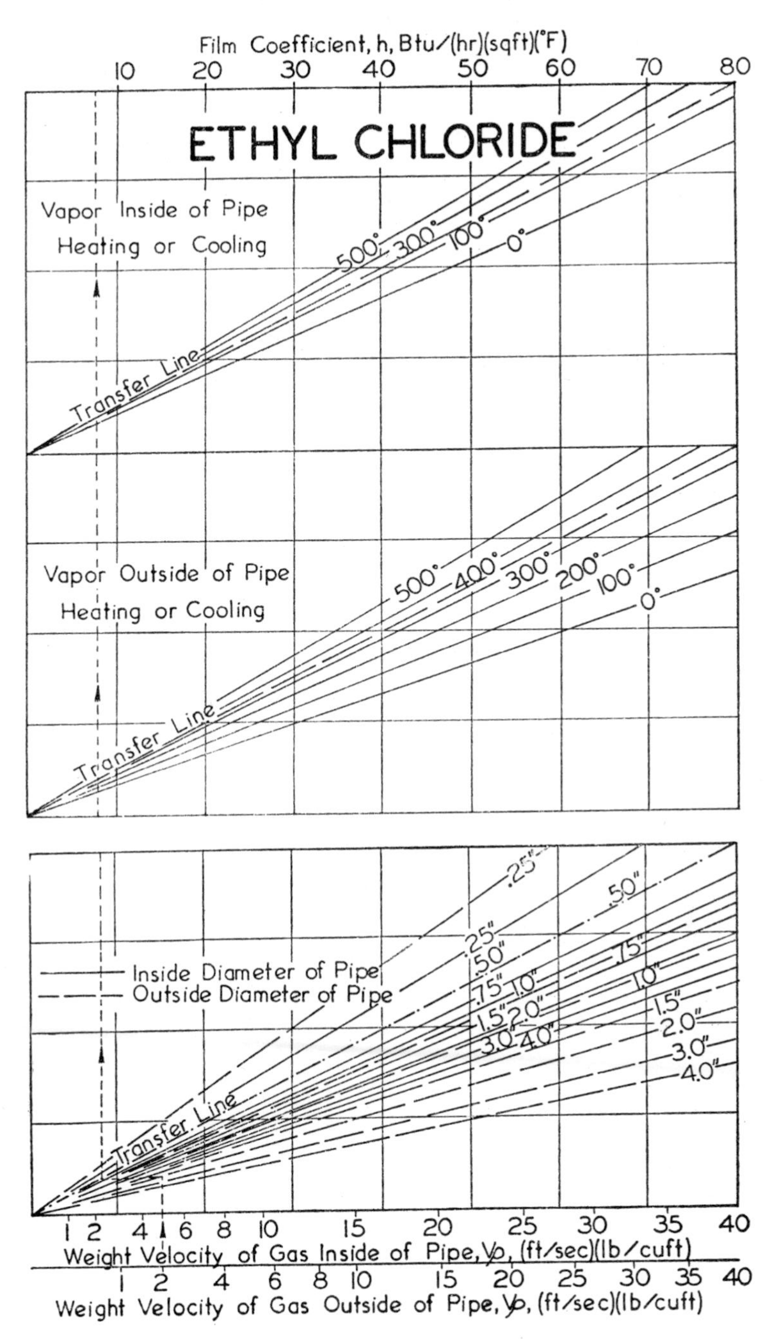
Film Coefficient, h, Btu/(hr)(sqft)(°F)
10 20 30 40 50 60 70 80
ETHYL CHLORIDE
Vapor Inside of Pipe
Heating or Cooling
500° 300° 100° 0°
Transfer Line
Vapor Outside of Pipe
Heating or Cooling
500° 400° 300° 200° 100° 0°
Transfer Line
Inside Diameter of Pipe
Outside Diameter of Pipe
.25" .50" .75" 1.0" 1.5" 2.0" 3.0" 4.0"
Transfer Line
1 2 4 6 8 10 15 20 25 30 35 40
Weight Velocity of Gas Inside of Pipe, Vρ, (ft/sec)(lb/cuft)
1 2 4 6 8 10 15 20 25 30 35 40
Weight Velocity of Gas Outside of Pipe, Vρ, (ft/sec)(lb/cuft)

Figure 6.63

Ethyl Ether (Vapor)

Ethyl Ether (vapor) heating or cooling in turbulent flow within a tube or in turbulent flow outside and normal to a single tube.

Equations: Gas or vapor heating or cooling within a tube:

$$Nu = 0.023\,(Re)^{0.8}\,(Pr)^{0.4}$$

Gas or vapor heating or cooling outside and normal to a single tube: $Nu = 0.385\,(Re)^{0.56}\,(Pr)^{0.3}$

Text References: Chapter VI; equations 6.5, 6.9, 6.12, and 6.14.

Extensions: Refer to section 6.5 for extensions to annular spaces, tube bundles, and flow through helical coils.

Special Conditions: For a gas or vapor heating or cooling within a tube, do not use the graph unless the weight velocity, $V\rho$ (ft/sec) (lb/cu ft), exceeds 0.5 at 1 atmosphere, 2 at 10 atmospheres, or 3.0 at 20 atmospheres.

For a gas or vapor flowing outside and normal to a single tube, do not use the graph for $V\rho$ less than 0.1 unless the Reynolds number exceeds 100.

Example: Ethyl Ether (vapor) at —100 F is being cooled while flowing through an annular space in a double-pipe heat exchanger for which the equivalent inside diameter (equation 6.16) is 1 inch. The weight velocity is 30 (ft/sec) (lb/cu ft). Determine the inside film coefficient.*

Solution: The film coefficient is directly determinable from the graph as indicated by the dashed example line, Fig. 6.64. The resultant value, 62, is the film coefficient for the outside of the inner pipe of the annular exchanger and its units are Btu per hour per °F per square foot of outer surface of the inner pipe.

***Note:** To determine other heat transfer coefficients for Ethyl Ether, use Fig. 6.64 but refer to the examples on the following pages for the appropriate method: Outside film coefficient, page 280; inside film coefficient, page 278; outside film coefficient per lineal foot, page 276; inside film coefficient per lineal foot, use method similar to that for outside film coefficient per lineal foot.

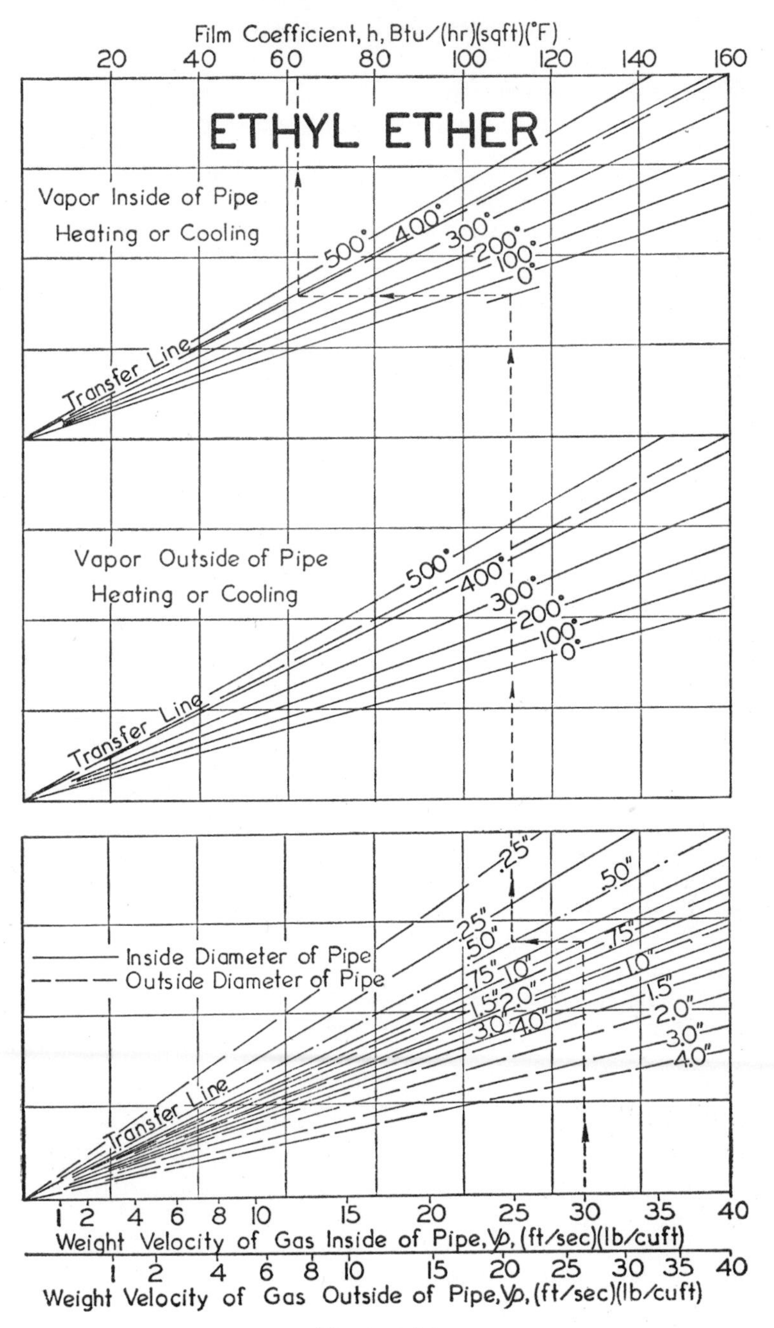
Film Coefficient, h, Btu/(hr)(sqft)(°F)
20 40 60 80 100 120 140 160
ETHYL ETHER
Vapor Inside of Pipe
Heating or Cooling
500° 400° 300° 200° 100° 0°
Transfer Line
Vapor Outside of Pipe
Heating or Cooling
500° 400° 300° 200° 100° 0°
Transfer Line
Inside Diameter of Pipe
Outside Diameter of Pipe
.25" .50" .75" 1.0" 1.5" 2.0" 3.0" 4.0"
.25" .50" .75" 1.0" 1.5" 2.0" 3.0" 4.0"
Transfer Line
1 2 4 6 8 10 15 20 25 30 35 40
Weight Velocity of Gas Inside of Pipe, Vρ, (ft/sec)(lb/cuft)
1 2 4 6 8 10 15 20 25 30 35 40
Weight Velocity of Gas Outside of Pipe, Vρ, (ft/sec)(lb/cuft)

Figure 6.64

Ethylene (Vapor)

Ethylene (vapor) heating or cooling in turbulent flow within a tube or in turbulent flow outside and normal to a single tube.

Equations: Gas or vapor heating or cooling within a tube:
$$Nu = 0.023\,(Re)^{0.8}\,(Pr)^{0.4}$$
Gas or vapor heating or cooling outside and normal to a single tube: $Nu = 0.385\,(Re)^{0.56}\,(Pr)^{0.3}$

Text References: Chapter VI; equations 6.5, 6.9, 6.12, and 6.14.

Extensions: Refer to section 6.5 for extensions to annular spaces, tube bundles, and flow through helical coils.

Special Conditions: For a gas or vapor heating or cooling within a tube, do not use the graph unless the weight velocity, $V\rho$ (ft/sec) (lb/cu ft), exceeds 0.5 at 1 atmosphere, 2 at 10 atmospheres, or 3.0 at 20 atmospheres.

For a gas or vapor flowing outside and normal to a single tube, do not use the graph for $V\rho$ less than 0.1 unless the Reynolds number exceeds 100.

Example: Ethylene (vapor) is heating at 200 F while flowing outside and normal to a ¾″ Type K copper tube; the weight velocity is 20 (ft/sec) (lb/cu ft). Determine the film coefficient per lineal foot of tube.*

Solution: The dashed example line on the graph (Fig. 6.65) shows the method of evaluating the outside film coefficient, for the stated conditions, in terms of one square foot of outside surface of the tube. To convert this value, 65 Btu/(hr) (sq ft) (°F), to a lineal basis Fig. 5.4 would ordinarily be used. However, in this case, the entering value of 65 Btu/(hr) (sq ft) (°F) would be at the low end of the scale where accurate use of the graph is difficult. Equation 5.9 is therefore used,

$$h_o' = h_o A_{o_L}$$
$$= 65 \times 0.229 = 15 \text{ Btu per hour per °F per lineal foot of tube}$$

*__Note:__ To determine other heat transfer coefficients for Ethylene, use Fig. 6.65 but refer to the examples on the following pages for the appropriate method: Outside film coefficient, page 280; inside film coefficient, page 278; inside film coefficient per lineal foot, use method similar to that for outside film coefficient per lineal foot; inside film coefficient for a double-pipe exchanger, page 282.

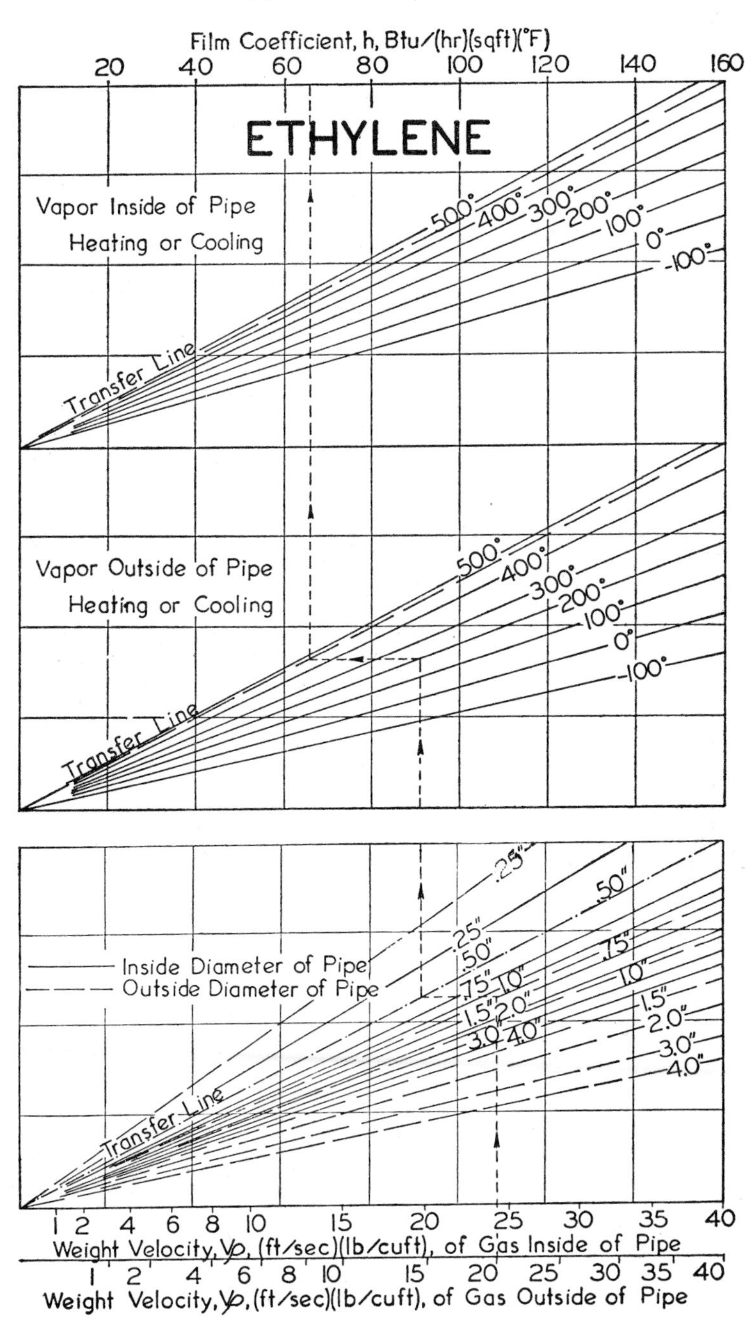
Film Coefficient, h, Btu/(hr)(sqft)(°F)
20 40 60 80 100 120 140 160
ETHYLENE
Vapor Inside of Pipe
Heating or Cooling
500° 400° 300° 200° 100° 0° -100°
Transfer Line
Vapor Outside of Pipe
Heating or Cooling
500° 400° 300° 200° 100° 0° -100°
Transfer Line
Inside Diameter of Pipe
Outside Diameter of Pipe
.25" .50" .75" 1.0" 1.5" 2.0" 3.0" 4.0"
.25" .50" .75" 1.0" 1.5" 2.0" 3.0" 4.0"
Transfer Line
1 2 4 6 8 10 15 20 25 30 35 40
Weight Velocity, Vρ, (ft/sec)(lb/cuft), of Gas Inside of Pipe
1 2 4 6 8 10 15 20 25 30 35 40
Weight Velocity, Vρ, (ft/sec)(lb/cuft), of Gas Outside of Pipe

Figure 6.65

Helium (Gas)

Helium (gas) heating or cooling in turbulent flow within a tube or in turbulent flow outside and normal to a single tube.

Equations: Gas or vapor heating or cooling within a tube:

$$Nu = 0.023\,(Re)^{0.8}\,(Pr)^{0.4}$$

Gas or vapor heating or cooling outside and normal to a single tube: $Nu = 0.385\,(Re)^{0.56}\,(Pr)^{0.3}$

Text References: Chapter VI; equations 6.5, 6.9, 6.12, and 6.14.

Extensions: Refer to section 6.5 for extensions to annular spaces, tube bundles, and flow through helical coils.

Special Conditions: For a gas or vapor heating or cooling within a tube, do not use the graph unless the weight velocity, $V\rho$ (ft/sec) (lb/cu ft), exceeds 0.5 at 1 atmosphere, 2 at 10 atmospheres, or 3.0 at 20 atmospheres.

For a gas or vapor flowing outside and normal to a single tube, do not use the graph for $V\rho$ less than 0.1 unless the Reynolds number exceeds 100.

Example: Helium (gas) is being heated while flowing within a tube having an inside diameter of ¼ inch. The weight velocity is 10 (ft/sec) (lb/cu ft) and the mean temperature is 100 F. Determine the value of the inside film coefficient.*

Solution: Enter the bottom of the graph (Fig. 6.66) at a weight velocity of 10 and rise to intersect the radial line for a tube of ¼″ inside diameter. From this intersection move right to intersect the transfer line, then rise to the group of radials for fluid inside; intersect the radial for a temperature of 100 F then move left to the transfer line and from this intersection rise to read the answer at the top scale as 180 Btu/(hr) (sq ft) (°F).

***Note:** To determine other heat transfer coefficients for Helium, use Fig. 6.66 but refer to the examples on the following pages for the appropriate method: Outside film coefficient, page 280; outside film coefficient per lineal foot, page 284; inside film coefficient per lineal foot, use method similar to that for outside film coefficient per lineal foot; inside film coefficient for a double-pipe exchanger, page 282.

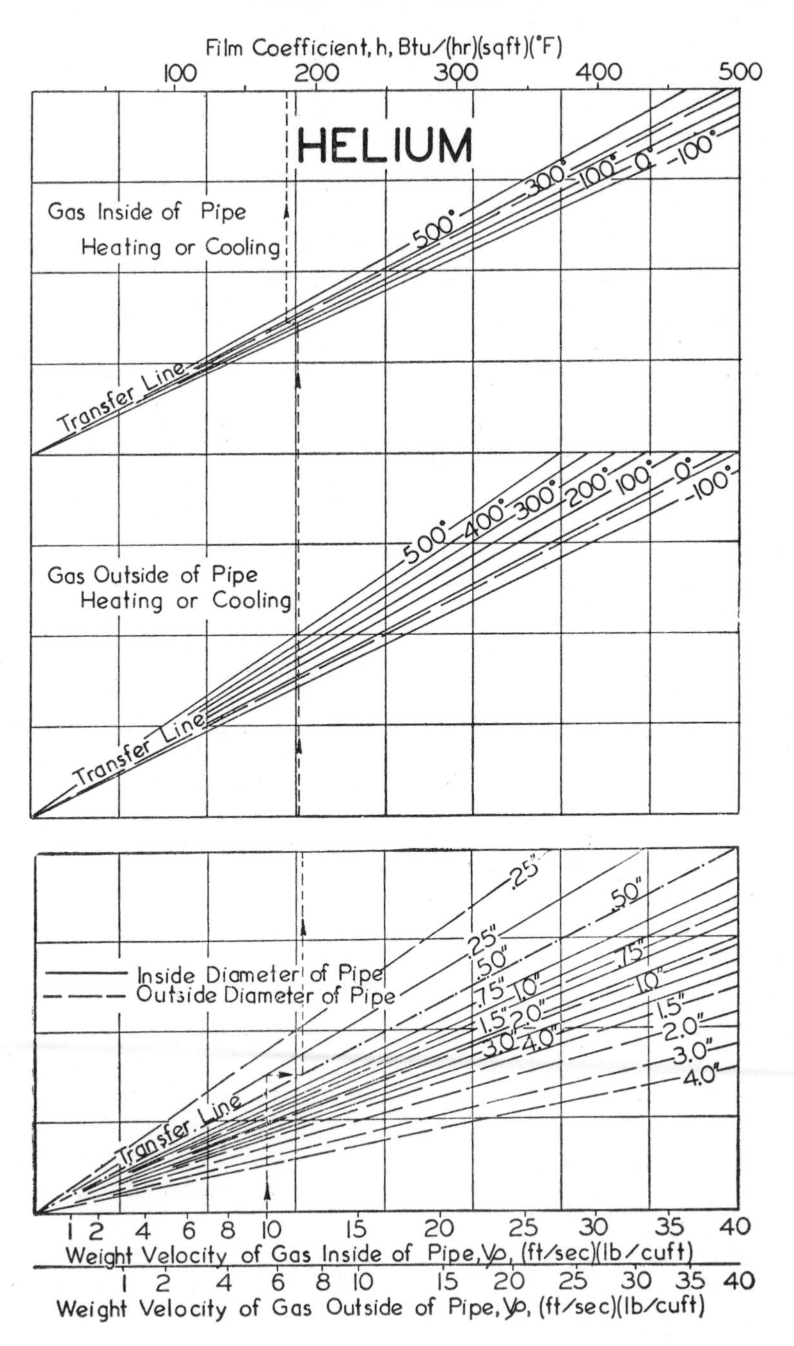
Film Coefficient, h, Btu/(hr)(sqft)(°F)
100
200
300
400
500
HELIUM
Gas Inside of Pipe
Heating or Cooling
500°
300°
100°
0°
-100°
Transfer Line
Gas Outside of Pipe
Heating or Cooling
500°
400°
300°
200°
100°
0°
-100°
Transfer Line
Inside Diameter of Pipe
Outside Diameter of Pipe
.25"
.50"
.75"
1.0"
1.5"
2.0"
3.0"
4.0"
Transfer Line
1 2 4 6 8 10 15 20 25 30 35 40
Weight Velocity of Gas Inside of Pipe, Vρ, (ft/sec)(lb/cuft)
1 2 4 6 8 10 15 20 25 30 35 40
Weight Velocity of Gas Outside of Pipe, Vρ, (ft/sec)(lb/cuft)

Figure 6.66

Hydrogen (Gas)

Hydrogen (gas) heating or cooling in turbulent flow within a tube or in turbulent flow outside and normal to a single tube.

Equations: Gas or vapor heating or cooling within a tube:
$$Nu = 0.023 (Re)^{0.8} (Pr)^{0.4}$$
Gas or vapor heating or cooling outside and normal to a single tube: $Nu = 0.385 (Re)^{0.56} (Pr)^{0.3}$

Text References: Chapter VI; equations 6.5, 6.9, 6.12, and 6.14.

Extensions: Refer to section 6.5 for extensions to annular spaces, tube bundles, and flow through helical coils.

Special Conditions: For a gas or vapor heating or cooling within a tube, do not use the graph unless the weight velocity, $V\rho$ (ft/sec) (lb/cu ft), exceeds 0.5 at 1 atmosphere, 2 at 10 atmospheres, or 3.0 at 20 atmospheres.

For a gas or vapor flowing outside and normal to a single tube, do not use the graph for $V\rho$ less than 0.1 unless the Reynolds number exceeds 100.

Example: Hydrogen (gas) is flowing outside and normal to a bundle of staggered 2 inch outside diameter tubes. The weight velocity through the narrowest section between tubes is 2 (ft/sec) (lb/cu ft) and the mean temperature of the gas, which is being cooled, is —100 F. Determine the outside film coefficient.*

Solution: The dashed example line on the graph (Fig. 6.67) shows that, for the stated conditions, the film coefficient for flow normal to a single tube would be 80. For flow across a staggered tube bundle the base value of the outside coefficient is raised by 30% (refer to part 6 of section 6.5) hence for this case the corrected coefficient is $1.3 \times 80 = 104$ Btu/(hr) (sq ft) (°F).

***Note:** To determine other heat transfer coefficients for Hydrogen, use Fig. 6.67 but refer to the examples on the following pages for the appropriate method: Inside film coefficient, page 286; outside film coefficient per lineal foot, page 284; inside film coefficient per lineal foot, use method similar to that for outside film coefficient per lineal foot; inside film coefficient for a double-pipe exchanger, page 282.

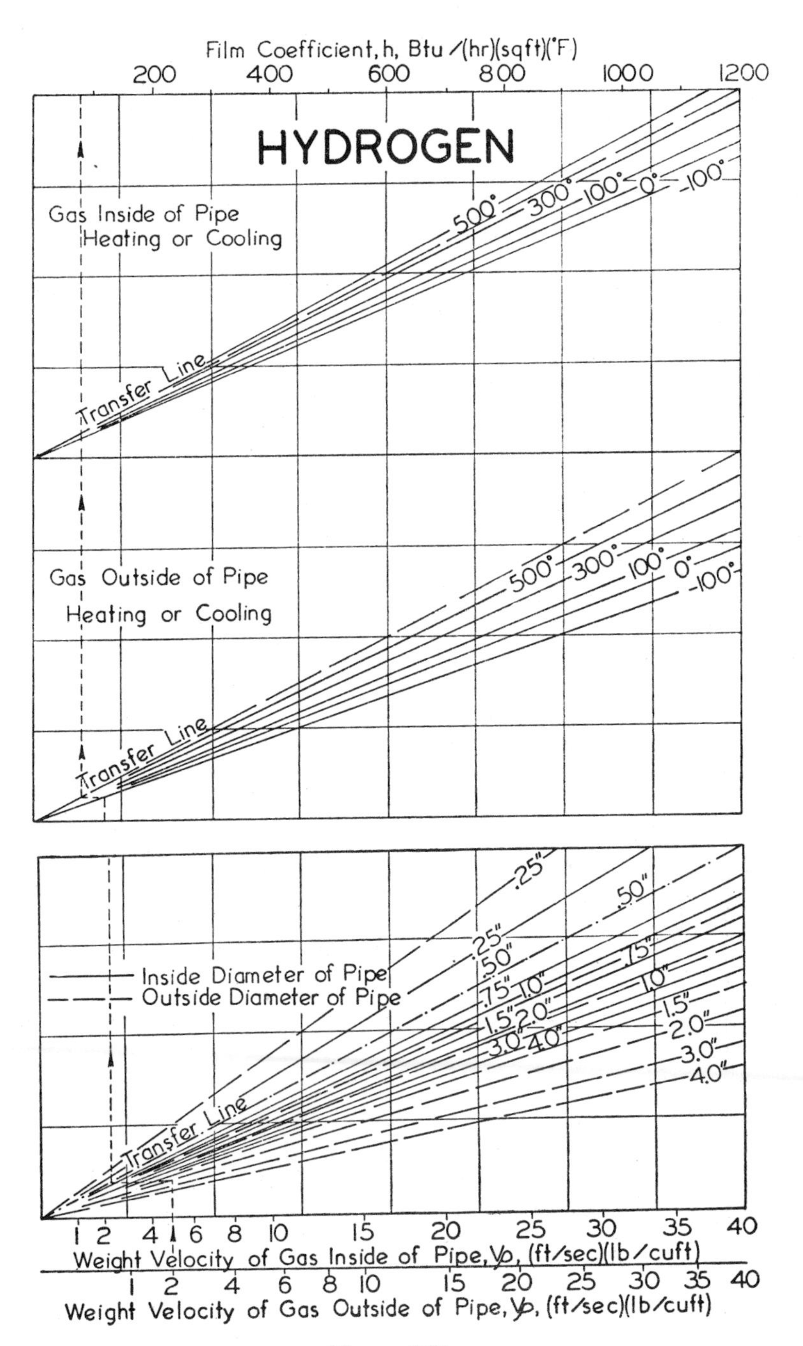
Film Coefficient, h, Btu /(hr)(sqft)(°F)
200 400 600 800 1000 1200
HYDROGEN
Gas Inside of Pipe
Heating or Cooling
500° 300° 100° 0° -100°
Transfer Line
Gas Outside of Pipe
Heating or Cooling
500° 300° 100° 0° -100°
Transfer Line
Inside Diameter of Pipe
Outside Diameter of Pipe
.25" .50" .75" 1.0" 1.5" 2.0" 3.0" 4.0"
.25" .50" .75" 1.0" 1.5" 2.0" 3.0" 4.0"
Transfer Line
1 2 4 6 8 10 15 20 25 30 35 40
Weight Velocity of Gas Inside of Pipe, Vρ, (ft/sec)(lb/cuft)
1 2 4 6 8 10 15 20 25 30 35 40
Weight Velocity of Gas Outside of Pipe, Vρ, (ft/sec)(lb/cuft)

Figure 6.67

Hydrogen Sulphide (Gas)

Hydrogen Sulfide (gas) heating or cooling in turbulent flow within a tube or in turbulent flow outside and normal to a single tube.

Equations: Gas or vapor heating or cooling within a tube:

$$Nu = 0.023\,(Re)^{0.8}\,(Pr)^{0.4}$$

Gas or vapor heating or cooling outside and normal to a single tube: $Nu = 0.385\,(Re)^{0.56}\,(Pr)^{0.3}$

Text References: Chapter VI; equations 6.5, 6.9, 6.12, and 6.14.

Extensions: Refer to section 6.5 for extensions to annular spaces, tube bundles, and flow through helical coils.

Special Conditions: For a gas or vapor heating or cooling within a tube, do not use the graph unless the weight velocity, $V\rho$ (ft/sec) (lb/cu ft), exceeds 0.5 at 1 atmosphere, 2 at 10 atmospheres, or 3.0 at 20 atmospheres.

For a gas or vapor flowing outside and normal to a single tube, do not use the graph for $V\rho$ less than 0.1 unless the Reynolds number exceeds 100.

Example: Hydrogen Sulfide (gas) at 100 F is being cooled while flowing through an annular space in a double-pipe heat exchanger for which the equivalent inside diameter (equation 6.16) is 1 inch. The weight velocity is 30 (ft/sec) (lb/cu ft). Determine the inside film coefficient.*

Solution: The film coefficient is directly determinable from the graph as indicated by the dashed example line, Fig. 6.68. The resultant value, 48, is the film coefficient for the outside of the inner pipe of the annular exchanger and its units are Btu per hour per °F per square foot of outer surface of the inner pipe.

***Note:** To determine other heat transfer coefficients for Hydrogen Sulphide, use Fig. 6.68 but refer to the examples on the following pages for the appropriate method: Outside film coefficient, page 288; inside film coefficient, page 286; outside film coefficient per lineal foot, page 284; inside film coefficient per lineal foot, use method similar to that for outside film coefficient per lineal foot.

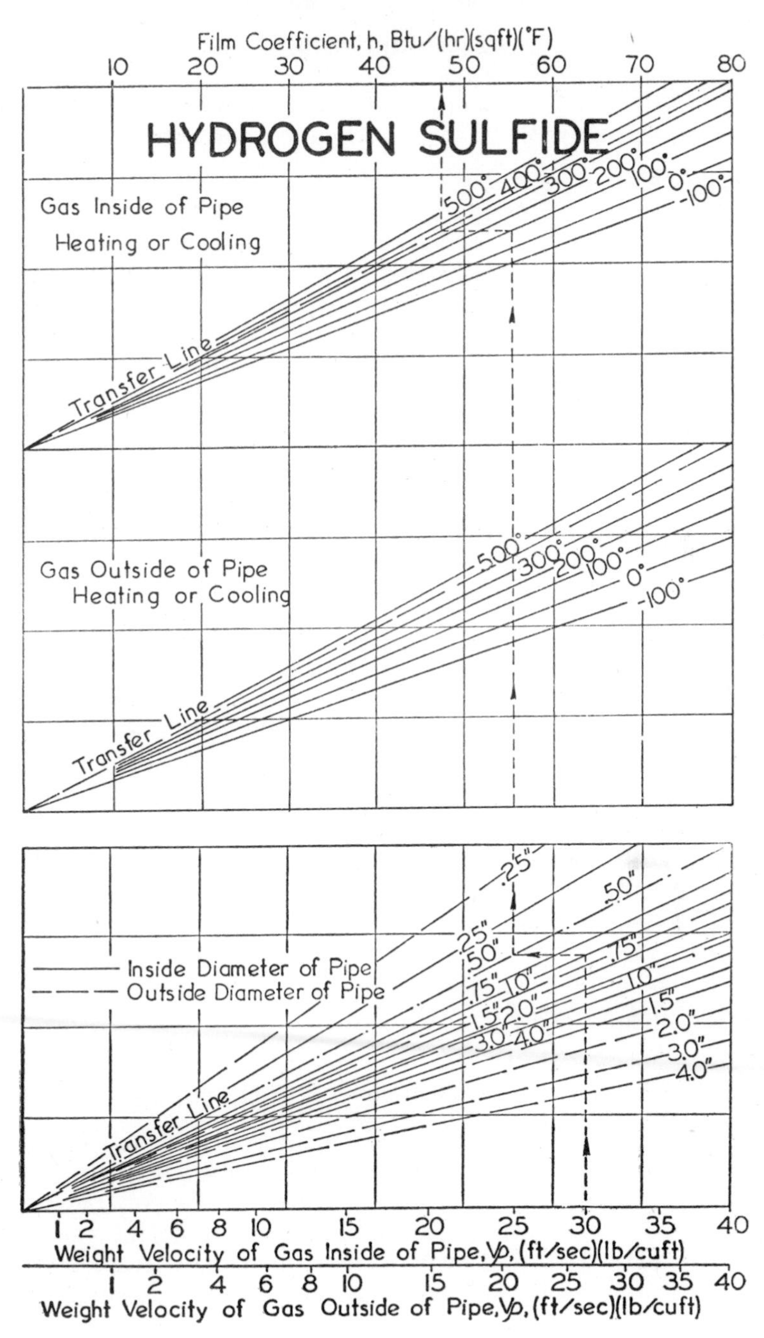
Film Coefficient, h, Btu/(hr)(sqft)(°F)
10 20 30 40 50 60 70 80
HYDROGEN SULFIDE
Gas Inside of Pipe
Heating or Cooling
500° 400° 300° 200° 100° 0° -100°
Transfer Line
Gas Outside of Pipe
Heating or Cooling
500° 300° 200° 100° 0° -100°
Transfer Line
Inside Diameter of Pipe
Outside Diameter of Pipe
.25" .50" .75" 1.0" 1.5" 2.0" 3.0" 4.0"
Transfer Line
1 2 4 6 8 10 15 20 25 30 35 40
Weight Velocity of Gas Inside of Pipe, Vρ, (ft/sec)(lb/cuft)
1 2 4 6 8 10 15 20 25 30 35 40
Weight Velocity of Gas Outside of Pipe, Vρ, (ft/sec)(lb/cuft)

Figure 6.68

Methane (Gas)

Methane (gas) heating or cooling in turbulent flow within a tube or in turbulent flow outside and normal to a single tube.

Equations: Gas or vapor heating or cooling within a tube:

$$Nu = 0.023\,(Re)^{0.8}\,(Pr)^{0.4}$$

Gas or vapor heating or cooling outside and normal to a single tube: $Nu = 0.385\,(Re)^{0.56}\,(Pr)^{0.3}$

Text References: Chapter VI; equations 6.5, 6.9, 6.12, and 6.14.

Extensions: Refer to section 6.5 for extensions to annular spaces, tube bundles, and flow through helical coils.

Special Conditions: For a gas or vapor heating or cooling within a tube, do not use the graph unless the weight velocity, $V\rho$ (ft/sec) (lb/cu ft), exceeds 0.5 at 1 atmosphere, 2 at 10 atmospheres, or 3.0 at 20 atmospheres.

For a gas or vapor flowing outside and normal to a single tube, do not use the graph for $V\rho$ less than 0.1 unless the Reynolds number exceeds 100.

Example: Methane (gas) is heating at 300 F while flowing outside and normal to a 3/4″ Type K copper tube; the weight velocity is 20 (ft/sec) (lb/cu ft). Determine the film coefficient per lineal foot of tube.*

Solution: The dashed example line on the graph (Fig. 6.69) shows the method of evaluating the outside film coefficient, for the stated conditions, in terms of one square foot of outside surface of the tube. To convert this value, 62 Btu/(hr) (sq ft) (°F), to a lineal basis Fig. 5.4 would ordinarily be used. However, in this case, the entering value of 62 Btu/(hr) (sq ft) (°F) would be at the low end of the scale where accurate use of the graph is difficult. Equation 5.9 is therefore used,

$$h_o' = h_o A_{o_L}$$
$$= 62 \times 0.229 = 14 \text{ Btu per hour per °F per lineal foot of tube}$$

***Note:** To determine other heat transfer coefficients for Methane, use Fig. 6.69 but refer to the examples on the following pages for the appropriate method: Outside film coefficient, page 288; inside film coefficient, page 286; inside film coefficient per lineal foot, use method similar to that for outside film coefficient per lineal foot; inside film coefficient for a double-pipe exchanger, page 290.

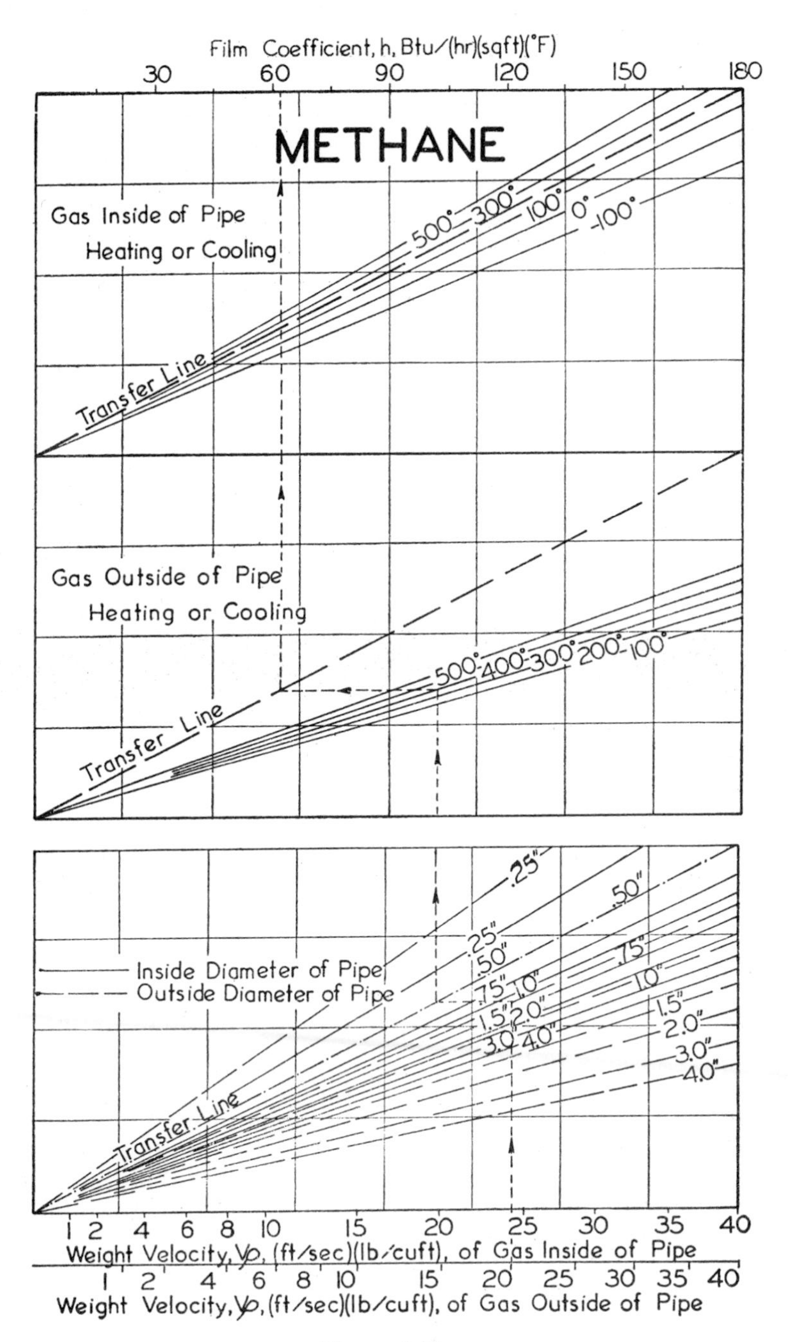
Film Coefficient, h, Btu/(hr)(sqft)(°F)
30 60 90 120 150 180
METHANE
Gas Inside of Pipe
Heating or Cooling
500° 300° 100° 0° -100°
Transfer Line
Gas Outside of Pipe
Heating or Cooling
500° 400° 300° 200° 100°
Transfer Line
Inside Diameter of Pipe
Outside Diameter of Pipe
.25" .50" .75" 1.0" 1.5" 2.0" 3.0" 4.0"
Transfer Line
1 2 4 6 8 10 15 20 25 30 35 40
Weight Velocity, Vρ, (ft/sec)(lb/cuft), of Gas Inside of Pipe
1 2 4 6 8 10 15 20 25 30 35 40
Weight Velocity, Vρ, (ft/sec)(lb/cuft), of Gas Outside of Pipe

Figure 6.69

Methyl Chloride (Vapor)

Methyl Chloride (vapor) heating or cooling in turbulent flow within a tube or in turbulent flow outside and normal to a single tube.

Equations: Gas or vapor heating or cooling within a tube:
$Nu = 0.023\,(Re)^{0.8}\,(Pr)^{0.4}$
Gas or vapor heating or cooling outside and normal to a single tube: $Nu = 0.385\,(Re)^{0.56}\,(Pr)^{0.3}$

Text References: Chapter VI; equations 6.5, 6.9, 6.12, and 6.14.

Extensions: Refer to section 6.5 for extensions to annular spaces, tube bundles, and flow through helical coils.

Special Conditions: For a gas or vapor heating or cooling within a tube, do not use the graph unless the weight velocity, $V\rho$ (ft/sec) (lb/cu ft), exceeds 0.5 at 1 atmosphere, 2 at 10 atmospheres, or 3.0 at 20 atmospheres.

For a gas or vapor flowing outside and normal to a single tube, do not use the graph for $V\rho$ less than 0.1 unless the Reynolds number exceeds 100.

Example: Methyl Chloride (vapor) is being heated while flowing within a tube having an inside diameter of 1/4 inch. The weight velocity is 10 (ft/sec) (lb/cu ft) and the mean temperature is 0 F. Determine the value of the inside film coefficient.*

Solution: Enter the bottom of the graph (Fig. 6.70) at a weight velocity of 10 and rise to intersect the radial line for a tube of 1/4″ inside diameter. From this intersection move right to intersect the transfer line, then rise to the group of radials for fluid inside; intersect the radial for a temperature of 0 F then move left to the transfer line and from this intersection rise to read the answer at the top scale as 20 Btu/ (hr) (sq ft) (°F).

*__Note:__ To determine other heat transfer coefficients for Methyl Chloride, use Fig. 6.70 but refer to the examples on the following pages for the appropriate method: Outside film coefficient, page 288; outside film coefficient per lineal foot, page 292; inside film coefficient per lineal foot, use method similar to that for outside film coefficient per lineal foot; inside film coefficient for a double-pipe exchanger, page 290.

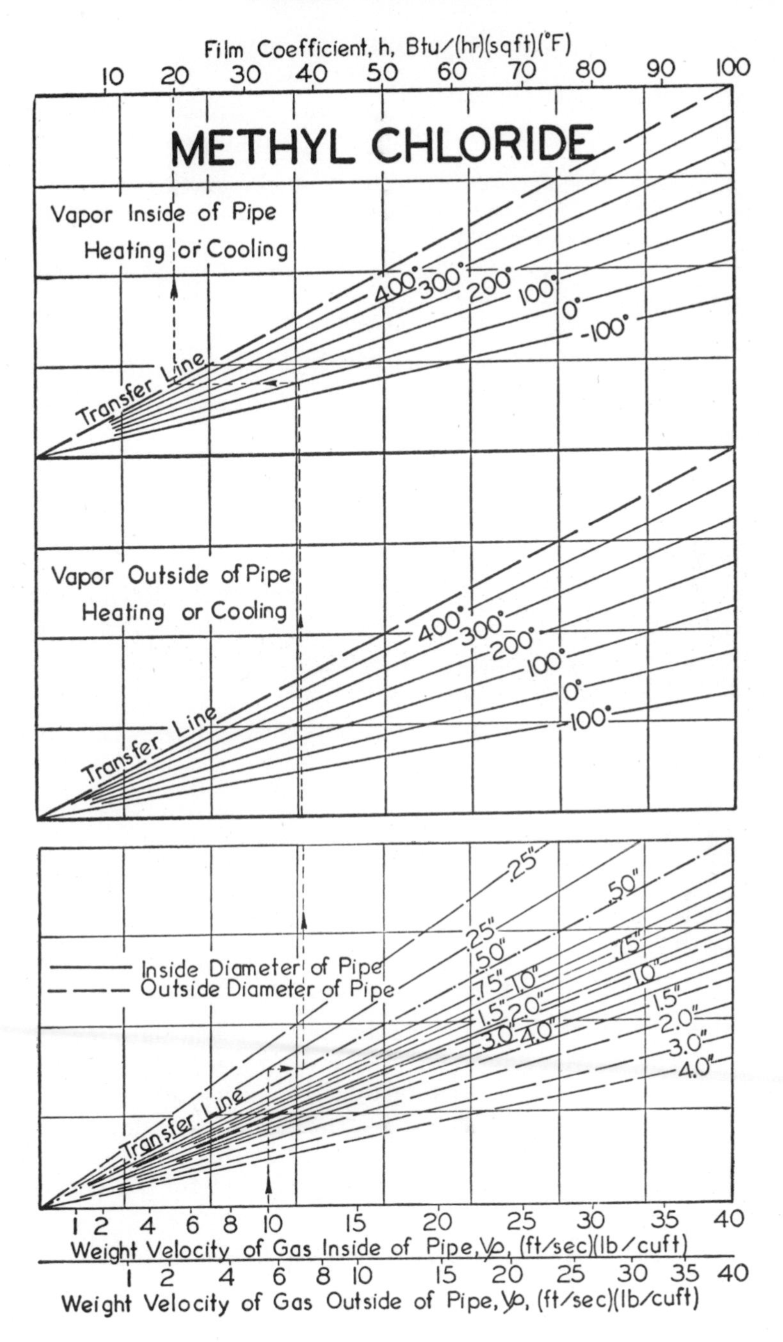

Film Coefficient, h, Btu/(hr)(sqft)(°F)
10 20 30 40 50 60 70 80 90 100
METHYL CHLORIDE
Vapor Inside of Pipe
Heating or Cooling
400° 300° 200° 100° 0° -100°
Transfer Line
Vapor Outside of Pipe
Heating or Cooling
400° 300° 200° 100° 0° -100°
Transfer Line
Inside Diameter of Pipe
Outside Diameter of Pipe
.25" .50" .75" 1.0" 1.5" 2.0" 3.0" 4.0"
.25" .50" .75" 1.0" 1.5" 2.0" 3.0" 4.0"
Transfer Line
1 2 4 6 8 10 15 20 25 30 35 40
Weight Velocity of Gas Inside of Pipe, Vρ, (ft/sec)(lb/cuft)
1 2 4 6 8 10 15 20 25 30 35 40
Weight Velocity of Gas Outside of Pipe, Vρ, (ft/sec)(lb/cuft)

Figure 6.70

Nitric Oxide (Gas)

Nitric Oxide (gas) heating or cooling in turbulent flow within a tube or in turbulent flow outside and normal to a single tube.

Equations: Gas or vapor heating or cooling within a tube:
$Nu = 0.023\,(Re)^{0.8}\,(Pr)^{0.4}$
Gas or vapor heating or cooling outside and normal to a single tube: $Nu = 0.385\,(Re)^{0.56}\,(Pr)^{0.3}$

Text References: Chapter VI; equations 6.5, 6.9, 6.12, and 6.14.

Extensions: Refer to section 6.5 for extensions to annular spaces, tube bundles, and flow through helical coils.

Special Conditions: For a gas or vapor heating or cooling within a tube, do not use the graph unless the weight velocity, $V\rho$ (ft/sec) (lb/cu ft), exceeds 0.5 at 1 atmosphere, 2 at 10 atmospheres, or 3.0 at 20 atmospheres.

For a gas or vapor flowing outside and normal to a single tube, do not use the graph for $V\rho$ less than 0.1 unless the Reynolds number exceeds 100.

Example: Nitric Oxide (gas) is flowing outside and normal to a bundle of staggered 2 inch outside diameter tubes. The weight velocity through the narrowest section between tubes is 2 (ft/sec) (lb/cu ft) and the mean temperature of the gas, which is being cooled, is —100 F. Determine the outside film coefficient.*

Solution: The dashed example line on the graph (Fig. 6.71) shows that, for the stated conditions, the film coefficient for flow normal to a single tube would be 7. For flow across a staggered tube bundle the base value of the outside coefficient is raised by 30% (refer to part 6 of section 6.5) hence for this case the corrected coefficient is $1.3 \times 7 = 9$ (Btu/(hr) (sq ft) (°F).

*__Note:__ To determine other heat transfer coefficients for Nitric Oxide, use Fig. 6.71 but refer to the examples on the following pages for the appropriate method: Inside film coefficient, page 294; outside film coefficient per lineal foot, page 292; inside film coefficient per lineal foot, use method similar to that for outside film coefficient per lineal foot; inside film coefficient for a double-pipe exchanger, page 290.

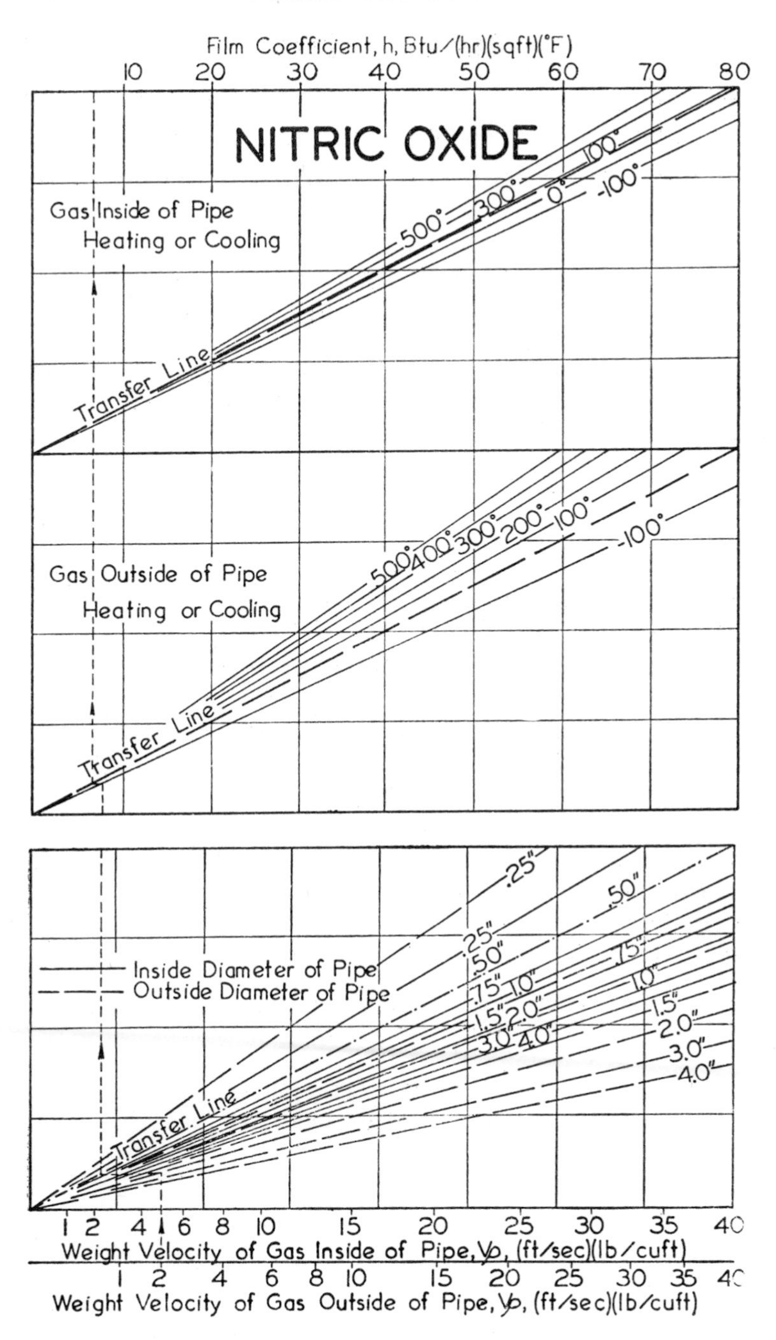
Film Coefficient, h, Btu/(hr)(sqft)(°F)
NITRIC OXIDE
Gas Inside of Pipe
Heating or Cooling
Transfer Line
500°
300°
100°
0°
-100°
Gas Outside of Pipe
Heating or Cooling
Transfer Line
500°
400°
300°
200°
100°
-100°
Inside Diameter of Pipe
Outside Diameter of Pipe
Transfer Line
.25"
.50"
.75"
1.0"
1.5"
2.0"
3.0"
4.0"
Weight Velocity of Gas Inside of Pipe, Vρ, (ft/sec)(lb/cuft)
Weight Velocity of Gas Outside of Pipe, Vρ, (ft/sec)(lb/cuft)

Figure 6.71

Nitrogen (Gas)

Nitrogen (gas) heating or cooling in turbulent flow within a tube or in turbulent flow outside and normal to a single tube.

Equations: Gas or vapor heating or cooling within a tube:
$$Nu = 0.023\,(Re)^{0.8}\,(Pr)^{0.4}$$
Gas or vapor heating or cooling outside and normal to a single tube: $Nu = 0.385\,(Re)^{0.56}\,(Pr)^{0.3}$

Text References: Chapter VI; equations 6.5, 6.9, 6.12, and 6.14.

Extensions: Refer to section 6.5 for extensions to annular spaces, tube bundles, and flow through helical coils.

Special Conditions: For a gas or vapor heating or cooling within a tube, do not use the graph unless the weight velocity, $V\rho$ (ft/sec) (lb/cu ft), exceeds 0.5 at 1 atmosphere, 2 at 10 atmospheres, or 3.0 at 20 atmospheres.

For a gas or vapor flowing outside and normal to a single tube, do not use the graph for $V\rho$ less than 0.1 unless the Reynolds number exceeds 100.

Example: Nitrogen (gas) at 0 F is being cooled while flowing through an annular space in a double-pipe heat exchanger for which the equivalent inside diameter (equation 6.16) is 1 inch. The weight velocity is 30 (ft/sec) (lb/cu ft). Determine the inside film coefficient.*

Solution: The film coefficient is directly determinable from the graph as indicated by the dashed example line, Fig. 6.72. The resultant value, 60, is the film coefficient for the outside of the inner pipe of the annular exchanger and its units are Btu per hour per °F per square foot of outer surface of the inner pipe.

*__Note:__ To determine other heat transfer coefficients for Nitrogen, use Fig. 6.72 but refer to the examples on the following pages for the appropriate method: Outside film coefficient, page 296; inside film coefficient, page 294; outside film coefficient per lineal foot, page 292; inside film coefficient per lineal foot, use method similar to that for outside film coefficient per lineal foot.

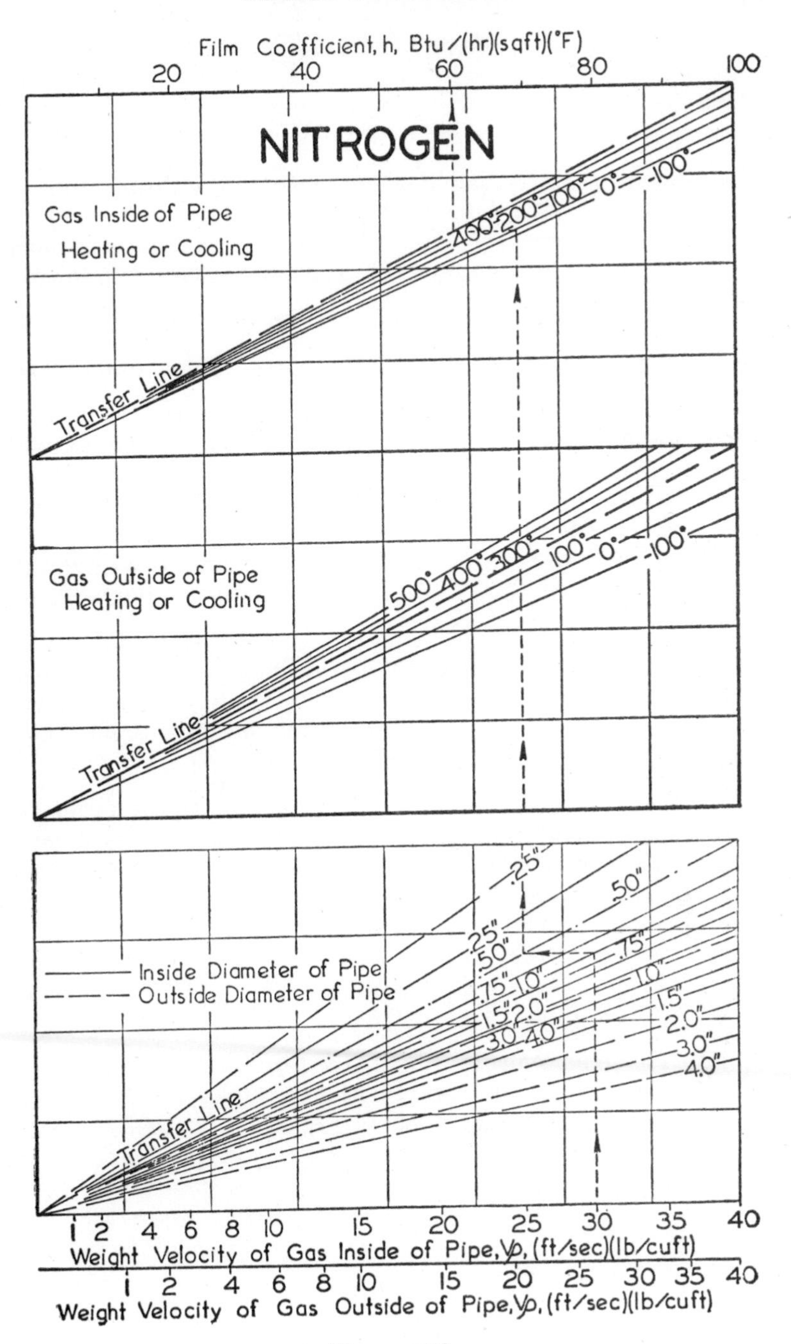
Film Coefficient, h, Btu/(hr)(sq ft)(°F)
20
40
60
80
100
NITROGEN
Gas Inside of Pipe
Heating or Cooling
400° 200° 100° 0° -100°
Transfer Line
Gas Outside of Pipe
Heating or Cooling
500° 400° 300° 100° 0° -100°
Transfer Line
Inside Diameter of Pipe
Outside Diameter of Pipe
.25"
.50"
.75"
1.0"
1.5"
2.0"
3.0"
4.0"
Transfer Line
1 2 4 6 8 10 15 20 25 30 35 40
Weight Velocity of Gas Inside of Pipe, Vρ, (ft/sec)(lb/cu ft)
1 2 4 6 8 10 15 20 25 30 35 40
Weight Velocity of Gas Outside of Pipe, Vρ, (ft/sec)(lb/cu ft)

Figure 6.72

Nitrous Oxide (Gas)

Nitrous Oxide (gas) heating or cooling in turbulent flow within a tube or in turbulent flow outside and normal to a single tube.

Equations: Gas or vapor heating or cooling within a tube:
$$Nu = 0.023\,(Re)^{0.8}\,(Pr)^{0.4}$$
Gas or vapor heating or cooling outside and normal to a single tube: $Nu = 0.385\,(Re)^{0.56}\,(Pr)^{0.3}$

Text References: Chapter VI; equations 6.5, 6.9, 6.12, and 6.14.

Extensions: Refer to section 6.5 for extensions to annular spaces, tube bundles, and flow through helical coils.

Special Conditions: For a gas or vapor heating or cooling within a tube, do not use the graph unless the weight velocity, $V\rho$ (ft/sec) (lb/cu ft), exceeds 0.5 at 1 atmosphere, 2 at 10 atmospheres, or 3.0 at 20 atmospheres.

For a gas or vapor flowing outside and normal to a single tube, do not use the graph for $V\rho$ less than 0.1 unless the Reynolds number exceeds 100.

Example: Nitrous Oxide (gas) is heating at 300 F while flowing outside and normal to a ¾″ Type K copper tube; the weight velocity is 20 (ft/sec) (lb/cu ft). Determine the film coefficient per lineal foot of tube.*

Solution: The dashed example line on the graph (Fig. 6.73) shows the method of evaluating the outside film coefficient, for the stated conditions, in terms of one square foot of outside surface of the tube. To convert this value, 38 Btu/(hr) (sq ft) (°F), to a lineal basis refer to Fig. 5.4 and, using a method similar to that shown by the dashed example line, enter the graph at h of 38 and come out at the top scale with a film coefficient of 20 Btu per hour per °F per lineal foot of tube.

***Note:** To determine other heat transfer coefficients for Nitrous Oxide, use Fig. 6.73 but refer to the examples on the following pages for the appropriate method: Outside film coefficient, page 296; inside film coefficient, page 294; inside film coefficient per lineal foot, use method similar to that for outside film coefficient per lineal foot; inside film coefficient for a double-pipe exchanger, page 298.

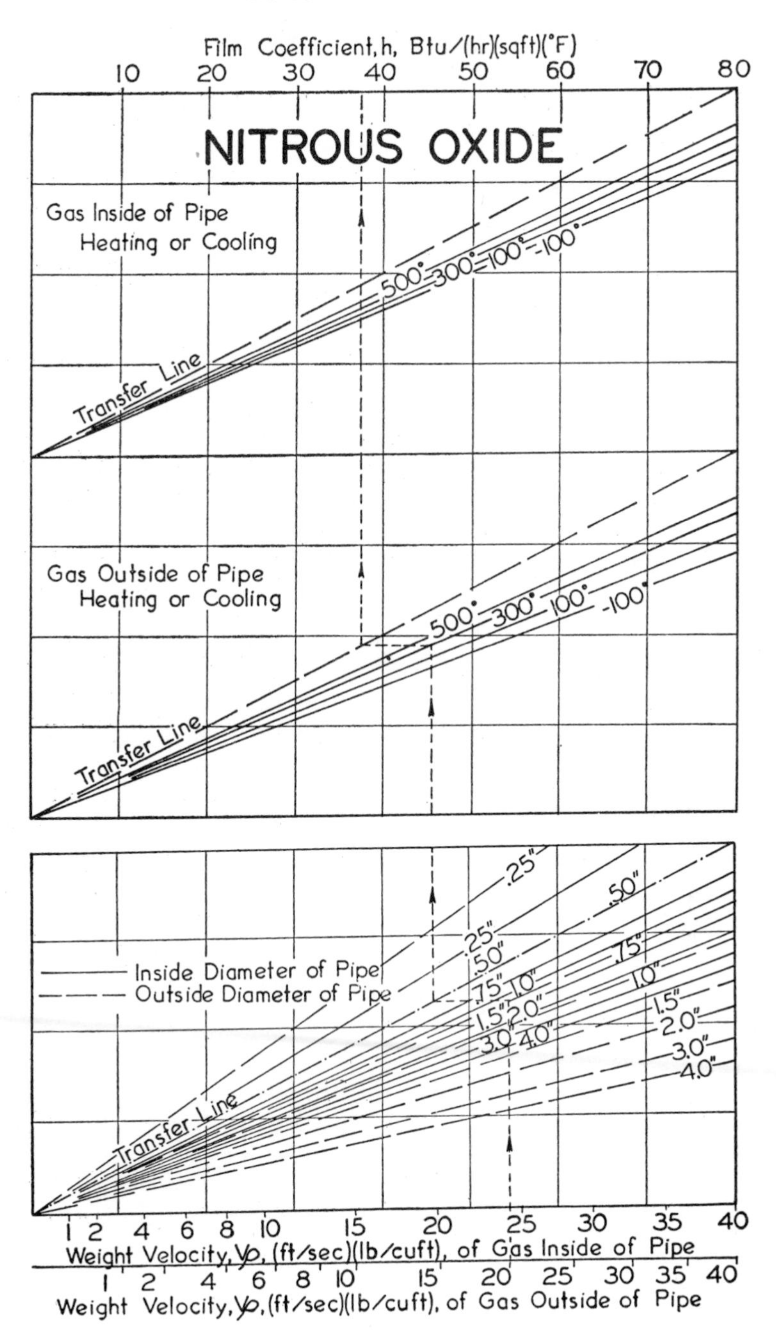
Film Coefficient, h, Btu/(hr)(sqft)(°F)
10 20 30 40 50 60 70 80
NITROUS OXIDE
Gas Inside of Pipe
Heating or Cooling
500° 300° 100° -100°
Transfer Line
Gas Outside of Pipe
Heating or Cooling
500° 300° 100° -100°
Transfer Line
.25" .50" .75" 1.0" 1.5" 2.0" 3.0" 4.0"
Inside Diameter of Pipe
Outside Diameter of Pipe
Transfer Line
1 2 4 6 8 10 15 20 25 30 35 40
Weight Velocity, Vρ, (ft/sec)(lb/cuft), of Gas Inside of Pipe
1 2 4 6 8 10 15 20 25 30 35 40
Weight Velocity, Vρ, (ft/sec)(lb/cuft), of Gas Outside of Pipe

Figure 6.73

Oxygen (Gas)

Oxygen (gas) heating or cooling in turbulent flow within a tube or in turbulent flow outside and normal to a single tube.

Equations: Gas or vapor heating or cooling within a tube:
$$Nu = 0.023(Re)^{0.8}(Pr)^{0.4}$$
Gas or vapor heating or cooling outside and normal to a single tube: $Nu = 0.385(Re)^{0.56}(Pr)^{0.3}$

Text References: Chapter VI; equations 6.5, 6.9, 6.12, and 6.14.

Extensions: Refer to section 6.5 for extensions to annular spaces, tube bundles, and flow through helical coils.

Special Conditions: For a gas or vapor heating or cooling within a tube, do not use the graph unless the weight velocity, $V\rho$ (ft/sec) (lb/cu ft), exceeds 0.5 at 1 atmosphere, 2 at 10 atmospheres, or 3.0 at 20 atmospheres.

For a gas or vapor flowing outside and normal to a single tube, do not use the graph for $V\rho$ less than 0.1 unless the Reynolds number exceeds 100.

Example: Oxygen (gas) is heating at 200 F while flowing outside and normal to a ¾″ Type K copper tube; the weight velocity is 20 (ft/sec) (lb/cu ft). Determine the film coefficient per lineal foot of tube.*

Solution: The dashed example line on the graph (Fig. 6.74) shows the method of evaluating the outside film coefficient, for the stated conditions, in terms of one square foot of outside surface of the tube. To convert this value, 53 Btu/(hr) (sq ft) (°F), to a lineal basis refer to Fig. 5.4 and, using a method similar to that shown by the dashed example line, enter the graph at h of 53 and come out at the top scale with a film coefficient of 25 Btu per hour per °F per lineal foot of tube.

***Note:** To determine other heat transfer coefficients for Oxygen, use Fig. 6.74 but refer to the examples on the following pages for the appropriate method: Outside film coefficient, page 296; inside film coefficient, page 294; inside film coefficient per lineal foot, use method similar to that for outside film coefficient per lineal foot; inside film coefficient for a double-pipe exchanger, page 298.

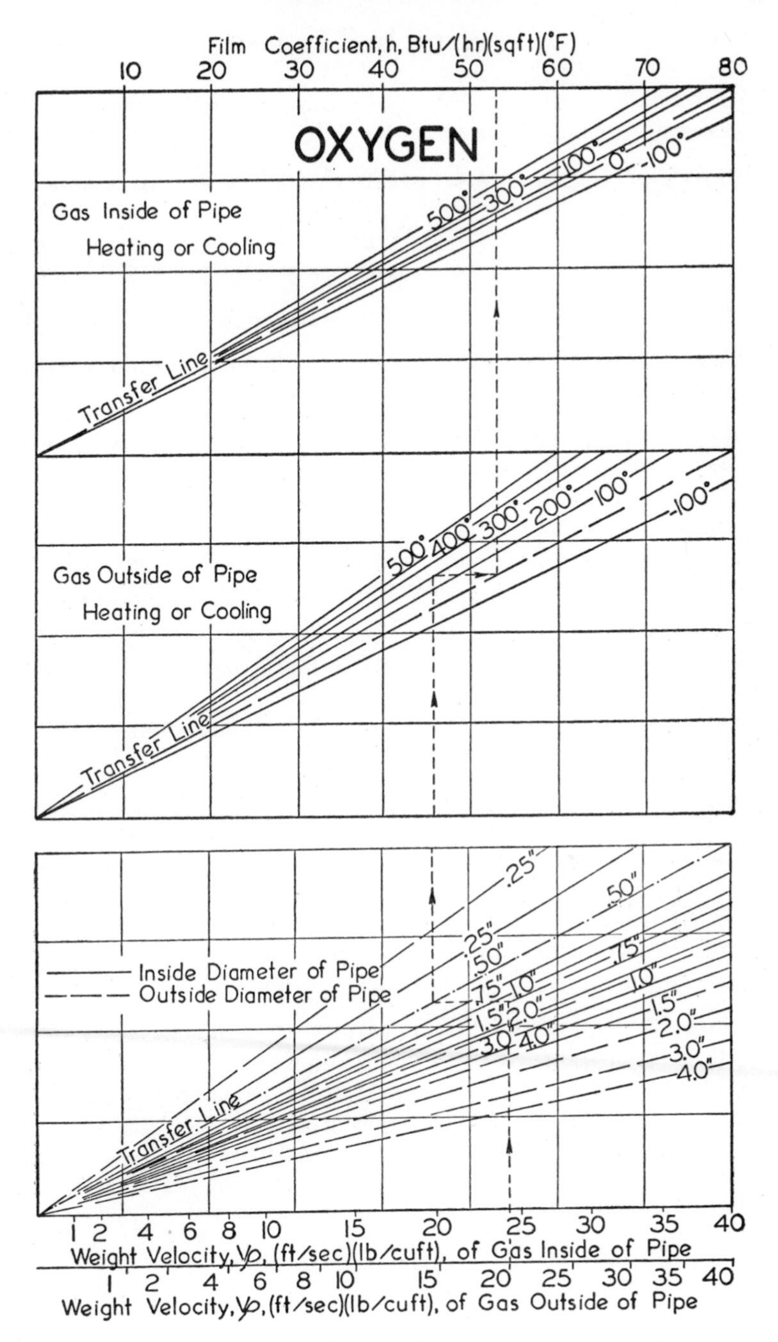
Film Coefficient, h, Btu/(hr)(sqft)(°F)
10 20 30 40 50 60 70 80
OXYGEN
Gas Inside of Pipe
Heating or Cooling
500° 300° 100° 0° -100°
Transfer Line
Gas Outside of Pipe
Heating or Cooling
500° 400° 300° 200° 100° -100°
Transfer Line
Inside Diameter of Pipe
Outside Diameter of Pipe
.25" .50" .75" 1.0" 1.5" 2.0" 3.0" 4.0"
.25" .50" .75" 1.0" 1.5" 2.0" 3.0" 4.0"
Transfer Line
1 2 4 6 8 10 15 20 25 30 35 40
Weight Velocity, Vρ, (ft/sec)(lb/cuft), of Gas Inside of Pipe
1 2 4 6 8 10 15 20 25 30 35 40
Weight Velocity, Vρ, (ft/sec)(lb/cuft), of Gas Outside of Pipe

Figure 6.74

Pentane, Iso (Vapor)

Pentane, Iso (vapor) heating or cooling in turbulent flow within a tube or in turbulent flow outside and normal to a single tube.

Equations: Gas or vapor heating or cooling within a tube:
$Nu = 0.023\,(Re)^{0.8}\,(Pr)^{0.4}$
Gas or vapor heating or cooling outside and normal to a single tube: $Nu = 0.385\,(Re)^{0.56}\,(Pr)^{0.3}$

Text References: Chapter VI; equations 6.5, 6.9, 6.12, and 6.14.

Extensions: Refer to section 6.5 for extensions to annular spaces, tube bundles, and flow through helical coils.

Special Conditions: For a gas or vapor heating or cooling within a tube, do not use the graph unless the weight velocity, $V\rho$ (ft/sec) (lb/cu ft), exceeds 0.5 at 1 atmosphere, 2 at 10 atmospheres, or 3.0 at 20 atmospheres.

For a gas or vapor flowing outside and normal to a single tube, do not use the graph for $V\rho$ less than 0.1 unless the Reynolds number exceeds 100.

Example: Pentane, Iso (vapor) is being heated while flowing within a tube having an inside diameter of ¼ inch. The weight velocity is 10 (ft/sec) (lb/cu ft) and the mean temperature is 100 F. Determine the value of the inside film coefficient.*

Solution: Enter the bottom of the graph (Fig. 6.75) at a weight velocity of 10 and rise to intersect the radial line for a tube of ¼″ inside diameter. From this intersection move right to intersect the transfer line, then rise to the group of radials for fluid inside; intersect the radial for a temperature of 100 F then move left to the transfer line and from this intersection rise to read the answer at the top scale as 43 Btu/(hr) (sq ft) (°F).

***Note:** To determine other heat transfer coefficients for Pentane, Iso, use Fig. 6.75 but refer to the examples on the following pages for the appropriate method: Outside film coefficient, page 296; outside film coefficient per lineal foot, page 302; inside film coefficient per lineal foot, use method similar to that for outside film coefficient per lineal foot; inside film coefficient for a double-pipe exchanger, page 298.

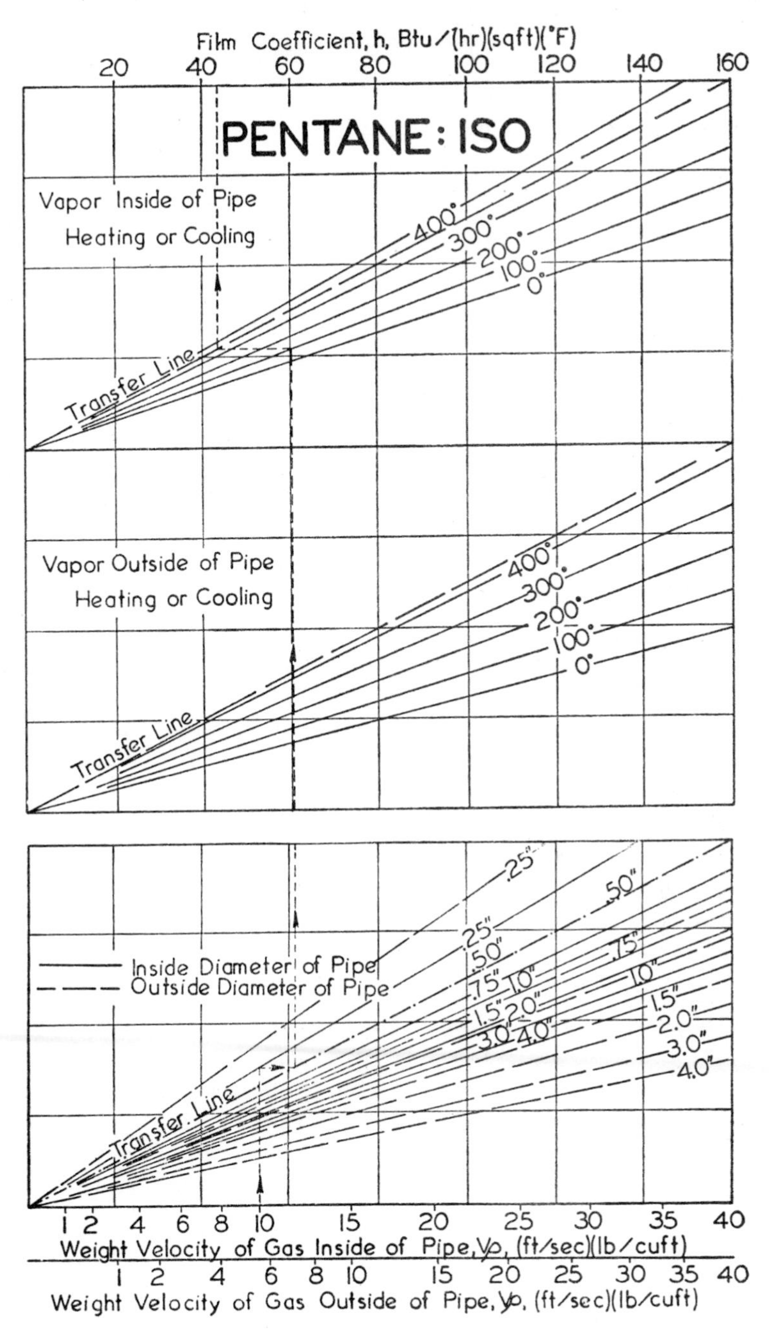
Film Coefficient, h, Btu/(hr)(sqft)(°F)
20 40 60 80 100 120 140 160
PENTANE: ISO
Vapor Inside of Pipe
Heating or Cooling
400°
300°
200°
100°
0°
Transfer Line
Vapor Outside of Pipe
Heating or Cooling
400°
300°
200°
100°
0°
Transfer Line
Inside Diameter of Pipe
Outside Diameter of Pipe
.25"
.50"
.75"
1.0"
1.5"
2.0"
3.0"
4.0"
Transfer Line
1 2 4 6 8 10 15 20 25 30 35 40
Weight Velocity of Gas Inside of Pipe, Vρ, (ft/sec)(lb/cuft)
1 2 4 6 8 10 15 20 25 30 35 40
Weight Velocity of Gas Outside of Pipe, Vρ, (ft/sec)(lb/cuft)

Figure 6.75

Steam (Vapor)

Steam (vapor) heating or cooling in turbulent flow within a tube or in turbulent flow outside and normal to a single tube.

Equations: Gas or vapor heating or cooling within a tube:
$$Nu = 0.023(Re)^{0.8}(Pr)^{0.4}$$
Gas or vapor heating or cooling outside and normal to a single tube: $Nu = 0.385(Re)^{0.56}(Pr)^{0.3}$

Text References: Chapter VI; equations 6.5, 6.9, 6.12, and 6.14.

Extensions: Refer to section 6.5 for extensions to annular spaces, tube bundles, and flow through helical coils.

Special Conditions: For a gas or vapor heating or cooling within a tube, do not use the graph unless the weight velocity, $V\rho$ (ft/sec) (lb/cu ft), exceeds 0.5 at 1 atmosphere, 2 at 10 atmospheres, or 3.0 at 20 atmospheres.

For a gas or vapor flowing outside and normal to a single tube, do not use the graph for $V\rho$ less than 0.1 unless the Reynolds number exceeds 100.

Example: Steam (vapor) is flowing outside and normal to a bundle of staggered 2 inch outside diameter tubes. The weight velocity through the narrowest section between tubes is 2 (ft/sec) (lb/cu ft) and the mean temperature of the vapor, which is being cooled, is 500 F. Determine the outside film coefficient.*

Solution: The dashed example line on the graph (Fig. 6.76) shows that, for the stated conditions, the film coefficient for flow normal to a single tube would be 15. For flow across a staggered tube bundle the base value of the outside coefficient is raised by 30% (refer to part 6 of section 6.5) hence for this case the corrected coefficient is $1.3 \times 15 = 20$ Btu/(hr) (sq ft) (°F).

***Note:** To determine other heat transfer coefficients for Steam, use Fig. 6.76 but refer to the examples on the following pages for the appropriate method: Inside film coefficient, page 304; outside film coefficient per lineal foot, page 302; inside film coefficient per lineal foot, use method similar to that for outside film coefficient per lineal foot; inside film coefficient for a double-pipe exchanger, page 298.

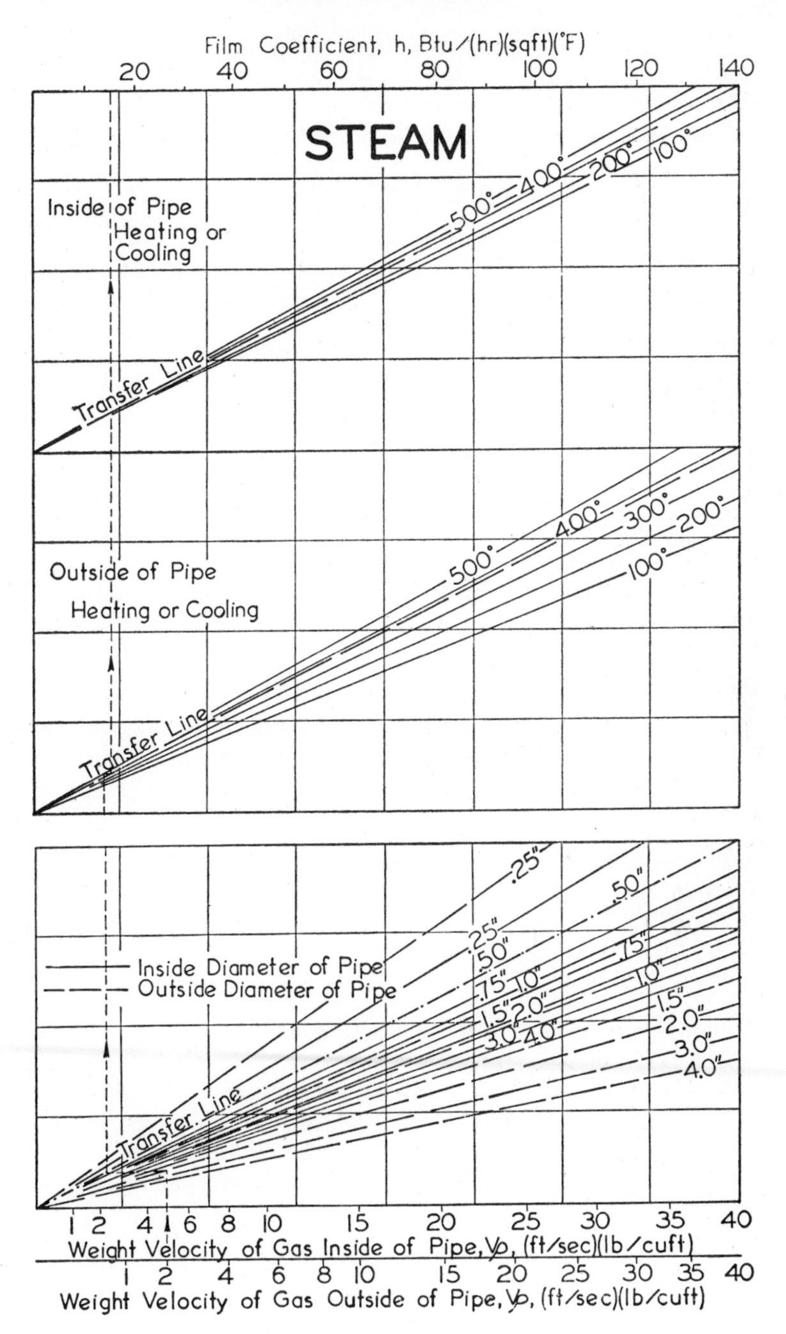
Film Coefficient, h, Btu/(hr)(sqft)(°F)
20 40 60 80 100 120 140
STEAM
Inside of Pipe
Heating or Cooling
500° 400° 200° 100°
Transfer Line
Outside of Pipe
Heating or Cooling
500° 400° 300° 200° 100°
Transfer Line
Inside Diameter of Pipe
Outside Diameter of Pipe
.25" .50" .75" 1.0" 1.5" 2.0" 3.0" 4.0"
Transfer Line
1 2 4 6 8 10 15 20 25 30 35 40
Weight Velocity of Gas Inside of Pipe, Vρ, (ft/sec)(lb/cuft)
1 2 4 6 8 10 15 20 25 30 35 40
Weight Velocity of Gas Outside of Pipe, Vρ, (ft/sec)(lb/cuft)

Figure 6.76

Sulfur Dioxide (Vapor)

Sulfur Dioxide (vapor) heating or cooling in turbulent flow within a tube or in turbulent flow outside and normal to a single tube.

Equations: Gas or vapor heating or cooling within a tube:
$Nu = 0.023 (Re)^{0.8} (Pr)^{0.4}$
Gas or vapor heating or cooling outside and normal to a single tube: $Nu = 0.385 (Re)^{0.56} (Pr)^{0.3}$

Text References: Chapter VI; equations 6.5, 6.9, 6.12, and 6.14.

Extensions: Refer to section 6.5 for extensions to annular spaces, tube bundles, and flow through helical coils.

Special Conditions: For a gas or vapor heating or cooling within a tube, do not use the graph unless the weight velocity, $V\rho$ (ft/sec) (lb/cu ft), exceeds 0.5 at 1 atmosphere, 2 at 10 atmospheres, or 3.0 at 20 atmospheres.

For a gas or vapor flowing outside and normal to a single tube, do not use the graph for $V\rho$ less than 0.1 unless the Reynolds number exceeds 100.

Example: Sulfur Dioxide (vapor) at 100 F is being cooled while flowing through an annular space in a double-pipe heat exchanger for which the equivalent inside diameter (equation 6.16) is 1 inch. The weight velocity is 30 (ft/sec) (lb/cu ft). Determine the inside film coefficient.*

Solution: The film coefficient is directly determinable from the graph as indicated by the dashed example line, Fig. 6.77. The resultant value, 29.5, is the film coefficient for the outside of the inner pipe of the annular exchanger and its units are Btu per hour per °F per square foot of outer surface of the inner pipe.

***Note:** To determine other heat transfer coefficients for Sulfur Dioxide, use Fig. 6.77 but refer to the examples on the following pages for the appropriate method: Outside film coefficient, page 306; inside film coefficient, page 304; outside film coefficient per lineal foot, page 302; inside film coefficient per lineal foot, use method similar to that for outside film coefficient per lineal foot.

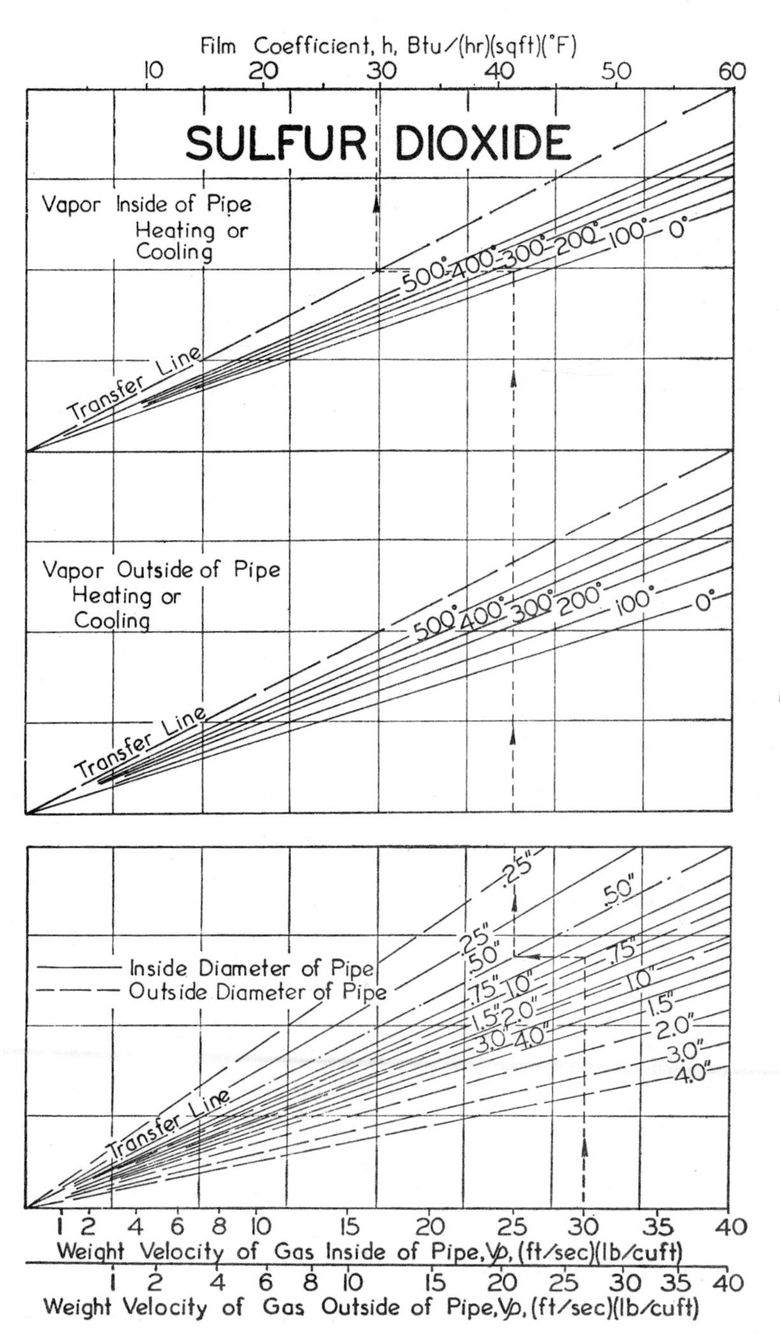

Film Coefficient, h, Btu/(hr)(sqft)(°F)
10 20 30 40 50 60
SULFUR DIOXIDE
Vapor Inside of Pipe
Heating or
Cooling
Transfer Line
500° 400° 300° 200° 100° 0°
Vapor Outside of Pipe
Heating or
Cooling
Transfer Line
500° 400° 300° 200° 100° 0°
Inside Diameter of Pipe
Outside Diameter of Pipe
Transfer Line
.25" .50" .75" 1.0" 1.5" 2.0" 3.0" 4.0"
.25" .50" .75" 1.0" 1.5" 2.0" 3.0" 4.0"
1 2 4 6 8 10 15 20 25 30 35 40
Weight Velocity of Gas Inside of Pipe, Vρ, (ft/sec)(lb/cuft)
1 2 4 6 8 10 15 20 25 30 35 40
Weight Velocity of Gas Outside of Pipe, Vρ, (ft/sec)(lb/cuft)

Figure 6.77

Appendix

Table 1. Properties of Materials*

Name of Material	Apparent Density, ρ, lb/cu ft	Specific Heat c_p, Btu/(lb) (°F)	Thermal Conductivity, k, Btu/(hr) (sq ft) (°F/ft)			Normal Total Emissivity, e.
			0°F	100°F	212°F	
Metals						
Aluminum (polished plate)	169	0.214	117	—	119	0.04
Brass, 70% Cu (polished plate)	532	0.092	56	—	60	0.04
Carbon steel 1% (polished)	487	0.113	25	—	25	0.55
Cast iron (polished)	454	0.10	32	—	30	0.21
Constantin, 60% Cu	557	0.098	—	—	13	—
Copper (polished)	559	0.092	224	—	218	0.02
Duralumin	174	0.211	92	—	105	—
German silver, 62% cu	538	0.094	—	—	18	—
Lead (polished)	708	0.031	20	—	19	0.06
Magnesium	109	0.242	99	—	97	—
Nickel (polished)	556	0.107	36	—	34	0.05
Red brass, 85% Cu (polished)	544	0.092	34	—	41	0.03
Silver (polished)	657	0.056	242	—	238	0.03
Tin	456	0.054	36	—	34	0.05
Tungsten	1208	0.032	96	—	87	0.30
Wrought iron (dull)	490	0.11	—	—	32	0.94
Zinc (polished)	446	0.092	65	—	64	0.05
Building and Insulating Materials						
Asbestos	36	0.20	0.087	—	0.111	0.96
Asphalt	132	—	—	0.43	—	0.93
Brick (common building)	112	0.2	—	0.4	—	0.93
Concrete	130	0.21	—	0.6	—	—
Corkboard	10	—	—	0.025	—	—
Felt, wool	20	—	—	0.03	—	—
Fiber insulating board	15	0.2	—	0.028	—	—
Glass	140	0.2	—	0.5	—	0.94
Gypsum	78	—	—	0.25	—	—
Hair felt	17	—	—	0.021	—	—
Limestone	103	0.22	—	0.54	—	—
Magnesia, 85%	—	—	—	—	0.041	—
Mineral wool	9	0.16	0.225	0.03	—	—
Rubber, hard	75	0.48	—	0.087	—	0.95
Sand	95	0.22	—	0.19	—	—
Wallboard, insulating	15	—	—	0.028	—	—
Wood: Fir, white	28	0.65	—	0.06	—	—
Oak	52	0.57	—	0.12	—	0.89
Pine, white	34	0.67	—	0.09	—	—
Sawdust	12	—	—	0.034	—	—
Miscellaneous Solids						
Cotton	5	—	0.032	—	0.039	—
Ice	58	0.49	1.3	—	—	0.92
Lampblack	10	—	—	0.038	—	0.95
Leather	63	—	—	0.09	—	—
Silk	6.3	—	—	0.026	—	—
Snow	34.7	—	0.27	—	—	—

*Compiled from references listed in the Bibliography

Table 2. Dimensional and Capacity Data For Schedule 40 Pipe

Diameter, Inches			Wall Thick-ness, In.	Cross-Sectional Area, Sq. In.			Weight per Foot, Lb.		
Nom-inal	Actual Inside	Actual Outside		Out-side	In-side	Metal	Of Pipe Alone	Of Water in Pipe	Of Pipe and Water
1/8	0.269	0.405	0.068	0.129	0.057	0.072	0.25	0.028	0.278
1/4	0.364	0.540	0.088	0.229	0.104	0.125	0.43	0.045	0.475
3/8	0.493	0.675	0.091	0.358	0.191	0.167	0.57	0.083	0.653
1/2	0.622	0.840	0.109	0.554	0.304	0.250	0.86	0.132	0.992
3/4	0.824	1.050	0.113	0.866	0.533	0.333	1.14	0.232	1.372
1	1.049	1.315	0.133	1.358	0.864	0.494	1.68	0.375	2.055
1 1/4	1.380	1.660	0.140	2.164	1.495	0.669	2.28	0.649	2.929
1 1/2	1.610	1.900	0.145	2.835	2.036	0.799	2.72	0.882	3.602
2	2.067	2.375	0.154	4.431	3.356	1.075	3.66	1.454	5.114
2 1/2	2.469	2.875	0.203	6.492	4.788	1.704	5.80	2.073	7.873
3	3.068	3.500	0.216	9.621	7.393	2.228	7.58	3.201	10.781
3 1/2	3.548	4.000	0.226	12.568	9.888	2.680	9.11	4.287	13.397
4	4.026	4.500	0.237	15.903	12.730	3.173	10.80	5.516	16.316
5	5.047	5.563	0.258	24.308	20.004	4.304	14.70	8.674	23.374
6	6.065	6.625	0.280	34.474	28.890	5.584	19.00	12.52	31.52
8	7.981	8.625	0.322	58.426	50.030	8.396	28.60	21.68	50.28
10	10.020	10.750	0.365	90.79	78.85	11.90	40.50	34.16	74.66
12	11.938	12.750	0.406	127.67	113.09	15.77	53.60	48.50	102.10
14	13.126	14.000	0.437	153.94	135.33	18.61	63.30	58.64	121.94
16	15.000	16.000	0.500	201.06	176.71	24.35	82.80	76.58	159.38
18	16.876	18.000	0.562	254.47	223.68	30.79	105.00	96.93	201.93
20	18.814	20.000	0.593	314.16	278.01	36.15	123.00	120.46	243.46

Nom-inal Dia., In.	Circumference, Inches		Sq. Ft. of Surface per Lineal Foot		Contents of Pipe per Lineal Foot		Lineal Feet to Contain		
	Out-side	In-side	Out-side	In-side	Cu. Ft.	Gal.	1 Cu. Ft.	1 Gal.	1 Lb. of Water
1/8	1.27	0.84	0.106	0.070	0.0004	0.003	2533.775	338.74	35.714
1/4	1.69	1.14	0.141	0.095	0.0007	0.005	1383.789	185.00	22.222
3/8	2.12	1.55	0.177	0.129	0.0013	0.010	754.360	100.85	12.048
1/2	2.65	1.95	0.221	0.167	0.0021	0.016	473.906	63.36	7.576
3/4	3.29	2.58	0.275	0.215	0.0037	0.028	270.034	36.10	4.310
1	4.13	3.29	0.344	0.274	0.0062	0.045	166.618	22.28	2.667
1 1/4	5.21	4.33	0.435	0.361	0.0104	0.077	96.275	12.87	1.541
1 1/2	5.96	5.06	0.497	0.422	0.0141	0.106	70.733	9.46	1.134
2	7.46	6.49	0.622	0.540	0.0233	0.174	42.913	5.74	0.688
2 1/2	9.03	7.75	0.753	0.654	0.0332	0.248	30.077	4.02	0.482
3	10.96	9.63	0.916	0.803	0.0514	0.383	19.479	2.60	0.312
3 1/2	12.56	11.14	1.047	0.928	0.0682	0.513	14.565	1.95	0.233
4	14.13	12.64	1.178	1.052	0.0884	0.660	11.312	1.51	0.181
5	17.47	15.84	1.456	1.319	0.1390	1.040	7.198	0.96	0.115
6	20.81	19.05	1.734	1.585	0.2010	1.500	4.984	0.67	0.080
8	27.09	25.07	2.258	2.090	0.3480	2.600	2.878	0.38	0.046
10	33.77	31.47	2.814	2.622	0.5470	4.100	1.826	0.24	0.029
12	40.05	37.70	3.370	3.140	0.7850	5.870	1.273	0.17	0.021
14	47.12	44.76	3.930	3.722	1.0690	7.030	1.067	0.14	0.017
16	53.41	51.52	4.440	4.310	1.3920	9.180	0.814	0.11	0.013
18	56.55	53.00	4.712	4.420	1.5530	11.120	0.644	0.09	0.010
20	62.83	59.09	5.236	4.920	1.9250	14.400	0.517	0.07	0.008

Table 3. Dimensional and Capacity Data For Schedule 80 Pipe

Diameter, In.			Wall Thickness, In.	Cross-Sectional Area, Sq. In.			Weight per Foot, Lb.		
Nominal	Actual Inside	Actual Outside		Outside	Inside	Metal	Of Pipe	Of Water in Pipe	Of Pipe and Water
1/8	0.215	0.405	0.095	0.129	0.036	0.093	0.314	0.016	0.330
1/4	0.302	0.540	0.119	0.229	0.072	0.157	0.535	0.031	0.566
3/8	0.423	0.675	0.126	0.358	0.141	0.217	0.738	0.061	0.799
1/2	0.546	0.840	0.147	0.554	0.234	0.320	1.087	0.102	1.189
3/4	0.742	1.050	0.154	0.866	0.433	0.433	1.473	0.213	1.686
1	0.957	1.315	0.179	1.358	0.719	0.639	2.171	0.312	2.483
1 1/4	1.278	1.660	0.191	2.164	1.283	0.881	2.996	0.555	3.551
1 1/2	1.500	1.900	0.200	2.835	1.767	1.068	3.631	0.765	4.396
2	1.939	2.375	0.218	4.431	2.954	1.477	5.022	1.280	6.302
2 1/2	2.323	2.875	0.276	6.492	4.238	2.254	7.661	1.830	9.491
3	2.900	3.500	0.300	9.621	6.605	3.016	10.252	2.870	13.122
3 1/2	3.364	4.000	0.318	12.568	8.890	3.678	12.505	3.720	16.225
4	3.826	4.500	0.337	15.903	11.496	4.407	14.983	4.970	19.953
5	4.813	5.563	0.375	24.308	18.196	6.112	20.778	7.940	28.718
6	5.761	6.625	0.432	34.474	26.069	8.405	28.573	11.300	39.873
8	7.625	8.625	0.500	58.426	45.666	12.760	43.388	19.800	63.188
10	9.564	10.750	0.593	90.79	71.87	18.92	64.400	31.130	95.530
12	11.376	12.750	0.687	127.67	101.64	26.03	88.600	44.040	132.640
14	12.500	14.000	0.750	153.94	122.72	31.22	107.000	53.180	160.180
16	14.314	16.000	0.843	201.06	160.92	40.14	137.000	69.730	206.730
18	16.126	18.000	0.937	254.47	204.24	50.23	171.000	88.500	259.500
20	17.938	20.000	1.031	314.16	252.72	61.44	209.000	109.510	318.510

Nominal Dia., In.	Circumference, Inches		Sq. Ft. of Surface per Lineal Foot		Contents of Pipe per Lineal Foot		Lineal Foot to Contain		
	Outside	Inside	Outside	Inside	Cu. Ft.	Gal.	1 Cu. Ft.	1 Gal.	1 Lb. of Water
1/8	1.27	0.675	0.106	0.056	0.00033	0.0019	3070	527	101.01
1/4	1.69	0.943	0.141	0.079	0.00052	0.0037	1920	271	32.26
3/8	2.12	1.328	0.177	0.111	0.00098	0.0073	1370	137	16.39
1/2	2.65	1.715	0.221	0.143	0.00162	0.0122	616	82	9.80
3/4	3.29	2.330	0.275	0.194	0.00300	0.0255	334	39.2	4.69
1	4.13	3.010	0.344	0.251	0.00500	0.0374	200	26.8	3.21
1 1/4	5.21	4.010	0.435	0.334	0.00880	0.0666	114	15.0	1.80
1 1/2	5.96	4.720	0.497	0.393	0.01230	0.0918	81.50	10.90	1.31
2	7.46	6.090	0.622	0.507	0.02060	0.1535	49.80	6.52	0.78
2 1/2	9.03	7.320	0.753	0.610	0.02940	0.220	34.00	4.55	0.55
3	10.96	9.120	0.916	0.760	0.0460	0.344	21.70	2.91	0.35
3 1/2	12.56	10.580	1.047	0.882	0.0617	0.458	16.25	2.18	0.27
4	14.13	12.020	1.178	1.002	0.0800	0.597	12.50	1.675	0.20
5	17.47	15.150	1.456	1.262	0.1260	0.947	7.95	1.055	0.13
6	20.81	18.100	1.734	1.510	0.1820	1.355	5.50	0.738	0.09
8	27.09	24.000	2.258	2.000	0.3180	2.380	3.14	0.420	0.05
10	33.77	30.050	2.814	2.503	0.5560	4.165	1.80	0.241	0.03
12	40.05	35.720	3.370	2.975	0.7060	5.280	1.42	0.189	0.02
14	47.12	39.270	3.930	3.271	0.8520	6.380	1.18	0.157	0.019
16	53.41	44.970	4.440	3.746	1.1170	8.360	0.895	0.119	0.014
18	56.55	50.660	4.712	4.220	1.4180	10.610	0.705	0.094	0.011
20	62.83	56.350	5.236	4.694	1.7550	13.130	0.570	0.076	0.009

Table 4. Dimensional and Capacity Data For Type K Copper Tubing

Diameter, Inches			Wall Thickness, In.	Cross-Sectional Area, Sq. In.			Weight per Foot, Lb.		
Nominal	Actual Inside	Actual Outside		Outside	Inside	Metal	Of Tube Alone	Of Water in Tube	Of Tube and Water
1/4	0.311	0.375	0.032	0.110	0.076	0.034	0.134	0.033	0.167
3/8	0.402	0.500	0.049	0.196	0.127	0.069	0.269	0.055	0.324
1/2	0.527	0.625	0.049	0.307	0.218	0.089	0.344	0.094	0.438
5/8	0.652	0.750	0.049	0.442	0.334	0.108	0.418	0.145	0.563
3/4	0.745	0.875	0.065	0.601	0.436	0.165	0.641	0.189	0.830
1	0.995	1.125	0.065	0.993	0.777	0.216	0.839	0.338	1.177
1 1/4	1.245	1.375	0.065	1.484	1.217	0.267	1.04	0.53	1.57
1 1/2	1.481	1.625	0.072	2.072	1.722	0.350	1.36	1.22	2.58
2	1.959	2.125	0.083	3.546	3.013	0.533	2.06	1.31	3.37
2 1/2	2.435	2.625	0.095	5.409	4.654	0.755	2.93	2.02	4.95
3	2.907	3.125	0.109	7.669	6.634	1.035	4.00	2.88	6.88
3 1/2	3.385	3.625	0.120	10.321	8.999	1.322	5.12	3.91	9.03
4	3.857	4.125	0.134	13.361	11.682	1.679	6.51	5.07	11.58
5	4.805	5.125	0.160	20.626	18.126	2.500	9.67	7.87	17.54
6	5.741	6.125	0.192	29.453	25.874	3.579	13.9	11.2	25.1
8	7.583	8.125	0.271	51.826	45.138	6.888	25.9	19.6	45.5
10	9.449	10.125	0.338	80.463	70.085	10.378	40.3	30.4	70.7
12	11.315	12.125	0.405	115.395	100.480	14.915	57.8	43.6	101.4

Nominal Dia., In.	Circumference, Inches		Sq. Ft. of Surface per Lineal Foot		Contents of Tube per Lineal Foot		Lineal Feet to Contain		
	Outside	Inside	Outside	Inside	Cu. Ft.	Gal.	1 Cu. Ft.	1 Gal.	1 Lb. of Water
1/4	1.178	0.977	0.098	0.081	.00052	.00389	1923	257	30.8
3/8	1.570	1.262	0.131	0.105	.00088	.00658	1136	152	18.2
1/2	1.963	1.655	0.164	0.138	.00151	.01129	662	88.6	10.6
5/8	2.355	2.047	0.196	0.171	.00232	.01735	431	57.6	6.90
3/4	2.748	2.339	0.229	0.195	.00303	.02664	330	37.5	5.28
1	3.533	3.124	0.294	0.260	.00540	.04039	185	24.8	2.96
1 1/4	4.318	3.909	0.360	0.326	.00845	.06321	118	15.8	1.89
1 1/2	5.103	4.650	0.425	0.388	.01958	.14646	51.1	6.83	0.817
2	6.673	6.151	0.556	0.513	.02092	.15648	47.8	6.39	0.765
2 1/2	8.243	7.646	0.688	0.637	.03232	.24175	30.9	4.14	0.495
3	9.813	9.128	0.818	0.761	.04607	.34460	21.7	2.90	0.347
3 1/2	11.388	10.634	0.949	0.886	.06249	.46745	15.8	2.14	0.257
4	12.953	12.111	1.080	1.009	.08113	.60682	12.3	1.65	0.197
5	16.093	15.088	1.341	1.257	.12587	.94151	7.94	1.06	0.127
6	19.233	18.027	1.603	1.502	.17968	1.3440	5.56	0.744	0.089
8	25.513	23.811	2.126	1.984	.31345	2.3446	3.19	0.426	0.051
10	31.793	29.670	2.649	2.473	.48670	3.4405	2.05	0.291	0.033
12	38.073	35.529	3.173	2.961	.69778	5.2194	1.43	0.192	0.023

Table 5. Dimensional and Capacity Data For Type L Copper Tubing

Diameter, Inches			Wall Thickness, In.	Cross-Sectional Area, Sq. In.			Weight per Foot, Lb.		
Nominal	Actual Inside	Actual Outside		Outside	Inside	Metal	Of Tube Alone	Of Water in Tube	Of Tube and Water
1/4	0.315	0.375	0.030	0.110	0.078	0.032	0.126	0.034	0.160
3/8	0.430	0.500	0.035	0.196	0.145	0.051	0.198	0.063	0.261
1/2	0.545	0.625	0.040	0.307	0.233	0.074	0.285	0.101	0.386
5/8	0.666	0.750	0.042	0.442	0.348	0.094	0.362	0.151	0.513
3/4	0.785	0.875	0.045	0.601	0.484	0.117	0.455	0.210	0.665
1	1.025	1.125	0.050	0.993	0.825	0.168	0.655	0.358	1.013
1 1/4	1.265	1.375	0.055	1.484	1.256	0.228	0.884	0.545	1.429
1 1/2	1.505	1.625	0.060	2.072	1.778	0.294	1.14	0.77	1.91
2	1.985	2.125	0.070	3.546	3.093	0.453	1.75	1.34	3.09
2 1/2	2.465	2.625	0.080	5.409	4.770	0.639	2.48	2.07	4.55
3	2.945	3.125	0.090	7.669	6.808	0.861	3.33	2.96	6.29
3 1/2	3.425	3.625	0.100	10.321	9.214	1.107	4.29	4.00	8.29
4	3.905	4.125	0.110	13.361	11.971	1.390	5.38	5.20	10.58
5	4.875	5.125	0.125	20.626	18.659	1.967	7.61	8.10	15.71
6	5.845	6.125	0.140	29.453	26.817	2.636	10.2	11.6	21.8
8	7.725	8.125	0.200	51.826	46.849	4.977	19.3	20.3	39.6
10	9.625	10.125	0.250	80.463	72.722	7.741	30.1	31.6	61.7
12	11.565	12.125	0.280	115.395	104.994	10.401	40.4	45.6	86.0

Nominal Dia., In.	Circumference, Inches		Sq. Ft. of Surface per Lineal Foot		Contents of Tube per Lineal Foot		Lineal Feet to Contain		
	Outside	Inside	Outside	Inside	Cu. Ft.	Gal.	1 Cu. Ft.	1 Gal.	1 Lb. of Water
1/4	1.178	0.989	0.098	0.082	.00054	.0040	1852	250	29.6
3/8	1.570	1.350	0.131	0.113	.00100	.0075	1000	133	16.0
1/2	1.963	1.711	0.164	0.143	.00162	.0121	617.3	82.6	9.87
5/8	2.355	2.091	0.196	0.174	.00242	.0181	413.2	55.2	6.61
3/4	2.748	2.465	0.229	0.205	.00336	.0251	297.6	40.5	4.76
1	3.533	3.219	0.294	0.268	.00573	.0429	174.5	23.3	2.79
1 1/4	4.318	3.972	0.360	0.331	.00872	.0652	114.7	15.3	1.83
1 1/2	5.103	4.726	0.425	0.394	.01237	.0925	80.84	10.8	1.29
2	6.673	6.233	0.556	0.519	.02147	.1606	46.58	6.23	0.745
2 1/2	8.243	7.740	0.688	0.645	.03312	.2478	30.19	4.04	0.483
3	9.813	9.247	0.818	0.771	.04728	.3537	21.15	2.83	0.338
3 1/2	11.388	10.760	0.949	0.897	.06398	.4786	15.63	2.09	0.251
4	12.953	12.262	1.080	1.022	.08313	.6218	12.03	1.61	0.192
5	16.093	15.308	1.341	1.276	.12958	.9693	7.220	1.03	0.123
6	19.233	18.353	1.603	1.529	.18622	1.393	5.371	0.718	0.0592
8	25.513	24.465	2.126	2.039	.32534	2.434	3.074	0.411	0.0492
10	31.793	30.223	2.649	2.519	.50501	3.777	1.980	0.265	0.0317
12	38.073	36.314	3.173	3.026	.72912	5.454	1.372	0.183	0.0219

Table 6. Dimensional and Capacity Data For Type M Copper Tubing

Diameter, Inches			Wall Thickness, In.	Cross-Sectional Area, Sq. In.			Weight per Foot, Lb.		
Nominal	Actual Inside	Actual Outside		Outside	Inside	Metal	Of Tube Alone	Of Water in Tube	Of Tube and Water
3/8	0.450	0.500	0.025	0.196	0.159	0.037	0.145	0.069	0.214
1/2	0.569	0.625	0.028	0.307	0.254	0.053	0.204	0.110	0.314
3/4	0.811	0.875	0.032	0.601	0.516	0.085	0.328	0.224	0.552
1	1.055	1.125	0.035	0.993	0.874	0.119	0.465	0.379	0.844
1 1/4	1.291	1.375	0.042	1.48	1.31	0.17	0.682	0.569	1.251
1 1/2	1.527	1.625	0.049	2.07	1.83	0.24	0.94	0.83	1.77
2	2.009	2.125	0.058	3.55	3.17	0.38	1.46	1.35	2.81
2 1/2	2.495	2.625	0.065	5.41	4.89	0.52	2.03	2.12	4.15
3	2.981	3.125	0.072	7.67	6.98	0.69	2.68	3.03	5.71
3 1/2	3.459	3.625	0.083	10.32	9.40	0.924	3.58	4.08	7.66
4	3.935	4.125	0.095	13.36	12.15	1.21	4.66	5.23	9.89
5	4.907	5.125	0.109	20.63	18.90	1.73	6.66	8.20	14.86
6	5.881	6.125	0.122	29.45	25.15	2.30	8.92	11.78	20.70
8	7.785	8.125	0.170	51.83	47.58	4.25	16.5	20.7	37.2
10	9.701	10.125	0.212	80.46	73.88	6.58	25.6	32.1	57.7
12	11.617	12.125	0.254	115.47	105.99	9.48	36.7	46.0	82.7

Nominal Dia., In.	Circumference, Inches		Sq. Ft. of Surface per Lineal Foot		Contents of Tube per Lineal Foot		Lineal Feet to Contain		
	Outside	Inside	Outside	Inside	Cu. Ft.	Gal.	1 Cu. Ft.	1 Gal.	1 Lb. of Water
3/8	1.570	1.413	0.131	0.118	.00110	.00823	909	122	14.5
1/2	1.963	1.787	0.164	0.149	.00176	.01316	568	76.0	9.09
3/4	2.748	2.547	0.229	0.212	.00358	.02678	379	37.3	4.47
1	3.533	3.313	0.294	0.276	.00607	.04540	164.7	22.0	2.64
1 1/4	4.318	4.054	0.360	0.338	.00910	.06807	109.9	14.7	1.76
1 1/2	5.103	4.795	0.425	0.400	.01333	.09971	75.02	10.0	1.20
2	6.673	6.308	0.556	0.526	.02201	.16463	45.43	6.08	0.727
2 1/2	8.243	7.834	0.688	0.653	.03396	.25402	29.45	3.94	0.471
3	9.813	9.360	0.818	0.780	.04847	.36256	20.63	2.76	0.330
3 1/2	11.388	10.867	0.949	0.906	.06525	.48813	15.33	2.05	0.246
4	12.953	12.356	1.080	1.030	.08368	.62593	11.95	1.60	0.191
5	16.093	15.408	1.341	1.284	.13125	.98175	7.62	1.02	0.122
6	19.233	18.466	1.603	1.539	.18854	1.410	5.30	0.709	0.849
8	25.513	24.445	2.126	2.037	.33044	2.472	3.03	0.405	0.484
10	31.793	30.461	2.649	2.538	.51306	3.838	1.91	0.261	0.312
12	38.073	36.477	3.173	3.039	.73569	5.503	1.36	0.182	0.217

BIBLIOGRAPHY

1. McAdams, *Heat Transmission,* McGraw-Hill, 1942

2. Jakob, *Heat Transfer:* Volume I, John Wiley & Sons, 1949

3. Stoever, *Applied Heat Transmission,* McGraw-Hill, 1941

4. Boelter, Cherry, Johnson, *Heat Transfer Notes,* Univ. of Cal., 1942

5. Eckert, *Introduction to the Transfer of Heat and Mass,* McGraw-Hill, 1950

6. Holme, *Warme,* (October 17, 1931), Berlin

7. Schmidt, *Foppls Festschrift* (p. 179), Springer, Berlin, 1924

8. Nessi and Nisolle, *Methodes graphiques pour l'etude des installations de chauffage et de refrigeration en regime discontinu,* Dunod, Paris, 1929

Note: All references in the text are to items in the bibliography.

INDEX TO GRAPHS

Graphs Relating to Free Convection, Streamline Flow, Convection With Gravity Flow, and Evaporation and Condensation of Water

Graphs Relating to Combined Heat Transmission

Graphs Relating to Forced Convection: General Relationships

INDEX

For classified index of graphical solutions see pages 317-319.

For classified index of graphical solutions see pages 317-319.

For classified index of graphical solutions see pages 317-319.

For classified index of graphical solutions see pages 317-319.

For classified index of graphical solutions see pages 317-319.

For classified index of graphical solutions see pages 317-319.

For classified index of graphical solutions see pages 317-319.